W9-CRP-963

JUNIOR GREAT BOOKS

SERIES 4

BOOK TWO

◆　◆　◆

The interpretive discussion program that moves

students toward excellence in reading comprehension,

critical thinking, and writing

JUNIOR GREAT BOOKS®

SERIES 4   BOOK TWO

THE GREAT BOOKS FOUNDATION

A nonprofit educational organization

Junior Great Books® is a registered trademark of the Great Books Foundation. Shared Inquiry™ is a trademark of the Great Books Foundation. The contents of this publication include proprietary trademarks and copyrighted materials, and may be used or quoted only with permission and appropriate credit to the Foundation.

Copyright © 2006 by The Great Books Foundation

Chicago, Illinois

All rights reserved

ISBN 978-1-933147-05-5

12 11 10

Printed in the United States of America

SUSTAINABLE FORESTRY INITIATIVE
Label applies to the text stock
Certified Sourcing
www.sfiprogram.org
SFI-00341

Published and distributed by

THE GREAT BOOKS FOUNDATION
A nonprofit educational organization

35 East Wacker Drive, Suite 400

Chicago, IL 60601

CONTENTS

9 SHREWD TODIE AND
LYZER THE MISER
Ukrainian folktale as told by Isaac Bashevis Singer

19 THE GOLDFISH
Eleanor Farjeon

29 THE GREAT BLACKBERRY PICK
Philippa Pearce

45 THE STORY OF WANG LI
Elizabeth Coatsworth

59 THE HEMULEN
WHO LOVED SILENCE

Tove Jansson

81 THE ENCHANTED STICKS

Steven J. Myers

93 THE ELEPHANT'S CHILD

Rudyard Kipling

105   MR. SINGER'S NICKNAMES

James Krüss

120   THE LITTLE HUMPBACKED HORSE

Russian folktale as told by Post Wheeler

151   ALI BABA AND
THE FORTY THIEVES

from The Arabian Nights

"Your tablespoon gave birth to a teaspoon."

SHREWD TODIE AND LYZER THE MISER

Ukrainian folktale
as told by Isaac Bashevis Singer

In a village somewhere in Ukraine, there lived a poor man called Todie. Todie had a wife, Shaindel, and seven children, but he could never earn enough to feed them properly. He tried many trades and failed in all of them. It was said of Todie that if he decided to deal in candles the sun would never set. He was nicknamed Shrewd Todie because whenever he managed to make some money, it was always by trickery.

This winter was an especially cold one. The snowfall was heavy, and Todie had no money to buy wood for the stove. His seven children stayed in bed all day to keep warm. When the frost burns outside, hunger is stronger than ever, but Shaindel's larder was empty. She reproached Todie bitterly, wailing, "If you can't feed your wife and children, I will go to the rabbi and get a divorce."

9

"And what will you do with it, eat it?" Todie retorted.

In the same village there lived a rich man called Lyzer. Because of his stinginess he was known as Lyzer the Miser. He permitted his wife to bake bread only once in four weeks because he had discovered that fresh bread is eaten up more quickly than stale.

Todie had more than once gone to Lyzer for a loan of a few gulden, but Lyzer had always replied, "I sleep better when the money lies in my strongbox rather than in your pocket."

Lyzer had a goat, but he never fed her. The goat had learned to visit the houses of the neighbors, who pitied her and gave her potato peelings. Sometimes, when there were not enough peelings, she would gnaw on the old straw of the thatched roofs. She also had a liking for tree bark. Nevertheless, each year the goat gave birth to a kid. Lyzer milked her but, miser that he was, did not drink the milk himself. Instead he sold it to others.

Todie decided that he would take revenge on Lyzer and at the same time make some much-needed money for himself.

One day, as Lyzer was sitting on a box eating borscht and dry bread (he used his chairs only on holidays so that the upholstery would not wear out), the door opened and Todie came in.

"Reb Lyzer," he said, "I would like to ask you a favor. My oldest daughter, Basha, is already fifteen and she's about to become engaged. A young man is coming from

Janev to look her over. My cutlery is tin, and my wife is ashamed to ask the young man to eat soup with a tin spoon. Would you lend me one of your silver spoons? I give you my holy word that I will return it to you tomorrow."

Lyzer knew that Todie would not dare to break a holy oath, and he lent him the spoon.

No young man came to see Basha that evening. As usual, the girl walked around barefoot and in rags, and the silver spoon lay hidden under Todie's shirt. In the early years of his marriage, Todie had possessed a set of silver tableware himself. He had, however, long since sold it all, with the exception of three silver teaspoons that were used only on Passover.

The following day, as Lyzer, his feet bare (in order to save his shoes), sat on his box eating borscht and dry bread, Todie returned.

"Here is the spoon I borrowed yesterday," he said, placing it on the table together with one of his own teaspoons.

"What is the teaspoon for?" Lyzer asked.

And Todie said, "Your tablespoon gave birth to a teaspoon. It is her child. Since I am an honest man, I'm returning both mother and child to you."

Lyzer looked at Todie in astonishment. He had never heard of a silver spoon giving birth to another. Nevertheless, his greed overcame his doubt, and he happily accepted both spoons. Such an unexpected piece

11

of good fortune! He was overjoyed that he had loaned Todie the spoon.

A few days later, as Lyzer (without his coat, to save it) was again sitting on his box eating borscht with dry bread, the door opened and Todie appeared.

"The young man from Janev did not please Basha because he had donkey ears, but this evening another young man is coming to look her over. Shaindel is cooking soup for him, but she's ashamed to serve him with a tin spoon. Would you lend me . . ."

Even before Todie could finish the sentence, Lyzer interrupted. "You want to borrow a silver spoon? Take it with pleasure."

The following day Todie once more returned the spoon and with it one of his own silver teaspoons. He again explained that during the night the large spoon had given birth to a small one, and in all good conscience he was bringing back the mother and newborn baby. As for the young man who had come to look Basha over, she hadn't liked him either, because his nose was so long that it reached to his chin. Needless to say, Lyzer the Miser was overjoyed.

Exactly the same thing happened a third time. Todie related that this time his daughter had rejected her suitor because he stammered. He also reported that Lyzer's silver spoon had again given birth to a baby spoon.

"Does it ever happen that a spoon has twins?" Lyzer inquired.

Todie thought it over for a moment. "Why not? I've even heard of a case where a spoon had triplets."

Almost a week passed by, and Todie did not go to see Lyzer. But on Friday morning, as Lyzer (in his underdrawers to save his pants) sat on his box eating borscht and dry bread, Todie came in and said, "Good day to you, Reb Lyzer."

"A good morning and many more to you," Lyzer replied in his friendliest manner. "What good fortune brings you here? Did you perhaps come to borrow a silver spoon? If so, help yourself."

"Today I have a very special favor to ask. This evening a young man from the big city of Lublin is coming to look Basha over. He is the son of a rich man, and I'm told he is clever and handsome as well. Not only do I need a silver spoon, but since he will remain with us over the Sabbath, I need a pair of silver candlesticks, because mine are brass and my wife is ashamed to place them on the Sabbath table. Would you lend me your candlesticks? Immediately after the Sabbath, I will return them to you."

Silver candlesticks are of great value and Lyzer the Miser hesitated, but only for a moment.

Remembering his good fortune with the spoons, he said, "I have eight silver candlesticks in my house. Take them all. I know you will return them to me just as you say. And if it should happen that any of them give birth, I have no doubt that you will be as honest as you have been in the past."

13

"Certainly," Todie said. "Let's hope for the best."

The silver spoon, Todie hid beneath his shirt as usual. But taking the candlesticks, he went directly to a merchant, sold them for a considerable sum, and brought the money to Shaindel. When Shaindel saw so much money, she demanded to know where he had gotten such a treasure.

"When I went out, a cow flew over our roof and dropped a dozen silver eggs," Todie replied. "I sold them and here is the money."

"I have never heard of a cow flying over a roof and laying silver eggs," Shaindel said doubtingly.

"There is always a first time," Todie answered. "If you don't want the money, give it back to me."

"There'll be no talk about giving it back," Shaindel said. She knew that her husband was full of cunning and tricks—but when the children are hungry and the larder is empty, it is better not to ask too many questions. Shaindel went to the marketplace and bought meat, fish, white flour, and even some nuts and raisins for a pudding. And since a lot of money still remained, she bought shoes and clothes for the children.

It was a very gay Sabbath in Todie's house. The boys sang and the girls danced. When the children asked their father where he had gotten the money, he replied, "It is forbidden to mention money during the Sabbath."

Sunday, as Lyzer (barefoot and almost naked to save his clothes) sat on his box finishing up a dry crust of bread with borscht, Todie arrived and, handing him his silver spoon, said, "It's too bad. This time your spoon did not give birth to a baby."

"What about the candlesticks?" Lyzer inquired anxiously.

Todie sighed deeply. "The candlesticks died."

Lyzer got up from his box so hastily that he overturned his plate of borscht.

"You fool! How can candlesticks die?" he screamed.

"If spoons can give birth, candlesticks can die."

Lyzer raised a great hue and cry and had Todie called before the rabbi. When the rabbi heard both sides of the story, he burst out laughing. "It serves you right," he said to Lyzer. "If you hadn't chosen to believe that spoons give birth, now you would not be forced to believe that your candlesticks died."

"But it's all nonsense," Lyzer objected.

"Did you not expect the candlesticks to give birth to other candlesticks?" the rabbi said admonishingly. "If you accept nonsense when it brings you profit, you must also accept nonsense when it brings you loss." And he dismissed the case.

The following day, when Lyzer the Miser's wife brought him his borscht and dry bread, Lyzer said to her, "I will eat only the bread. Borscht is too expensive a food, even without sour cream."

The story of the silver spoons that gave birth and the candlesticks that died spread quickly through the town.

All the people enjoyed Todie's victory and Lyzer the Miser's defeat. The shoemaker's and tailor's apprentices, as was their custom whenever there was an important happening, made up a song about it:

Lyzer, put your grief aside.
What if your candlesticks have died?
You're the richest man on earth
With silver spoons that can give birth
And silver eggs as living proof
Of flying cows above your roof.
Don't sit there eating crusts of bread—
To silver grandsons look ahead.

However, time passed and Lyzer's silver spoons never gave birth again.

He let the Goldfish dart through his fingers.

THE GOLDFISH

Eleanor Farjeon

There was once a Goldfish who lived in the sea in the days when all fishes lived there. He was perfectly happy and had only one care, and that was to avoid the net that floated about in the water, now here, now there. But all the fish had been warned by King Neptune, their father, to avoid the net, and in those days they did as they were bid. So the Goldfish enjoyed a glorious life, swimming for days and days in the blue and green water: sometimes low down close to the sand and shells and pearls and coral, and the big rocks where the anemones grew like clusters of gay flowers, and the seaweed waved in frills and fans of red and green and yellow; and sometimes he swam high up near the surface of the sea, where the white caps chased each other, and the great waves rose like mountains of glass and tumbled over themselves with a crash. When the Goldfish was as near the top as this, he sometimes saw swimming in the bright blue water far, far above him a great Gold Fish, as golden as himself, but as round as a jellyfish. And at other times, when that distant water was dark blue instead of bright, he saw a Silver Fish such as he had never met under the sea, and she too was often round in shape, though at times, when she seemed to swim sideways through the water, he could see her pointed silver fins. Our Goldfish felt a certain jealousy of the other Gold Fish, but with the Silver Fish he fell in love at sight and longed to be able to swim up to her. Whenever he tried to do this, something queer happened that made him lose his breath; and with a gasp he sank down into the ocean, so deep that he could see the Silver Fish no longer. Then, hoping she might descend to swim in his own water, he swam for miles and miles in search of her; but he never had the luck to find her.

One night as he was swimming about in very calm water, he saw overhead the motionless shadow of an enormous fish. One great long fin ran under its belly in the water, but all the rest of it was raised above the surface. The Goldfish knew every fish in the sea, but he had never before seen such a fish as this! It was bigger than the Whale, and as black as the ink of the Octopus. He swam all round it, touching it with his inquisitive little nose. At last he asked, "What sort of fish are *you*?"

The big black shadow laughed. "I am not a fish at all, I am a ship."

"What are you doing here if you are not a fish?"

"Just at present I am doing nothing, for I am becalmed. But when the wind blows I shall go on sailing round the world."

"What is the world?"

"All that you see and more."

"Am I in the world, then?" asked the Goldfish.

"Certainly you are."

The Goldfish gave a little jump of delight. "Good news! Good news!" he cried.

A passing Porpoise paused to ask, "What are you shouting for?"

"Because I am in the world!"

"Who says so?"

"The Ship-Fish!" said the Goldfish.

"Pooh!" said the Porpoise, "let him prove it!" and passed on.

The Goldfish stopped jumping, because his joy had been damped by doubt. "How can the world be more than I can see?" he asked the Ship. "If I am really in the world I ought to be able to see it *all*—or how can I be sure?"

"You must take my word for it," said the Ship. "A tiny fellow like you can never hope to see more than a scrap of the world. The world has a rim you can never see over; the world has foreign lands full of wonders that you can never look upon; the world is as round as an orange, but you will never see how round the world is."

Then the Ship went on to tell of the parts of the world that lay beyond the rim of things, of men and women and children, of flowers and trees, of birds with eyes in their tails—blue, gold, and green—of white and black elephants, and temples hung with tinkling bells. The Goldfish wept with longing because he could never see over the rim of things, because he could not see how round the world was, because he could not behold all at once all the wonders that were in the world.

How the Ship laughed at him! "My little friend," said he, "if you were the Moon yonder, why, if you were the Sun himself, you could only see one half of these things at a time."

"Who is the Moon yonder?" asked the Goldfish.

"Who else but that silver slip of light up in the sky?"

"Is that the sky?" said the Goldfish. "I thought it was another sea. And is that the Moon? I thought she was a Silver Fish. But who then is the Sun?"

"The Sun is the round gold ball that rolls through the sky by day," said the Ship. "They say he is her lover and gives her his light."

"But I will give her the world!" cried the Goldfish. And he leaped with all his tiny might into the air, but he could not reach the Moon and fell gasping into the sea. There he let himself sink like a little gold stone to the bottom of the ocean, where he lay for a week weeping his heart out. For the things the Ship had told him were more than he could understand; but they swelled him with great longings—longings to possess the Silver Moon, to be a mightier fish than the Sun, and to see the whole of the world from top to bottom and from side to side, with all the wonders within and beyond it.

Now it happened that King Neptune, who ruled the land under the waves, was strolling through a grove of white and scarlet coral, when he heard a chuckle that was something between a panting and a puffing; and peering through the branches of the coral-trees he beheld a plump Porpoise bursting its sleek sides with laughter. Not far off lay the Goldfish, swimming in tears.

King Neptune, like a good father, preferred to share in all the joys and sorrows of his children, so he stopped to ask the Porpoise, "What tickles you so?"

"Ho! ho! ho!" puffed the Porpoise. "I am tickled by the grief of the Goldfish there."

"Has the Goldfish a grief?" asked King Neptune.

"He has indeed! For seven days and nights he has wept because, ho! ho! ho! because he cannot marry the Moon, surpass the Sun, and possess the world!"

"And you," said King Neptune, "have you never wept for these things?"

"Not I!" puffed the Porpoise. "What! Weep for the Sun and the Moon that are nothing but two blobs in the distance? Weep for the world that no one can behold? No, Father! When my dinner is in the distance, I'll weep for *that*; and when I see death coming, I'll weep for *that*; but for the rest, I say pooh!"

"Well, it takes all sorts of fish to make a sea," said King Neptune, and stooping down he picked up the Goldfish and admonished it with his finger.

"Come, child," said he, "tears may be the beginning, but they should not be the end of things. Tears will get you nowhere. Do you really wish to marry the Moon, surpass the Sun, and possess the world?"

"I do, Father, I do!" quivered the Goldfish.

"Then since there is no help for it, you must get caught in the net—do you see it floating yonder in the water? Are you afraid of it?"

"Not if it will bring me all I long for," said the Goldfish bravely.

"Risk all, and you will get your desires," promised King Neptune. He let the Goldfish dart through his fingers and saw him swim boldly to the net, which was waiting to catch what it could. As the meshes closed upon him, King Neptune stretched out his hand and slipped a second fish inside it; and then, stroking his green beard, he continued his stroll among his big and little children.

And what happened to the Goldfish?

He was drawn up into the Fisherman's boat that lay in wait above the net; and in the same cast a Silver Fish was taken, a lovely creature with a round body and silky fins like films of moonlit cloud. "There's a pretty pair!" thought the Fisherman, and he carried them home to please his little daughter. And to make her pleasure more complete, he first bought a globe of glass, and sprinkled sand and shells and tiny pebbles at the bottom, and set among them a sprig of coral and a strand of seaweed. Then he filled the globe with water, dropped in the Gold and Silver Fishes, and put the little glass world on a table in his cottage window.

The Goldfish, dazed with joy, swam towards the Silver Fish, crying, "You are the Moon come out of the sky! Oh see, how round the world is!"

And he looked through one side of the globe and saw flowers and trees in the garden. And he looked through another side of the globe and saw on the mantelpiece black and white elephants of ebony and ivory that the Fisherman had brought from foreign parts. And through another side of the globe he saw on the wall a fan of peacock's feathers, with eyes of gold and blue and green. And through the fourth side, on a bracket, he saw a little Chinese temple hung with bells. And he looked at the bottom of the globe and saw his own familiar world of coral, sand, and shells. And he looked at the top of the globe and saw a man, a woman, and a child smiling down at him over the rim.

And he gave a little jump of joy and cried to his Silver Bride:

"Oh Moonfish, I am greater than the Sun! For I give you not half, but the whole of the world, the top and the bottom and all the way round, with all the wonders that are in it and beyond it!"

And King Neptune under the sea, who had ears for all that passed, laughed in his beard and said:

"It was a shame ever to let such a tiny fellow loose in the vast ocean. He needed a world more suited to his size."

And ever since then, the world of the Goldfish has been a globe of glass.

From inside came a smell of roast meat and of delicious baking.

THE GREAT BLACKBERRY PICK

Philippa Pearce

Dad was against waste—waste of almost anything: electricity, time, crusts of bread. Wasted food was his special dread. Just after the summer holidays, nearing the second or third Saturday of term: "Sun now," he would say, "frost later, and pounds and pounds and pounds and pounds of blackberries out in the hedges going to waste. Good food wasted: bramble jelly"—their mother flinched, perhaps remembering stained bags hanging from hooks in the kitchen—"jelly, and jam, and blackberry-and-apple pies. . . ." He smacked his lips. Dad seemed to think he must mime enjoyment to make them understand.

Val said eagerly, "I love blackberries."

Her father beamed on her.

Chris said, "I don't. I don't like the pips between my teeth."

"Worse under your plate," their mother murmured.

29

Like their mother, Dad had false teeth, but he did not acknowledge them. He said scornfully, "In *bought* jam the pips are artificial. Tiny chips of wood. Put in afterwards."

"Nice job, carving 'em to shape," said Chris.

Peter was not old enough to think that funny, and Val decided not to laugh; so nobody did.

Peter said, "Do we have to go?"

"Bicycles," said Dad. "Everyone on bicycles and off into the country, blackberry picking. Five of us should gather a good harvest."

"I'll make the picnic," Val said. She liked that kind of thing. She looked anxiously round her family. Their mother had turned her face away from them to gaze out of the window. Peter and Chris had fixed their eyes upon Dad: Peter would have to go, although much bicycling made his legs ache; but Chris, the eldest of them, as good as grown up—Chris said, "I'm not coming."

"Oh, Chris!" Val cried.

Dad said, "Not coming?"

"No."

"And why not?"

"I've been asked to go somewhere else on Saturday. I'm doing something else. I'm not coming."

No one had ever said that to Dad before. What would happen? Dad began to growl in his throat like a dog preparing to attack. Then the rumble died away. Dad said, "Oh, have it your own way then."

So that was one who wouldn't go blackberrying this year.

Nor did their mother go. When Saturday came, she didn't feel well, she said. She'd stay at home and have their tea ready for them.

Two fewer didn't matter, because Dad begged the two Turner children from next door. Mrs. Turner was glad to be rid of them for the day, and they had bicycles.

"Bicycles," said Dad, "checked in good order, tires pumped, brakes working, and so on. Then, the picnic." Val smiled and nodded. "Something to gather the blackberries in," went on Dad. "Not paper bags or rubbishy receptacles of that sort. Baskets, plastic carrier bags, anything like that. Something that will go into a bicycle basket, or can be tied on somewhere. Something that will bear a weight of blackberries. Right?"

Val said, "Yes," so that Dad could go on. "All assemble in the road at nine thirty. I'll have the map."

There they were on this fine Saturday morning in September at half past nine: Val and Peter and their dad and the two Turner children from next door, all on bicycles.

They had about four miles on the main road, riding very carefully, two by two or sometimes in single file, with Dad in the rear shouting to them. Then Dad directed them to turn off the main road into a side road, and after that it was quiet country roads all the way. As

Chris had once said, you had to hand it to Dad: Dad was good with a map; he knew where he was going.

Country roads, and then lanes that grew doubtful of themselves and became mere grassy tracks. These were the tracks that, in the old days, people had made on foot or on horseback, going from one village to the next. Nowadays almost no one used them.

They were pushing their bikes now, or riding them with their teeth banging in their gums. The Turner children each fell off once, and one cried.

"Quiet now!" Dad said severely, as though the blackberries were shy wild creatures to be taken by surprise.

They left their bicycles stacked against each other and followed Dad on foot, walking steeply through an afforestation of pines, and then out into a large clearing on a hillside, south facing and overgrown with brambles.

You had to hand it to Dad, it was a marvellous place.

The bushes were often more than a man's height and densely growing, but with irregular passages between them. The pickers could edge through narrow gaps or stoop under stems arched to claw and clutch. For most of the time they wore their anoraks with the hoods up.

The blackberries grew thickly. They were very big and ripe—many already overripe, with huge bluebottles squatting on them.

"Eat what you want, to begin with," said Dad. "Soon enough you won't want to eat any more. Then just pick and go on picking." He smiled. He was good tempered. Everything was going well.

They separated at once to pick. They went burrowing about among the bushes, meeting each other, exclaiming, drawn to each other's blackberry clumps, because always someone else's blackberries seemed bigger, riper.

They picked and picked and picked and picked. Their teeth and tongues and lips were stained, but their fingers were stained the most deeply, because they went on picking—on and on and on—after they had stopped eating. Dad had been right about that, too. But himself, he never ate any blackberries at all, just picked.

The brambles scratched them. Val had a scratch on her forehead that brought bright blood oozing down into her eyebrow. "Nothing!" said Dad. He tied her head with a handkerchief to stop the bleeding. The handkerchief had been a present to him; it was red with white spots. When he had tied it round Val's head, he called her his pirate-girl.

Then he looked into her plastic carrier bag. "Why, pirate-girl, you've picked more blackberries than anyone else!"

When Dad had gone off again, Peter began to dance round Val. "Pirate-girl! Pirate-girl!" Val didn't mind; no, she really enjoyed it. She felt happy to have picked more blackberries than anyone else, and for Dad to have said so, and to be wearing Dad's handkerchief and to be teased for what he had called her. The Turner children appeared round a bramble corner, and she was glad of the audience. Peter was good humoured, too. His legs had stopped aching, and he had forgotten that they would ache again. The children were in early afternoon sunshine and blackberry-scented air. They had picked enough blackberries to be proud of, the picnic would be any time now, and Dad was in a good temper.

"Pirate-girl!" Peter teased. He set down his basket of blackberries to pick a solitary stem of hogweed, dry and straight and stiff. With this he made cutlass-slashes at Val.

There was no weapon to hand for Val, so she used her carrier bag to parry him. She swung the bag to and fro, trying to bang his stem and break it. The weight in the carrier made it swing slowly, heavily, like a pendulum. Val was getting nowhere in the fight, but she was enjoying it. She hissed fiercely between her teeth. Peter dodged. The bag swung.

Dad came back round the bushes and saw them. Val couldn't stop the swinging at once, and at once an awful thing began to happen. The swinging was too much for the weight of the blackberries in the bag. The bottom did not fall out—after all, the bag was plastic; but the plastic where she gripped it began to stretch. The handle holes elongated swiftly and smoothly. Swiftly and smoothly the plastic round them thinned, thinned out into nothingness. No ripping, no violent severance, but the bag gave way.

The blackberries shot out at Dad's feet. They pattered impudently over his Wellington boots, nestled there in a squashy heap. Val, looking down at them, knew they were wasted. She had gathered them, and she had literally thrown them away. She lifted her eyes to Dad's face; his brows were heavy, his lips open and drawn back, his teeth showed, ground together.

Then he growled, in his way.

She turned and ran. She ran and ran, as fast as she could, to get away. Fast and far she ran. Now, as she ran, there were pine trees on either side of her, an audience that watched her. Then she tripped and fell painfully over metal, and realized that she had reached the bicycles. She pulled her own bicycle from the heap and got on it and rode. The way was downhill and rough, and she was riding too fast for carefulness. She was shaken violently, as though someone were shaking a wicked child.

She followed the track by which they had come; then diverged into another. The way grew smoother; she passed a farmhouse; the surface under her wheels was made up now. She took another turn and another, and was in a narrow road between high hedges. She cycled on and came to a crossroads; two quiet country roads quietly meeting and crossing, with no signpost saying anything. Without consideration she took the turn towards the downward sloping of the sun and cycled on more slowly. She knew that she was lost, and she was glad of it.

She found that she had a headache. She was surprised at the headache and wondered if the tight-tied handkerchief had caused it. Then she connected the feeling in her head with a feeling in her stomach: she was hungry. They had all been hungry for the picnic even before the pirate-fight, and she had ridden away without eating.

She was so tired and hungry that she cried a little as she pedalled along. She knew she had nearly twenty pence in the pocket of her anorak. She could buy herself some food.

But these were not roads with shops on them. Another farm, a derelict cottage, and suddenly a bungalow with a notice at the gate: "Fruit. Veg."

She leant her bicycle against the hedge and went up the path towards the front door. But the front door had a neglected look, and a motor mower was parked right against it, under the shelter of the porch. She turned and went round the side of the bungalow, following a path but also a faint, enticing smell. The smell grew stronger, more exciting. The side door she came to was also a kitchen door, and it stood ajar. From inside came a smell of roast meat and of delicious baking.

Val went right up to the door and peered in. The kitchen was empty of people. A meal had just been finished. A baby's highchair stood near the table, its tray spattered with mashed potato and gravy. There was no food left on the table except more mashed potato and the remains of a treacle tart in a baking tin.

And there was the smell, overwhelming now.

Val inhaled and looked.

A door opened and a young woman came into the kitchen. She picked up the tin with the treacle tart in it, evidently to put it away somewhere. Then she saw Val's face at the crack of the door. She gave a gasp.

Val pushed the door wide open to show how harmless she was, and with the same intention said, "I saw the notice at the gate."

"Oh," said the woman, recovering, "that shouldn't be there still. Should have come down last week. We've not much stuff left, you see. What did you want? Vegetable marrow?"

"Something to eat now," said Val. The woman had put the treacle tart down on the table again.

"Blackberries?" the woman suggested.

"No," said Val. "Not blackberries. Thank you."

The woman had been staring at her. "Why's your head tied up? Have you had an accident? You're very pale."

"No," said Val. "I'm all right really." The woman's hand was still on the treacle tart tin; she remained staring.

"You have had an accident."

"Not really." Val didn't want to think of what had happened among the brambles. "I fell off my bike."

The woman left the treacle tart and came across to Val. She slipped the handkerchief from her head and laid it aside. She examined Val's brow. "It's really only a scratch, but it's bled a lot. You sit down." She cleaned the wound and then dressed it with a plaster. Then, "You'd better have some tea. I was going to make a pot while the baby slept." She boiled the kettle and made the tea. She also cleared the kitchen table, taking the treacle tart away and shutting it into a larder. Val watched it go, over the cup of tea the woman poured for her.

Next the woman opened the oven door just a crack. A smell of baking, hot, dry, delicious, came out and made straight for Val. The woman was peering into the oven; "Ah," she said. "Yes." She opened the oven door wide and took out two tin trays of scones, done to a turn. She got out a wire rack and began to transfer the scones one by one from the trays to the rack. They were so hot that she picked each one up by the tips of her fingers and very quickly.

"Have another cup," she said hospitably to Val.

"I won't have any more to drink, thank you," Val said. The scones sat on their wire rack, radiating heat and smell. The woman finished with the trays and began washing up.

There were footsteps outside and a young man appeared, carrying a pig-bucket. He left it just outside and came in. "Hello!" he said to Val. "Where've you sprung from?"

"She fell off her bike. I've given her a cup of tea." The woman dried her hands. "You might like a scone, too?"

Val nodded. She couldn't say anything.

The woman slit a scone, buttered it, and handed it to her.

"What about me?" asked the man.

"You!" said the woman. From the rack she chose a scone, misshapen but huge, made from the last bits of dough clapped together. She slit it, pushed a hunk of butter inside, and gave it to him.

"Would you like another?" she asked Val.

Val said she would. The woman watched her eating the second scone. "Haven't you had much dinner?"

Val didn't decide what she was going to say. It came at once. "The others all rode away from me when I fell off my bike. Rode off with the picnic."

The woman was indignant. "But didn't you try to catch up with them again?"

"I got lost."

The woman gave Val a third scone and her husband a second. She went to the larder and came back with the treacle tart, which she set before Val. "There's a nice surprise for you," she said.

They asked where Val lived, and when she told them, the man said, "Quite a way on a bike."

Val said, "If you could tell me how to get to the main road from here, all these lanes, and not many signposts . . ."

"Tricky," said the man.

Then the woman said, "Weren't you taking the van to the garage some time to get that part?"

"Ah," said the man. "Yes. I could set her on her way. Room for the bike in the back."

"No hurry," the woman said to Val. "You sit there."

Away somewhere a baby began to cry, and the woman went to fetch it. While she was out of the kitchen, the man helped himself to another scone and butter, winking at Val. The woman came back with the baby in her arms. "You!" she said to the man. He kissed her with his mouth full of scone, and kissed the baby.

The woman said to Val, "You hold her while I finish the washing up." So Val held the baby, smelling of cream cheese and warm woollies and talcum powder. The baby seemed to like her.

"Well," the man said to Val, "I'll be back for you later."

His wife gave him the old mashed potato and other remains for the pig-bucket. "It wasn't worth your coming for it specially," she said.

"No," he said. "But I remembered about the scones."

"You!" she said.

He laughed and went off with his pig-bucket again.

Val nursed the baby, and gave it a rusk, and helped to change its nappies, and played with it.

The mother cleared and cleaned the kitchen and washed out the nappies.

It all took some time. Then the man came again.

"Ready?" he said to Val. Val took her anorak, that the baby had been sucking, and went with him. He had already hoisted the bicycle into the back of the van. The woman came to the gate with the baby in her arms. The baby slapped at the notice saying "Fruit. Veg." "You never got round to taking that notice down," the woman said to her husband. He grunted, busy with the van. Val kissed goodbye to the baby, who took a piece of her cheek and twisted it.

Then Val got into the van and they drove off. Val was not noticing the way they took; she was thinking of the warm, sweet-smelling kitchen they had left. As they drove along, she half-thought they passed one of the two farmhouses she had noticed earlier when she was cycling, but that was all.

She began to think of what it would be like when she got home.

They reached the main road at last and drove along it a short way to the garage. Here the man lifted Val's bicycle out of the van, and she mounted it. He gave her clear directions to get her on her way, ending with, "You should be home well before dusk."

So she was, and they were all waiting for her. Even Chris was there. The Turner children had wanted to stay, too, but Dad had packed them off home.

There was a great explosion from Dad about what had happened at the blackberry pick and after. Val was given some tea, but the row from Dad went on during it and after it. Their mother started her ironing; Chris settled down to TV; Peter played a quiet but violent game with soldiers and tanks behind the couch. Dad went on and on.

"And what about that sticking-plaster?" he shouted suddenly. Their mother knocked the iron against the ironing board, almost toppling it. "Where's my red handkerchief that I lent you?"

In a flash of memory Val saw the red handkerchief laid aside on the dresser in that scone-smelling, baby-smelling kitchen. "A woman gave me a cup of tea," she said. "She took the handkerchief off and put the plaster on instead. I must have left the handkerchief there."

"My red handkerchief!" Dad shouted.

"Oh," muttered Chris, without taking his eyes off TV, "a red cotton handkerchief!"

"I'm sorry," Val said to Dad.

"Sorry!"

Then Dad cross-questioned her: who was this woman, and where did she live? All Val could say was that she lived quite a way from the bramble patch and from the main road, in a bungalow with a notice at the gate saying "Fruit. Veg."

"Right," said Dad. "You'll come with me tomorrow. You'll cycle back the way you came. You'll help me search until we find that bungalow and the woman and my red handkerchief."

So the next day—Sunday—Val cycled with her father alone into the country. Just the two of them—once she would have loved that.

He led them systematically to and fro among the country lanes. "Do you recognize this road? Could that be the bungalow? Look, girl, *look*!" Dad knew his map, and he was thorough in his crisscrossing of the countryside; but they saw few bungalows, and none with a notice at the gate saying "Fruit. Veg."

As they passed one bungalow, Val looked up the path to the front door. Against it, under the shelter of the porch, was parked a motor mower. Also a pole with a board at the top; the inscription on the board faced the front door. And behind the glass of a window Val thought she saw movement—the odd, top-heavy shape of someone carrying a child. But they were cycling past too quickly for her to be sure.

When they got home at last, Dad was too tired to go on with the row. He just said, "A day wasted!"

Val was even more tired, and she said nothing.

He beheld a most beautiful sight.

THE STORY OF WANG LI

Elizabeth Coatsworth

Once in China many many years ago there lived a young man named Wang Li, with his old mother, on a small farm under the shadow of the Hill of the Seven Stars. When he was a boy he studied letters and charms with a famous sage who lived by himself in the Wind Cave halfway up the mountain. But when he had studied for several years he declared one morning that he would climb the rough path no more.

His mother was in despair.

"How hard have I labored without your help in the fields!" she cried. "Why, in a few years you could have called the cranes out of the sky to carry us anywhere we wished or turned flower petals into money to buy whatever we desired! Ungrateful son! Return to your studies!"

But Wang Li only shook his head.

"I have learned all that I need," he replied. *"A big heart is better than a big house."*

Upon hearing a proverb quoted at her, Wang Li's mother grew furious, and seizing her broom, beat Wang Li over the shoulders until she was tired. He, being a filial son in most matters, waited until she had stopped, and then brought her a drink of cold water fresh from the well.

After that Wang Li helped his mother in the fields, but often he slipped away to the forests at the foot of the Hill of the Seven Stars with his bow and arrow, to wander in their green shades and perhaps bring back a hare for their dinner, until he became as expert a hunter as there was in the countryside.

So the days went by and at last there came a dry spring. Week after week passed and still no rain fell and the young rice and millet shoots stood small and yellow in the fields, and the mulberry leaves hung withered on the trees, unfit for the silkworms, and the melon vines lay brittle as straws on the baked ground. Prayers were said all day long in the Temple of the God of the Soil. Incense burned in great twisted ropes of sweetness about his nostrils, gongs were sounded before him, and offerings of fish and chickens and pork lay heaped on his altars.

But still no rain fell.

Early one morning Wang Li was wandering in the forest when he saw something above his head that looked like a flight of great swans, slowly settling down toward the clear waters of Heaven Mirror Lake. Creeping without sound through the underbrush, he at last came to a thicket at the very edge of the water, and parting the leaves with careful hands, he beheld a most beautiful sight. The creatures whom he had seen were not swans but winged maidens who were playing about on the surface, splashing the water until it shone like the crystal beads in their elaborate headdresses, shaking their white wings with a sound like music, clapping their delicate hands, and pursuing one another in sport.

It happened that during their games the most beautiful of the damsels passed close to the thicket where Wang Li was hidden. Swift as a hawk he seized one snow-white wing in his strong hand, and while the other maidens rose screaming into the air, he drew his lovely captive to the shore.

For a little while she wept, but glancing at him through her lashes, she was reassured and ceased to sob. Still holding the edge of one bright wing, he questioned her.

"What is your name, beautiful one?" he asked.

"I am called the Sky Damsel and am the youngest daughter of the Cloud Dragon," she answered timidly. And then went on: "You are the first human being

I have ever seen. If you will come with me I will take you to the sixteen palaces of my father that are built upon the clouds. One palace is of white jade and silver, and butterflies guard the gates; another palace is built of marble inlaid with rose quartz, and its gardens are famous for their peonies; another palace has walls of gold and is overlooked by a high pagoda on which stands the bird of the sun to crow to the dawn; and the last palace is built of ebony with pavilions of scarlet lacquer, and Lightning stands on the left of the gate and Thunder on the right. If you will come, you shall be my husband and live in whichever palace you please, and you shall ride on steeds of vapor and pluck the stars as you pass."

"I am a poor man," said Wang Li, "and the son of a poor man. How should I live in a palace? But if I give you your freedom, Sky Damsel, will you swear to me that in return you will ask your august parent to send upon this unfortunate countryside the requisite rains, so that the crops shall flourish and the people may not die? And he might keep a special eye on my mother's little farm at the foot of Seven Stars Hill," he added, "for she works hard and likes her garden to do well."

"It shall be as you have said," replied the Sky Damsel, and she flew away, often looking back and weeping.

But Wang Li returned home, and as he neared his mother's house the rain began to fall, soft and warm, filling all the ditches with the gurgle of running water.

"Rejoice," cried his mother as he entered, "the drought is over! And just in time, too! Now the crops will be spared. I wonder how it occurred?"

"Oh, I know all about *that,*" said Wang Li, and he told her what had happened by the lonely shore of Heaven Mirror Lake.

At once his mother flew into a rage.

"And you only asked for rain," she screamed, "when we might have lived in palaces, and worn silk woven from moonlight, and fed on the fruit of the immortals! Oh, you undutiful son!"

And she fell to beating him with her broom. But when at last she stopped, exhausted, he only remarked: *"A chicken coop is still a chicken coop even when covered with cloth of gold."* And he lifted a pot of dumplings which was in danger of boiling over.

Now the next year it happened that Roving Horse River was in flood, spreading out over its banks, ruining fields, and carrying away houses. Its waters came up nearly to the door of the cottage where Wang Li and his mother lived, and threatened her mulberry trees. She was in despair and wept bitterly, but Wang Li took his bow and arrow from the wall.

"Are you going hunting at such a time?" she screamed. "Oh, that I should have borne a son with no heart!"

But he only said: *"If you know how, a thing is not hard; if it is hard, then you don't know how."* And he left her with her mouth open, not understanding what he meant.

"I wish that boy would stop quoting proverbs," she muttered to herself. "He is as clever a boy as ever breathed, but what good does it do us?"

Meantime Wang Li walked along beside the bank of the river. And he saw the flood coming down in a great white wave. And having very keen eyes he saw in the midst of the wave a youth and a maiden, clothed in garments of white silk, riding white horses with silver bits. And attendants on white horses followed them.

Then Wang Li drew his bow, fitted an arrow into the string, and let it fly straight into the heart of the young man, who fell dead from his horse. At that the others turned their horses and rode away at full speed, and the flood receded with them.

But as they rode, Wang Li sent another arrow after them which pierced the high headdress of the noble lady and shone there like a long ornament. And after a few paces, she reined in her horse and slowly rode back to where Wang Li stood.

"Here is your arrow," she said, giving it to him. "I suppose I should thank you for not sending it through my heart as you did through my cousin's, the Prince of Roving Horse River."

"I could never do anything so discourteous," murmured Wang Li.

The lady regarded him for a long time.

"Since you have spared my person," she said, "I suppose it should be yours. If you will come with me you shall be my husband, and reign in the palaces of the River Dragons. You shall sit on a throne of coral in halls of jade and crystal, and the River Maidens shall dance before you the Dance of the Ripples, and the River Warriors shall dance to please you the Dance of the Tempest."

"And what will happen to the countryside while they dance?" asked Wang Li. "No, no, I am a poor man and the son of a poor man. What should I do in palaces? If you wish to show your gratitude, make me a pledge that the river shall hereafter stay within its banks, and perhaps you might be especially careful along the edge of my mother's farm, for she is a poor woman and it grieves her to see her work washed away."

The lady raised her hand in agreement, and turned her horse and rode off. But before she disappeared forever, she looked back for a last glimpse of Wang Li, and he saw that she was weeping. A little sad, he returned to his mother's house and, as he walked, he noticed how the waters were draining off the land, leaving behind them, as tribute, pools filled with round-mouthed fish.

His mother met him at the door.

"See! see!" she cried. "The waters are withdrawing! But you, you wicked son, you left me here to drown and little you cared!"

51

"Indeed, I only went to bring you help!" said Wang Li, and he told his mother all that had happened. At hearing the story she nearly choked with rage.

"What! We might have lived in river palaces and dined off turtle eggs and carps' tongues every day!" she cried. "And I might have ridden on a dragon forty feet long when I went calling! All this might have been mine but you refused it, you ungrateful son!" And she seized her broom.

Whack!

"Take that!"

Whack!

"And that!"

Whack! Whack! Whack!

"And that! and that! and that!"

But when at last her arm fell, Wang Li politely helped her to her chair and brought her a fan.

"Peace in a thatched hut—that is happiness," he said, once more quoting an old proverb.

"Be off with you!" replied his mother. "You are a wicked, ungrateful son and have no right to be using the words of wise men. Besides, they hadn't been offered palaces, I'm sure."

So the months passed and the rain fell when it was needed, and the river remained within its banks and reflected on its smooth waters the sun by day and the moon by night. But after some time the country was greatly disturbed by earthquakes. People were awakened from their sleep by the tremblings of their beds, the dishes danced on the tables, sheds fell flat to the earth, and everyone waited with horror for the final quake that should bring their roofs down about their heads.

"Now," wept Wang Li's old mother, "I shall die a violent death, I who might have slept safe beside the Silver Stream of Heaven or walked in the gardens of the river, if it had not been for this great foolish son."

But Wang Li took his spear and went to the mouth of the Cave of the Evening Sun which is on the west side of the Hill of the Seven Stars. Then he looked carefully at the ground beneath his feet, which was rounded up as though a huge mole had passed under it, and choosing a certain spot, drove his spear deep into the loosened soil.

"Whoever walks along that path again will scratch his back," he said to himself with satisfaction, and was about to return home when he noticed a beautiful girl who sat beside a rock spinning, and weeping as she spun.

"Why do you scatter the pearls of your eyes, young maiden?" asked Wang Li gently. And she, raising her tear-wet eyes to him, said:

"Alas, I am Precious Jade, the only daughter of the former Dragon King of the Mountains. But my ungrateful uncle has risen against his elder brother and imprisoned him in the innermost prison of the hills, and he has driven me out to work with unaccustomed hands, living in this coarse robe, and eating roots and berries, and sleeping under the stars."

Wang Li looked at her in her rough brown garments, and her beauty seemed like a flower bursting from its sheath.

"I think I have stopped the path of your uncle who has been disturbing us with his wanderings, and now perhaps he will stay in his cavern palaces. But for you I can do nothing, I fear, though I would gladly serve you."

At that Precious Jade looked at him shyly.

"If you would deign to take me away with you and allow me to serve your mother with my poor strength, I should no longer weep alone on this desolate mountain," she whispered.

"And what gifts would you bring my mother if I took you home as a bride?" asked Wang Li.

Then Precious Jade wrung her hands. "Alas," she said, "I have no gifts but only my will to serve you both." And she wept very bitterly.

At that Wang Li laughed and lifted her up in his arms and carried her home to his mother.

"Mercy!" cried the old woman. "Whom have we here?"

"It is Precious Jade, the daughter of the former Dragon King of the Mountains," said Wang Li, "and she has returned here to be your daughter-in-law."

The old woman was all in a flutter.

"I must have an hour to get ready before I can present myself at court. How many guests will there be at the feast, my little dove? And how many rooms shall I have in the palace? And what color are the lanterns, or does light shine from the gems themselves in the Kingdom of the Mountain Dragons?"

"Alas!" said Precious Jade. "My father is a prisoner and I am only an exile."

"Pshaw!" exclaimed the old woman. "What a daughter-in-law for you to bring back, you senseless oaf! Look at the robe she is wearing, and her hands are fit for nothing! Go and bring me a pail of water, you useless girl! As for you," she cried, turning to her son, "you shall feel if my old arms are withered yet!" And she caught up her broom and began belaboring him with it.

"*A thin horse has long hair,*" remarked Wang Li philosophically when she had done, and he went out into the garden to find her a peach to refresh her after so much effort.

"I shall have to make the best of it," she grumbled to herself, when she had eaten the peach. "The boy has ears of stone. He follows his own way. *If the mountain will not turn, I must be the road and do the turning myself.*" After that she was kind to Precious Jade, who tried to be of help to her mother-in-law in every possible way.

So they lived together in peace and happiness, working hard, incurring no debts, and showing kindness to all. Throughout the district the rains fell punctually, no one had any complaint of Roving Horse River, and the earth was no longer shaken by the burrowing of dragons. In time Precious Jade bore a beautiful son whom they named Little Splendor and there were never four happier people in the world. One day, not long afterward, as Wang Li and Precious Jade sat alone beneath a grapevine trellis, which Wang Li had recently made, Precious Jade began, laying down her embroidery:

"My dear husband, a message has reached me from my father. It seems that my unworthy uncle, issuing forth hastily from his palace, struck himself against the point of your spear and after some time died. My father is again on his jewel throne, and naturally feels a deep gratitude towards you." She paused.

"Now you are going to tell me about the palaces under the mountains which I may have for the asking," said Wang Li.

"I always hated palaces. There was never anything to do," said Precious Jade, smiling. Then she went back to her embroidery.

"My husband is the proudest man in the world," she remarked to a yellow silk butterfly which she had not quite finished.

"Proud?" asked Wang Li. "Yet here I am and I might be a prince."

"You're too proud to be a prince," she replied, "and that is why I love you. I always wanted to marry the proudest man in the world."

"Maybe it's pride and maybe it's wisdom," said Wang Li, "but there are palaces and terraces of the mind I would not exchange for all the riches of the dragons."

And Precious Jade understood. In time Wang Li became so famous for his wisdom and benevolence that sages traveled from the farthest provinces to walk with him as he followed his plow. But sometimes when he was busy and the old mother needed a new silk gown or the baby wanted sweetmeats, Precious Jade would softly shake the leaves of the tree beside the door, and down would fall a light shower of silver coins. And Wang Li never noticed what it was that Precious Jade gathered under the mulberry tree.

The wet park was glittering all around him.

THE HEMULEN WHO LOVED SILENCE

Tove Jansson

Once upon a time there was a hemulen who worked in a pleasure ground, which doesn't necessarily mean having a lot of fun. The hemulen's job was to punch holes in tickets, so that people wouldn't have fun more than once, and such a job is quite enough to make anyone sad if you have to do it all your life.

The hemulen punched and punched, and while punching he used to dream of the things he would do when he got his pension at last.

In case someone doesn't know what a pension is, it means that you can do what you like in all the peace you wish for, when you're old enough. At least that was how the hemulen's relatives had explained it to him.

He had terribly many relatives, a great lot of enormous, rollicking, talkative hemulens who went

59

about slapping each others' backs and bursting into gigantic laughs.

They were joint owners of the pleasure ground, and in their spare time they blew the trombone or threw the hammer, told funny stories, and frightened people generally. But they did it all with the best of intentions. The hemulen himself didn't own anything because he was on the sideline, which means only half a relative, and as he never could put his foot down about anything to anyone he always had to do the babysitting, to work the big bellows of the merry-go-round, and, most of the time, to punch tickets.

"You're lonely and have nothing to do," the other hemulens used to tell him in their friendly way. "So it might cheer you up a bit to lend a hand and be among people."

"But I'm never lonely," the hemulen tried to explain. "I can't find the time to be. There's always such a lot of people who want to cheer me up. If you don't mind, I'd like so much to . . ."

"Splendid," the relatives said and slapped his back. "That's the thing. Never lonely, always on the go."

The hemulen punched along, dreaming about a great wonderful silent loneliness, and hoped he would grow old as soon as possible.

The whirligigs whirled, the trombones trumpeted, gaffsies and whompers and mymbles shrieked in the roller coaster every night. Edward the Booble won a first prize in china smashing, and all around the sad and dreamy hemulen people danced and whooped, laughed and quarreled, and ate and drank, and by and by the hemulen grew simply afraid of noisy people who were enjoying themselves.

He used to sleep in the hemulen children's dormitory, that was bright and nice in the daytime, and at night when the kiddies awoke and cried he comforted them with a barrel organ.

The rest of his spare time he lent a hand anywhere it was needed in a large house full of hemulens, and so he had company around the clock, and everybody was in high spirits and told him all about everything they thought and did and planned to do. Only they never gave him time to reply properly.

"Won't I grow old soon?" the hemulen once asked at dinner.

"Old? You?" his uncle shouted. "Far from it. Buck up, buck up, nobody's older than he feels."

"But I feel really old," the hemulen said hopefully.

"Pish, posh," the uncle said. "We're going to have an extra spot of fireworks tonight, and the brass band will play until sunrise."

But the fireworks never were touched off, because that same afternoon a great rain started to fall. It continued all night and all the next day, and the next one after that, and then all the following week.

To tell the truth, this rain kept up for eight weeks without a stop. No one had ever seen the like.

The pleasure ground lost its colors, shrunk, and withered away like a flower. It paled and rusted, and then it slowly started to disperse, because it was built on sand.

The roller coaster railway caved in with a sigh, and the merry-go-rounds went slowly turning around in large gray pools and puddles, until they were swept off, faintly tinkling, by the new rivers that were formed by the rain. All small kiddies, toffles and woodies and whompers and mymbles, and so forth, were standing days on end with their snouts pressed to the windowpanes, looking at their July becoming drenched and their color and music floating away.

The House of Mirrors came crashing
down in millions of wet splinters, and pink
drenched paper roses from the Miracle
Garden went bobbing off in hundreds
over the fields. Over it all rose the wailing
chorus of the kiddies.

They were driving their parents to
desperation, because they hadn't a single
thing to do except grieve over the lost pleasure ground.

Streamers and empty balloons were drooping from
the trees, the Happy House was filled with mud, and
the three-headed alligator swam off to the sea. He left
two of his heads behind him, because they had been
glued on.

The hemulens took it all as a splendid joke. They
stood at their windows, laughing and pointing and
slapping backs, and shouted:

"Look! There goes the curtain to the Arabian Nights!
The dancing floor has come loose! There's five black bats
from the Cave of Horror on the fillyjonk's roof! Did
you ever!"

They decided in the best of spirits to start a skating
rink instead, when the water froze, of course—and they
tried to comfort the hemulen by promising him the
ticket-punching job again as soon as they could get
things going.

"No," the hemulen suddenly said. "No, no, no.
I don't want to. I want my pension. I want to do what

I feel like doing, and I want to be absolutely alone in some silent place."

"But my dear nephew," one of his uncles said with enormous astonishment, "do you mean what you say?"

"I do," said the hemulen. "Every word of it."

"But why haven't you told us before?" the perplexed relatives asked him. "We've always believed that you've enjoyed yourself."

"I never dared tell you," the hemulen admitted.

At this they all laughed again and thought it terribly funny that the hemulen had had to do things he disliked all his life, only because he hadn't been able to put his foot down.

"Well, now, what *do* you want to do?" his maternal aunt asked cheerfully.

"I'd like to build myself a doll's house," the hemulen whispered. "The most beautiful doll's house in the world, with lots and lots of rooms, and all of them silent and solemn and empty."

Now the hemulens laughed so hard that they had to sit down. They gave each other enormous nudges and shouted, "A doll's house! Did you hear that! He said a doll's house!" and then they laughed themselves into tears and told him:

"Little dear, by all means do exactly as you like! You can have grandma's big park, very probably it's silent as a grave nowadays. That's the very place for you to rummage about in and play to your heart's content. Good luck to you, and hope you like it!"

"Thanks," the hemulen said, feeling a little shrunken inwardly. "I know you've always wished me well."

His dream about the doll's house with the calm and beautiful rooms vanished; the hemulens had laughed it to pieces. But it really was no fault of theirs. They would have felt sincerely sorry if anyone had told them that they had spoiled something for the hemulen. And it's a risky thing to talk about one's most secret dreams a bit too early.

The hemulen went along to grandma's old park that was now his own. He had the key in his pocket.

The park had been closed and never used since grandma had set fire to her house with fireworks and moved elsewhere with all her family.

That was long ago, and the hemulen was even a little uncertain about the way to the park.

The wood had grown, and ways and paths were underwater. While he was splashing along, the rain stopped as suddenly as it had started eight weeks ago. But the hemulen didn't notice it. He was wholly occupied with grieving over his lost dream and with feeling sorry because he didn't want to build a doll's house anymore.

Now he could see the park wall. A little of it had tumbled down, but it was still quite a high wall. The single gate was rusty and very hard to unlock.

The hemulen went in and locked the gate behind him. Suddenly he forgot about the doll's house. It was the first time in his life that he had opened a door of his own and shut it behind him. He was home. He didn't live in someone else's house.

The rain clouds were slowly drifting away and the sun came out. The wet park was steaming and glittering all around him. It was green and unworried. No one had cut or trimmed or swept it for a very, very long time. Trees were reaching branches down to the ground, bushes were climbing the trees and crisscrossing, and in the luscious grass tinkled the brooks that grandma had led through the park in her time. They didn't take care of the watering any longer, they took care only of themselves, but many of the little bridges were still standing even if the garden paths had disappeared.

The hemulen threw himself headlong into the green, friendly silence, he made capers in it, he wallowed in it, and he felt younger than he ever had before.

Oh, how wonderful to be old and pensioned at last, he thought. How much I like my relatives! And now I needn't even think of them.

He went wading through the long, sparkling grass, he threw his arms around the trees, and finally he went to sleep in the sunshine in a clearing in the middle of the park. It was the place where grandma's house had been. Her great fireworks parties were finished long ago. Young trees were coming up all around him, and in grandma's bedroom grew an enormous rosebush with a thousand red hips.

Night fell, lots of large stars came out, and the hemulen loved his park all the better. It was wide and mysterious, one could lose one's way in it and still be at home.

He wandered about for hours.

He found grandma's old fruit orchard where apples and pears lay strewn in the grass, and for a moment he thought, What a pity. I can't eat half of them. One ought to . . . And then he forgot the thought, enchanted by the loneliness of the silence.

He was the owner of the moonlight on the ground, he fell in love with the most beautiful of the trees, he made wreaths of leaves and hung them around his neck. During this first night he hardly had the heart to sleep at all.

In the morning the hemulen heard a tinkle from the old bell that still hung by the gate. He felt worried.

Someone was outside and wanted to come in, someone wanted something from him. Silently he crept in under the bushes along the wall and waited without a word. The bell jangled again. The hemulen craned his neck and saw a very small whomper waiting outside the gate.

"Go away," the hemulen called anxiously. "This is private ground. I live here."

"I know," the small whomper replied. "The hemulens sent me here with some dinner for you."

"Oh, I see, that was kind of them," the hemulen replied willingly. He unlocked the gate and took the basket from the whomper. Then he shut the gate again. The whomper remained where he was for a while but didn't say anything.

"And how are you getting on?" the hemulen asked impatiently. He stood fidgeting and longed to be back in his park again.

"Badly," the whomper replied honestly. "We're in a bad way all of us. We who are small. We've got no pleasure ground anymore. We're just grieving."

"Oh," the hemulen said, staring at his feet. He didn't want to be asked to think of dreary things, but he was so accustomed to listening that he couldn't go away either.

"You must be grieving, too," the whomper said with compassion. "You used to punch the tickets. But if one was very small and ragged and dirty you punched beside it. And we could use it two or three times."

"My eyesight wasn't so good," the hemulen explained. "They're waiting for you at home, aren't they?"

The whomper nodded but stayed on. He came close to the gate and thrust his snout through it. "I must tell you," he whispered. "We've got a secret."

The hemulen made a gesture of fright, because he disliked other people's secrets and confidences. But the whomper continued excitedly:

"We've rescued nearly all of it. We keep it in the fillyjonk's barn. You can't believe how much we've worked. Rescued and rescued. We stole out at nights in the rain and pulled things out of the water and down from the trees and dried them and repaired them, and now it's nearly right!"

"What is?" asked the hemulen.

"The pleasure ground of course!" the whomper cried. "Or as much of it as we could find, all the pieces there were left! Splendid, isn't it! Perhaps the hemulens will put it together again for us, and then you can come back and punch the tickets."

"Oh," the hemulen mumbled and put the basket on the ground.

"Fine, what! That made you blink," the whomper said, laughed, waved his hand, and was off.

Next morning the hemulen was anxiously waiting by the gate, and when the whomper came with the dinner basket he called at once: "Well? What did they say?"

"They didn't want to," the whomper said dejectedly. "They want to run a skating rink instead. And most of us go to sleep in winter, and anyway, where'd we get skates from . . ."

"That's too bad," the hemulen said, feeling quite relieved.

The whomper didn't reply, he was so disappointed. He just put down the basket and turned back.

Poor children, the hemulen thought for a moment. Well, well. And then he started to plan the leaf hut he was going to build on grandma's ruins.

The hemulen worked at his building all day and enjoyed himself tremendously. He stopped only when it was too dark to see anything, and then he went to sleep, tired and contented, and slept late the next morning.

When he went to the gate to fetch his food the whomper had been there already. On the basket lid he found a letter signed by several kiddies. "Dear pleasure puncher," the hemulen read. "You can have all of it because you are all right, and perhaps you will let us play with you sometime because we like you."

The hemulen didn't understand a word, but a horrible suspicion began burrowing in his stomach.

Then he saw. Outside the gate the kiddies had heaped all the things they had rescued from the pleasure ground. It was a lot. Most of it was broken and tattered and wrongly reassembled, and all of it looked strange. It was a lost and miscellaneous collection of boards, canvas, wire, paper, and rusty iron. It was looking sadly and unexpectantly at the hemulen, and he looked back in a panic.

Then he fled into his park and started on his leaf hut again.

He worked and worked, but nothing went quite right. His thoughts were elsewhere, and suddenly the roof came down and the hut laid itself flat on the ground.

No, said the hemulen. I don't want to. I've only just learned to say no. I'm pensioned. I do what I like. Nothing else.

He said these things several times over, more and more menacingly. Then he rose to his feet, walked through the park, unlocked the gate, and began to pull all the blessed junk and scrap inside.

The kiddies were sitting perched on the high wall around the hemulen's park. They resembled gray sparrows but were quite silent.

At times someone whispered, "What's he doing now?"

"Hush," said another. "He doesn't like to talk."

The hemulen had hung some lanterns and paper roses in the trees and turned all broken and ragged parts out of sight. Now he was assembling something that had once been a merry-go-round. The parts did not fit together very well, and half of them seemed to be missing.

"It's no use," he shouted crossly. "Can't you see? It's just a lot of scrap and nothing else! No!! I won't have any help from you."

A murmur of encouragement and sympathy was carried down from the wall, but not a word was heard.

The hemulen started to make the merry-go-round into a kind of house instead. He put the horses in the grass and the swans in the brook, turned the rest upside down, and worked with his hair on end. Doll's house! he thought bitterly. What it all comes to in the end is a lot of tinsel and gewgaws on a dustheap, and a noise and racket like it's been all my life. . . .

Then he looked up and shouted:

"What are you staring at? Run along to the hemulens and tell them I don't want any dinner tomorrow! Instead they might send me nails and a hammer and candles and ropes and some two-inch battens, and they'd better be quick about it."

The kiddies laughed and ran off.

"Didn't we tell him," the hemulens cried and slapped each other's backs. "He has to have something to do. The poor little thing's longing for his pleasure ground."

And they sent him twice what he had asked for and, furthermore, food for a week, and ten yards of red velvet, gold and silver paper in rolls, and a barrel organ just in case.

"No," said the hemulen. "No music box. Nothing that makes a noise."

"Of course not," the kiddies said and kept the barrel organ outside.

The hemulen worked, built, and constructed. And while building he began to like the job, rather against his will. High in the trees thousands of mirror glass splinters glittered, swaying with the branches in the winds. In the treetops the hemulen made little benches and soft nests where people could sit and have a drink of juice without being observed, or just sleep. And from the strong branches hung the swings.

The roller coaster railway was difficult. It had to be only a third of its former size, because so many parts were missing. But the hemulen comforted himself with the thought that no one could be frightened enough to scream in it now. And from the last stretch one was dumped in the brook, which is great fun to most people.

But still the railway was a bit too much for the hemulen to struggle with single-handed. When he had got one side right the other side fell down, and at last he shouted, very crossly:

"Lend me a hand, someone! I can't do ten things at once all alone."

The kiddies jumped down from the wall and came running.

After this they built it jointly, and the hemulens sent them such lots of food that the kiddies were able to stay all day in the park.

In the evening they went home,
but by sunrise they stood waiting
at the gate. One morning
they had brought along the
alligator on a string.

"Are you sure he'll keep quiet?" the hemulen asked
suspiciously.

"Quite sure," the whomper replied. "He won't say a
word. He's so quiet and friendly now that he's got rid of
his other heads."

One day the fillyjonk's son found the boa constrictor
in the porcelain stove. As it behaved nicely it was
immediately brought along to grandma's park.

Everybody collected strange things for the hemulen's
pleasure ground, or simply sent him cakes, kettles,
window curtains, toffee, or whatever. It became a fad

to send along presents with the kiddies in the mornings, and the hemulen accepted everything that didn't make a noise.

But he let no one inside the wall, except the kiddies.

The park grew more and more fantastic. In the middle of it the hemulen lived in the merry-go-round house. It was gaudy and lopsided, resembling most of all a large toffee paper bag that somebody had crumpled up and thrown away.

Inside it grew the rosebush with all the red hips.

And one beautiful, mild evening all was finished. It was definitely finished, and for one moment the sadness of completion overtook the hemulen.

They had lighted the lanterns and stood looking at their work.

Mirror glass, silver, and gold gleamed in the great dark trees; everything was ready and waiting—the ponds, the boats, the tunnels, the switchback, the juice stand, the swings, the dart boards, the trees for climbing, the apple boxes . . .

"Here you are," the hemulen said. "Just remember that this is *not* a pleasure ground, it's the Park of Silence."

The kiddies silently threw themselves into the enchantment they had helped to build. But the whomper turned and asked:

"And you won't mind that you've no tickets to punch?"

"No," said the hemulen. "I'd punch the air in any case."

He went into the merry-go-round and lighted the moon from the Miracle House. Then he stretched himself out in the fillyjonk's hammock and lay looking at the stars through a hole in the ceiling.

Outside all was silent. He could hear nothing except the nearest brook and the night wind.

Suddenly the hemulen felt anxious. He sat up, listening hard. Not a sound.

Perhaps they don't have any fun at all, he thought worriedly. Perhaps they're not able to have any fun without shouting their heads off. . . . Perhaps they've gone home?

He took a leap up on Gaffsie's old chest of drawers and thrust his head out of a hole in the wall. No, they hadn't gone home. All the park was rustling and seething with a secret and happy life. He could hear a splash, a giggle, faint thuds and thumps, padding feet everywhere. They *were* enjoying themselves.

Tomorrow, thought the hemulen, tomorrow I'll tell them they may laugh and possibly even hum a little if they feel like it. But not more than that. Absolutely not.

He climbed down and went back to his hammock. Very soon he was asleep and not worrying over anything.

Outside the wall, by the locked gate, the hemulen's uncle was standing. He looked through the bars but saw very little.

Doesn't sound as if they had much fun, he thought. But then, everyone has to make what he can out of life. And my poor relative always was a bit queer.

He took the barrel organ home with him because he had always loved music.

He quietly sat and enjoyed the world around him.

THE ENCHANTED STICKS

Steven J. Myers

Long ago in Japan, near the city of Kyoto, there was an old man who gathered wood in the forest. He picked up fallen limbs and sticks and traded them to the people of a nearby village for rice and tea.

He lived in a small hut at the edge of the forest by the side of a stream. He caught fish with his bare hands and ate them with his rice. After his evening meal he would sit in his doorway, slowly sip his tea, and quietly enjoy the world around him. He listened to the stream flowing by and the breeze in the leaves of the forest. He smelled the scents of the flowers and grass and fresh water. He felt the air soft and delicate on his skin.

One day when he was out gathering wood a band of twenty robbers jumped out from behind the trees. These robbers were both vicious and fearless. They respected no one and stole and killed without mercy.

The robber chief shouted at the old man and flashed his samurai sword.

The old man bowed in greeting, but showed no fear.

"Do you know who we are?" the robber chief asked.

The old man nodded.

"With this sword I could cut you into a thousand pieces to feed the crows. I could do that and it wouldn't bother me at all."

The old man nodded again.

"Oh, you're too stupid to be afraid!"

The old man bowed once more and smiled.

In the thick forest dark there were only a few shafts of light breaking through from the sky. There was the glint and slashing flash of the robber chief's sword in the rare light. Then, shouting "Hai!" he leaped into the air and with one swift slash he cut off the low limb of a tree. Before it hit the ground, he shouted and slashed so quickly that the limb flew apart in a shower of sticks.

The robber chief laughed and snorted. "Old man, *that* should have been you." And then with a wiggling, waltzing swagger-walk he headed toward Kyoto with his men following in poor and ragged imitation.

The old man gathered up the sticks cut by the robber chief. He took the largest one for a walking stick, and then he tied the rest into a bundle separate from the others because they were green and not much good for kindling.

Walking easily through the forest, slipping between the trees, he started home. Months passed and then one day when the old man was about to make a small fire to heat his tea, he dropped the sticks he was carrying. When he bent down he saw that they had fallen into the shape of the characters that spelled out: *Don't burn us!*

He shook his head and smiled. But when he tried to pick up the sticks, they wiggled in his hands and he dropped them again. And again they arranged themselves to say: *Don't burn us!*

This time he scrunched down to examine them closely. The sticks were from the bundle the robber chief had cut.

There was nothing unusual looking about them. They were just plain sticks. But as soon as the old man tried to pick up one, it wiggled loose and fell back into its place on the ground.

"All right," the old man said, "I won't burn you."

Then the sticks danced about and arranged themselves into a smiling face.

The old man laughed loudly and the sticks danced about. That only made him laugh more and the sticks dance more until the sticks and the old man were rolling around in dancing laughter.

After that the old man and the sticks *talked* every day. He shook the sticks a few times and tossed them into the air. They fell into words or, sometimes, whole sentences.

The old man and the sticks played tic-tac-toe. The old man was always the Os and the sticks were always the Xs. The sticks were good at the game, and the old man was pleased no matter who won.

And they would fence: mock sword fights between the old man and one of the sticks. The stick would dance about in the air, swinging and thrusting like the sword of an invisible samurai while the old man fought back with his walking stick. These carefree contests always ended in all the other sticks joining in to make the fight a wild clicking and light clattering of wood. And then the old man would fall down and surrender with laughter.

And when the old man hummed a song while he relaxed after his evening meal, the sticks clacked together beating time to the tune. Or on rare nights the sticks would take tufts of grass and strips of rag to dress themselves as dancers, actors, and animals. Then they would act out the legends from the far past. Afterward they danced, a slow formal dance, their makeshift kimonos flowing in soft waves in the moonlight.

And when the old man told a story, the sticks played the characters—the princes, the dragons, the lions, the lost maidens—as little stick figures, while the old man delighted in their dancing grace.

The old man was content with his life except—except that the band of robbers had grown larger and larger until now there were a hundred of them. No one was safe. They even attacked villages—taking food, clothes, anything they wanted. Then they burned the people's homes and escaped into the forest.

The emperor sent an army after them, but the robbers hid among the trees and thick brush. When the army entered the forest, a rain of arrows shot out of the green dark. Then the robbers jumped out with slashing swords and knives. They were so expert with bow and arrow and sword—especially the chief—that they easily scattered the army.

Then a band of eleven samurai—proud and brave and very skilled with sword and bow—went out to hunt down the robbers. But they got lost in the forest and wandered about, so that when they did find the robbers, the robber chief alone easily killed them.

A few months later the robbers boldly arrived at the outskirts of Kyoto itself, where they kidnapped a young maiden just as she was to marry a prince. The robber chief demanded a ransom so large that no one could pay. So he put the young girl in a bamboo cage and hung it from a tree. He gave her a samisen and ordered her to play and sing for him and his men.

She refused.

He told her that was fine with him, but she would only get rice if she sang. "A bird that doesn't sing isn't worth the bird seed," he said.

So she sang, but only sad songs. And all through the forest, people heard her sad music and soft song. But they thought that the robber chief had killed her and that it was only her ghost crying in the trees.

Every evening the old man listened to that song. He felt the sadness that thickened the air and dulled the quality of the light. Each note seemed a separate bird that settled on his skin and sank in to become an ache in his bones. Even the enchanted sticks no longer danced as easily or as lightly.

The old man knew something had to be done—but what? His mind was too clouded, too heavy. A clear stream of action couldn't flow from such a muddied source. So he meditated for three days. He just sat quietly by his hut—eating nothing, doing nothing.

Finally his mind was clear. He would ask the sticks.

He went to the stream for a long, cool drink, then into his hut for the enchanted sticks. He shook them and tossed them into the air.

They said: *You only need a small bundle of us. Follow the maiden's song.*

So he bundled the sticks in a strap, threw them over his shoulder, took his walking stick, and stepped out into the dark, night-tuned forest.

The maiden's music was a thread leading him through the night to the robbers' camp. In a few hours he was at the edge of a lake. Far out in the center he could see an island. By the light of four small fires he could see the shapes and shadows of men. He heard curses and rough voices. Then he saw a bamboo cage swaying from a high limb of a tree. The lovely sad song came from there.

The old man sat down at the edge of the water and waited all through the night. At first one fire was put out, then the second, the third, and finally the last one was only a soft orange-yellow glow. The music stopped. The cage swayed silently. Occasionally sounds of snoring came across the water.

The old man waited until morning. Then, in the early mist, he tossed the sticks into the air. They stuck together as if glued to form a ladder. Taking his walking stick, he climbed to the top. Then the enchanted sticks danced apart to become two tall stilts with the old man, his walking stick over his shoulder, calmly at ease upon them.

He walked out into the lake. The water rose slowly until at its deepest point it came up to his ankles. He paused to stir the water with his stick, rippling his strange reflection. Then he strode toward the island.

Two robbers guarded the island. They were half-asleep. They rubbed their eyes. They yawned. Suddenly one of them saw something move in the mist on the lake. He grabbed the other guard and tried to talk—but he was too frightened.

The second robber yelled, "Ghost! Ghost!" and ran away.

The other robbers, awakened by the screams, came running. The robber on guard jumped up and down and pointed. He still couldn't speak.

The old man continued toward them through the mist. The robbers rubbed their eyes. They thought he was walking on the lake. Some shouted. Others ran for their boats to escape. Others dove into the cold water and tried to swim away.

As the old man got closer to the island, the water became shallow. To the robbers, he appeared to grow taller and taller as he came with his eyes shining in the swirling mist.

The robber chief shouted at his men. He called them cowards. Screaming, "Kill the monster!" he rushed toward the old man.

But now the old man jumped down from his stilts. The sticks fell apart to become a bundle of arrows. He made his strap and walking stick into a bow and shot the enchanted arrows at the robbers. He couldn't miss. If a robber ducked, the arrow would whiz by, stop, and make a sharp turn to return to the target. Arrows curved around trees, jumped over rocks, went underground to pop up behind robbers and hit their bottoms.

Now, all the robbers ran away.

Except for the chief. He stood before the old man and flashed his sword.

The old man stepped forward and raised his walking stick to hit the robber chief.

The robber chief cut the stick in two.

The old man raised both pieces to hit the robber.

The robber slashed quicker than sight—and the 2 sticks were 4.

The old man then raised up 4 pieces to hit the robber.

The robber chief slashed and slashed.

Now the old man had 8 sticks.

The robber slashed.

The old man had 16 sticks.

The robber slashed sixteen times, cutting each stick in two.

The old man hit out with 32 sticks.

The robber, sweat pouring now, slashed thirty-two times.

The old man attacked with 64 sticks.

The robber chief cut those in two.

The old man had 128 sticks.

Now the robber chief was shouting and slashing about in a white-faced frenzy.

The old man attacked with 256 sticks.

The faster the robber chief slashed, the worse it got for him. He shouted "Hai! Hai! Hai!" as he cut and cut.

The old man struck with 512 sticks.

The robber chief was crying now. He was on his knees. Tears, dirt, and sweat covered his face. He tried once more, but his brilliant slashing gave the old man 1,024 sticks to attack with.

The robber fell face-down. Exhausted, he sobbed into the ground.

The old man shook his head, bent down to pick up the robber's sword, and threw it into the deep part of the lake. Then he walked over to the tree with the bamboo cage. He picked up several of his enchanted sticks and made a ladder. He climbed up to help the maiden from her cage. He placed her on his shoulders as he helped her down to the ground. Then he turned his sticks into stilts again. He carried the girl across the lake, where he made the sticks into a bundle. Then he put the girl on his shoulders once more and carried her all the way to her home.

When she told her father and family what had happened, everyone offered rich gifts to the old man.

But he said he only wanted the woods, the stream, and his hut.

The old man returned home, undid his bundle, and dropped the enchanted sticks. They scattered about, but said nothing. They formed no words, made no pictures. The old man tried again. Still nothing. Once more. No words.

He went to the stream, bent down, and scooped out two fish. He cleaned them and put them on a long stick. He got the bundle of enchanted sticks and arranged them into a tent-shaped pile. He took out his flint and struck it to light a handful of dry grass. He set the sticks on fire and cooked his fish. The fish were delicious and the fire crackled and the embers glowed for a long time.

Then the old man took a glowing stick and wrote on the evening air. With the glowing point he made designs, orange-yellow characters, warm-red profiles of lions, dragons, and fish.

And the old man laughed—as free and easy as a child.

This is the Elephant's Child having his nose pulled by the Crocodile. He is much surprised and astonished and hurt, and he is talking through his nose and saying, "Led go! You are hurtig be!" He is pulling very hard, and so is the Crocodile; but the Bi-Coloured-Python-Rock-Snake is hurrying through the water to help the Elephant's Child. All that black stuff is the banks of the great grey-green, greasy Limpopo River (but I am not allowed to paint these pictures), and the bottly tree with the twisty roots and the eight leaves is one of the fever trees that grow there.

Underneath the truly picture are shadows of African animals walking into an African ark. There are two lions, two ostriches, two oxen, two camels, two sheep, and two other things that look like rats, but I think they are rock-rabbits. They don't mean anything. I put them in because I thought they looked pretty. They would look very fine if I were allowed to paint them.   —R.K.

THE ELEPHANT'S CHILD

Rudyard Kipling

In the High and Far-Off Times the Elephant, O Best Beloved, had no trunk. He had only a blackish, bulgy nose, as big as a boot, that he could wriggle about from side to side; but he couldn't pick up things with it. But there was one Elephant—a new Elephant—an Elephant's Child—who was full of 'satiable curtiosity, and that means he asked ever so many questions. *And* he lived in Africa, and he filled all Africa with his 'satiable curtiosities. He asked his tall aunt, the Ostrich, why her tail feathers grew just so, and his tall aunt, the Ostrich, spanked him with her hard, hard claw. He asked his tall uncle, the Giraffe, what made his skin spotty, and his tall uncle, the Giraffe, spanked him with his hard, hard hoof. And still he was full of 'satiable curtiosity! He asked his broad aunt, the Hippopotamus, why her eyes were red, and his broad aunt, the Hippopotamus, spanked him with her broad, broad hoof; and he asked his hairy uncle, the Baboon, why melons tasted just so, and his hairy uncle, the Baboon, spanked him with his hairy, hairy paw. And *still* he was full of 'satiable curtiosity! He asked questions about everything that he saw, or heard, or felt, or smelt, or touched, and all his uncles and his aunts spanked him. And still he was full of 'satiable curtiosity!

One fine morning in the middle of the Precession of the Equinoxes this 'satiable Elephant's Child asked a new fine question that he had never asked before. He asked, "What does the Crocodile have for dinner?" Then everybody said, "Hush!" in a loud and dretful tone, and they spanked him immediately and directly, without stopping, for a long time.

By and by, when that was finished, he came upon Kolokolo Bird sitting in the middle of a wait-a-bit thorn bush, and he said, "My father has spanked me, and my mother has spanked me; all my aunts and uncles have spanked me for my 'satiable curtiosity; and *still* I want to know what the Crocodile has for dinner!"

Then Kolokolo Bird said, with a mournful cry, "Go to the banks of the great grey-green, greasy Limpopo River, all set about with fever trees, and find out."

That very next morning, when there was nothing left of the Equinoxes, because the Precession had preceded according to precedent, this 'satiable Elephant's Child took a hundred pounds of bananas (the little short red kind), and a hundred pounds of sugar cane (the long purple kind), and seventeen melons (the greeny-crackly kind), and said to all his dear families, "Goodbye. I am going to the great grey-green, greasy Limpopo River, all set about with fever trees, to find out what the Crocodile has for dinner." And they all spanked him once more for luck, though he asked them most politely to stop.

Then he went away, a little warm, but not at all astonished, eating melons and throwing the rind about, because he could not pick it up.

He went from Graham's Town to Kimberley, and from Kimberley to Khama's Country, and from Khama's Country he went east by north, eating melons all the time, till at last he came to the banks of the great grey-green, greasy Limpopo River, all set about with fever trees, precisely as Kolokolo Bird had said.

Now you must know and understand, O Best Beloved, that till that very week and day, and hour, and minute, this 'satiable Elephant's Child had never seen a Crocodile and did not know what one was like. It was all his 'satiable curtiosity.

The first thing that he found was a Bi-Coloured-Python-Rock-Snake curled round a rock.

" 'Scuse me," said the Elephant's Child most politely, "but have you seen such a thing as a Crocodile in these promiscuous parts?"

"*Have* I seen a Crocodile?" said the Bi-Coloured-Python-Rock-Snake, in a voice of dretful scorn. "What will you ask me next?"

" 'Scuse me," said the Elephant's Child, "but could you kindly tell me what he has for dinner?"

Then the Bi-Coloured-Python-Rock-Snake uncoiled himself very quickly from the rock and spanked the Elephant's Child with his scalesome, flailsome tail.

"That is odd," said the Elephant's Child, "because my father and my mother, and my uncle and my aunt, not to mention my other aunt, the Hippopotamus, and my other uncle, the Baboon, have all spanked me for my 'satiable curtiosity—and I suppose this is the same thing."

So he said goodbye very politely to the Bi-Coloured-Python-Rock-Snake, and helped to coil him up on the rock again, and went on, a little warm, but not at all astonished, eating melons, and throwing the rind about, because he could not pick it up, till he trod on what he thought was a log of wood at the very edge of the great grey-green, greasy Limpopo River, all set about with fever trees.

But it was really the Crocodile, O Best Beloved, and the Crocodile winked one eye—like this!

" 'Scuse me," said the Elephant's Child most politely, "but do you happen to have seen a Crocodile in these promiscuous parts?"

Then the Crocodile winked the other eye and lifted half his tail out of the mud; and the Elephant's Child stepped back most politely, because he did not wish to be spanked again.

"Come hither, Little One," said the Crocodile. "Why do you ask such things?"

" 'Scuse me," said the Elephant's Child, most politely, "but my father has spanked me, my mother has spanked me, not to mention my tall aunt, the Ostrich, and my tall uncle, the Giraffe, who can kick ever so hard, as well as my broad aunt, the Hippopotamus, and my hairy uncle, the Baboon, *and* including the Bi-Coloured-Python-Rock-Snake, with the scalesome, flailsome tail, just up the bank, who spanks harder than any of them; and *so*, if it's quite all the same to you, I don't want to be spanked any more."

"Come hither, Little One," said the Crocodile, "for I am the Crocodile," and he wept crocodile tears to show it was quite true.

Then the Elephant's Child grew all breathless, and panted, and kneeled down on the bank and said, "You are the very person I have been looking for all these long days. Will you please tell me what you have for dinner?"

"Come hither, Little One," said the Crocodile, "and I'll whisper."

Then the Elephant's Child put his head down close to the Crocodile's musky, tusky mouth, and the Crocodile caught him by his little nose, which up to that very week, day, hour, and minute, had been no bigger than a boot, though much more useful.

"I think," said the Crocodile—and he said it between his teeth, like this—"I think today I will begin with Elephant's Child!"

At this, O Best Beloved, the Elephant's Child was much annoyed, and he said, speaking through his nose, like this, "Led go! You are hurtig be!"

Then the Bi-Coloured-Python-Rock-Snake scuffled down from the bank and said, "My young friend, if you do not now, immediately and instantly, pull as hard as ever you can, it is my opinion that your acquaintance in the large-pattern leather ulster" (and by this he meant the Crocodile) "will jerk you into yonder limpid stream before you can say Jack Robinson."

This is the way Bi-Coloured-Python-Rock-Snakes always talk.

Then the Elephant's Child sat back on his little haunches, and pulled, and pulled, and pulled, and his nose began to stretch. And the Crocodile floundered into the water, making it all creamy with great sweeps of his tail, and *he* pulled, and pulled, and pulled.

And the Elephant's Child's nose kept on stretching; and the Elephant's Child spread all his little four legs and pulled, and pulled, and pulled, and his nose kept on stretching; and the Crocodile threshed his tail like an oar, and *he* pulled, and pulled, and pulled, and at each pull the Elephant's Child's nose grew longer and longer—and it hurt him hijjus!

Then the Elephant's Child felt his legs slipping, and he said through his nose, which was now nearly five feet long, "This is too butch for be!"

Then the Bi-Coloured-Python-Rock-Snake came down from the bank, and knotted himself in a double clove hitch round the Elephant's Child's hind legs, and said, "Rash and inexperienced traveller, we will now seriously devote ourselves to a little high tension, because if we do not, it is my impression that yonder self-propelling man-of-war with the armour-plated upper deck" (and by this, O Best Beloved, he meant the Crocodile) "will permanently vitiate your future career."

That is the way all Bi-Coloured-Python-Rock-Snakes always talk.

So he pulled, and the Elephant's Child pulled, and the Crocodile pulled; but the Elephant's Child and the Bi-Coloured-Python-Rock-Snake pulled hardest; and at last the Crocodile let go of the Elephant's Child's nose with a plop that you could hear all up and down the Limpopo.

Then the Elephant's Child sat down most hard and sudden; but first he was careful to say "Thank you" to the Bi-Coloured-Python-Rock-Snake; and next he was kind to his poor pulled nose, and wrapped it all up in cool banana leaves, and hung it in the great grey-green, greasy Limpopo to cool.

"What are you doing that for?" said the Bi-Coloured-Python-Rock-Snake.

" 'Scuse me," said the Elephant's Child, "but my nose is badly out of shape, and I am waiting for it to shrink."

"Then you will have to wait a long time," said the Bi-Coloured-Python-Rock-Snake. "Some people do not know what is good for them."

The Elephant's Child sat there for three days waiting for his nose to shrink. But it never grew any shorter, and, besides, it made him squint. For, O Best Beloved, you will see and understand that the Crocodile had pulled it out into a really truly trunk same as all Elephants have today.

At the end of the third day a fly came and stung him on the shoulder, and before he knew what he was doing he lifted up his trunk and hit that fly dead with the end of it.

" 'Vantage number one!" said the Bi-Coloured-Python-Rock-Snake. "You couldn't have done that with a mere-smear nose. Try and eat a little now."

Before he thought what he was doing the Elephant's Child put out his trunk and plucked a large bundle of grass, dusted it clean against his forelegs, and stuffed it into his own mouth.

" 'Vantage number two!" said the Bi-Coloured-Python-Rock-Snake. "You couldn't have done that with a mere-smear nose. Don't you think the sun is very hot here?"

"It is," said the Elephant's Child, and before he thought what he was doing he schlooped up a schloop of mud from the banks of the great grey-green, greasy Limpopo, and slapped it on his head, where it made a cool schloopy-sloshy mud-cap all trickly behind his ears.

" 'Vantage number three!" said the Bi-Coloured-Python-Rock-Snake. "You couldn't have done that with a mere-smear nose. Now how do you feel about being spanked again?"

" 'Scuse me," said the Elephant's Child, "But I should not like it at all."

"How would you like to spank somebody?" said the Bi-Coloured-Python-Rock-Snake.

"I should like it very much indeed," said the Elephant's Child.

"Well," said the Bi-Coloured-Python-Rock-Snake, "you will find that new nose of yours very useful to spank people with."

"Thank you," said the Elephant's Child, "I'll remember that; and now I think I'll go home to all my dear families and try."

So the Elephant's Child went home across Africa frisking and whisking his trunk. When he wanted fruit to eat he pulled fruit down from a tree, instead of waiting for it to fall as he used to do. When he wanted grass he plucked grass up from the ground, instead of going on his knees as he used to do. When the flies bit him he broke off the branch of a tree and used it as a flywhisk; and he made himself a new, cool, slushy-squshy mud-cap whenever the sun was hot. When he felt lonely walking through Africa he sang to himself down his trunk, and the noise was louder than several brass bands. He went especially out of his way to find a broad Hippopotamus (she was no relation of his), and he spanked her very hard, to make sure that the Bi-Coloured-Python-Rock-Snake had spoken the truth about his new trunk. The rest of the time he picked up the melon rinds that he had dropped on his way to the Limpopo—for he was a Tidy Pachyderm.

One dark evening he came back to all his dear families, and he coiled up his trunk and said, "How do you do?" They were very glad to see him and immediately said, "Come here and be spanked for your 'satiable curtiosity."

"Pooh," said the Elephant's Child. "I don't think you people know anything about spanking; but *I* do, and I'll show you."

Then he uncurled his trunk and knocked two of his dear brothers head over heels.

"O Bananas!" said they. "Where did you learn that trick, and what have you done to your nose?"

"I got a new one from the Crocodile on the banks of the great grey-green, greasy Limpopo River," said the Elephant's Child. "I asked him what he had for dinner, and he gave me this to keep."

"It looks very ugly," said his hairy uncle, the Baboon.

"It does," said the Elephant's Child. "But it's very useful," and he picked up his hairy uncle, the Baboon, by one hairy leg, and hove him into a hornet's nest.

Then that bad Elephant's Child spanked all his dear families for a long time, till they were very warm and greatly astonished. He pulled out his tall Ostrich aunt's tail feather; and he caught his tall uncle, the Giraffe, by the hind leg, and dragged him through a thorn bush; and he shouted at his broad aunt, the Hippopotamus, and blew bubbles into her ear when she was sleeping in the water after meals; but he never let anyone touch Kolokolo Bird.

At last things grew so exciting that his dear families went off one by one in a hurry to the banks of the great grey-green, greasy Limpopo River, all set about with fever trees, to borrow new noses from the Crocodile. When they came back nobody spanked anybody any more; and ever since that day, O Best Beloved, all the Elephants you will ever see, besides all those that you won't, have trunks precisely like the trunk of the 'satiable Elephant's Child.

"He acts like a stork."

MR. SINGER'S NICKNAMES

James Krüss

In the month of May of the year 1912, a steamboat came from the City of Hamburg to the Island of Helgoland. On its deck stood two gentlemen, talking to each other. One of them was stout, tall, and completely dressed in black. The other one was small and thin, had a pince-nez on his nose, and wore yellow spats over his shoes.

"Have you ever been on Helgoland?" the stout man asked the thin one.

"No," answered the gentleman with the pince-nez. "I am going over for the first time. I am to be the representative for the Society for the Care of Lobsterfishermen's Widows." He bowed and said, "May I introduce myself: Johann Jakob Singer!"

105

"I'm pleased to meet you, Mr. Singer. My name is Rasmussen, Pastor Rasmussen. But the islanders call me Thunder Pastor."

"Why Thunder Pastor?" asked Mr. Singer.

"Because I thunder into the consciences of the Helgolanders every Sunday," said the pastor. "You must know, Mr. Singer, that everyone who lives on Helgoland has an added name, a nickname."

"How dreadful!" exclaimed Mr. Singer. "But," he added, pursing his lips, "I am sure I will not be awarded any nickname. I am an honorable man who works and does his duty."

"Careful, Mr. Singer. Don't say that too loudly!"

"I shall say it as loudly as I please!" was the angry reply of the gentleman with the yellow spats. And pulling himself up with great dignity he added, "I am willing to wager that the Helgolanders will not give me a nickname!"

"I'll take that bet!" shouted Thunder Pastor with his booming voice. "If you do not have a nickname at the end of the first week, I will row around the island three times in a rowboat."

"Agreed," said Mr. Singer, and he put his skinny hand into the strong paw of the pastor. "Whoever loses the bet has to row around the island three times."

The pastor and the insurance representative promised each other to keep the bet secret and to take a walk together across the island in a week's time, the last Thursday in May, to find out whether or not Mr. Singer had been given a nickname.

It was afternoon when the little steamer reached Helgoland. The captain stopped the motor before they reached the island, let the anchor clank into the water, and lowered a rope ladder from the port side of the ship. Very soon a rowboat came over from the island, and all the passengers had to climb down the rope ladder into the boat. Pastor Rasmussen, who was used to this practice, was the first one down the ladder. He was followed by the timid Mr. Singer, who felt his way with shaky feet from rung to rung. The fishermen down in the boat stared in astonishment at the yellow spats; and the man at the tiller said, "He acts like a stork." Pastor Rasmussen smiled to himself.

When the boat made fast at the pier a quarter hour later, Helgolanders stood to the right and the left in two long lines. These two lines of people were called the razzers, since they tended to make remarks back and forth about newcomers that were not very flattering. When the pastor walked past the razzers, they called from both sides, "Welcome home, Pastor!" An old fisherman shouted, "We haven't had any good Sunday storms in a long time." And the plump owner of a rooming house called, "Hallelujah, it's going to Thunder again!"

The pastor threw a quick glance at Mr. Singer, and the poor insurance representative felt a little sick because he remembered that he didn't even know how to row.

Pastor Rasmussen also noticed a few whispered remarks that he didn't quite catch, which undoubtedly referred to the skinny Mr. Singer. For he did hear, to the left, someone whisper, "Our bird collection will get an owl!" And to the right, someone murmured, "Here comes an umbrella with a little man!"

The Thunder Pastor smiled. He was thinking of the bet. But by the same token he realized that the whispering was not very polite to a guest, and he decided to thunder a sermon on manners at the Helgolanders next Sunday.

Pastor Rasmussen delivered Mr. Singer at the Widow Broders's house on Treppen Street, since that was where the insurance representative was to be housed. He said goodbye to him and promised to call for him exactly a week later for the walk across the island. Then he made his way to the Upper Land to the parsonage.

But no sooner had the pastor climbed halfway up the stairs than the Widow Broders came panting after him calling, "Pastor, Pastor! Pastor!"

"What is it, Mrs. Broders?"

"Pastor, the little parrot that you brought me does not eat fish! What am I going to do? I can't buy meat for him every day. It's too expensive!"

"My dear Mrs. Broders," answered the pastor, raising his voice. "First of all, Mr. Singer is no parrot, remember that; and second, with God's help man can get used to anything, even to fish if it is well prepared. Good day!"

"Good day, I'm sorry to've bothered you," murmured the Widow Broders, tripping peaceably down the stairs. She had made up her mind to see that Mr. Singer got used to fish.

And that she did, and in a very simple way. She served him a whale cutlet and called it Wiener Schnitzel. She gave him smoked shark's belly and pretended it was pork belly right out of the smokehouse. The long and short of it was, she fooled him for several days; and on the fourth day, when Mr. Singer praised her cooking, she told him the truth: that he had eaten nothing but fish for three days.

The insurance representative was completely nonplussed at her announcement. He removed his pince-nez, sniffed the pork chop on his plate, and said, "Don't tell me this is swordfish!"

"Oh no, Mr. Singer," the Widow Broders said, laughing. "Today you are getting real pork, because it's Sunday."

During Johann Jakob Singer's first week on the island, he had many other surprises. For example, on the mainland he shook hands with all the people he met on the street that he knew, saying "Good day" and "How are you?" But on Monday morning this habit made him a whole hour late in getting to the office. During the short walk he met no less than fourteen people who were connected in some way with his insurance business. Fourteen times he held out his hand in greeting. Fourteen times he said, "Good day" and "How are you?" Fourteen times he reached out again in parting, and fourteen times he said, "Take care" and "Goodbye." This was time-consuming, and it was also very unusual on the island of Helgoland. The other people just shook hands when they left for the mainland or came back from there. Otherwise they merely said "Hello" or "Hoi" when they met someone.

The discussions he held in his insurance office also surprised Mr. Singer. As a correct man he always referred to his company as The Society for the Care of Lobsterfishermen's Widows. But the Helgolanders always spoke of it as "The Santa Claus Company." It took three or four days for Mr. Singer to find out that when they said this they meant his Lobsterfishermen's Widows' Insurance Company. The reason behind the name is simple. You see, St. Nicholas is the patron saint of all fishermen and seamen. So all companies that help seamen are called Santa Claus companies. And the representatives of such companies are simply called Nicholas. The representative of the Steamship Insurance Company at that time, for example, was called Nicholas One-two-three, because he always carried a walking cane with an iron tip, which he put down hard after every second step. It sounded like clap-clap-clip, or like one-two-three. The representative for Fisherman's Benefit Association was called Nicholas Pepper, because he showed a liking for highly seasoned food. And the representative of the Pilots' Insurance Company was called Pig Nicholas, because he owned the only pig on the whole island.

Johann Jakob Singer gradually learned all these names, but by the end of the week, as far as he knew, he was still without a nickname himself. And he was very proud of this. When Pastor Rasmussen called for him, as agreed, the last Thursday in May, the insurance representative said, "You have lost the wager, Pastor! I have been on Helgoland a whole week, and I still have no nickname."

"Just wait, Mr. Singer!" laughed the Thunder Pastor. "Let's take our walk first. Come along!"

The insurance representative donned his flowered chartreuse vest and decorated his thin ankles with his lemon-yellow spats. And he set out to accompany the pastor across the island. His office hours were over, since it was five o'clock in the afternoon.

As they climbed the steps to the Upper Land, they had to make a detour around Zangi, the old street sweeper, who was in the process of sweeping the one-hundred-eighty-three steps.

"How are things going, Zangi?" asked Pastor Rasmussen.

The old man answered without raising his head, "Downhill, Pastor!" As he spoke, his work took him down three more steps.

The Thunder Pastor called after him, "Tell me, Zangi, how old are you?"

"Seventy-five, Pastor!"

"Then it's about time for you to retire. Do you have any insurance?"

The old street sweeper hardly stopped sweeping as he answered. "Nope, Pastor, I'm not insured. I'll keep going until the end. Insurance companies just speculate and hope that you'll die early. I know those fellows! Nicholas One-two-three is as shrewd as the devil; Nicholas Pepper is a dunderhead; the Pig Nicholas doesn't like me; and the new Nicholas Lemonfoot isn't going to be much better either."

"Just a minute!" cried Mr. Singer. But by that time Zangi was already twelve steps down and couldn't hear him anymore. He was almost completely deaf.

Johann Jakob Singer stared at his yellow spats and asked, "Why did that fellow call me Lemonfoot? Yellow spats are the latest fashion in Hamburg."

"But not on Helgoland," answered the pastor, grinning. Then he took Mr. Singer's arm and said, "Come along. We'll visit Druggist Melleen."

Both gentlemen had now arrived at the top of the stairs, and they stepped into the old pharmacy, which stood just above the stairs at the edge of the rock. They were invited to sit down.

"I have heard a lot about you," said the pharmacist to Mr. Singer. "They call you the Dupe, right?"

"How is that again?" asked the insurance representative, shocked. "Dupe?"

"Oh, don't let it bother you," said Druggist Melleen. "Here no one is called by his right name. I am Ammonia-Peter. And you are called Dupe."

"Yes, but why, Mr. Druggist?"

"Well, Mr. Singer, it's like this: the Widow Broders has told everyone that you didn't like fish. But in her house, says the Widow Broders, you learned to eat fish. It took a bit of faking, she says. That's why people call you Dupe."

Pastor Rasmussen laughed so heartily he almost choked. But Mr. Singer only said, "How embarrassing!"

As both men sauntered on across the island, the Thunder Pastor said, "Well, you have two nicknames at least. I wonder if there is a third one."

"Two is enough!" said Johann Jakob Singer indignantly. He would have liked nothing better than to turn around. But the pastor dragged him on across the Upper Land, and even treated him to a grog in the tavern, "Joy of the North Sea."

The host himself, Genever-Harry, brought two glasses of grog and sat down with the two gentlemen.

"How do you like our island, Governor?" he asked Mr. Singer.

"I am not the Governor!" said Mr. Singer with dignity.

Genever-Harry laughed. "Of course, I know that you are an insurance agent. But I hear that you shake hands ten times a day with everybody. Only the Governor does that here; he comes to the island and shakes hands once a year. That's why people call you Governor. Quite a nice name."

Fortunately, Pastor Rasmussen did not choke this time. But he laughed just as hard. Mr. Singer only said, "Not bad!" because he liked the nickname, Governor. He almost enjoyed continuing his walk across the island with the pastor.

It was getting dark when both men approached the lighthouse, which rotated its three lightbeams tirelessly to warn the ships at sea.

At the foot of the lighthouse, they met Antje Howdjado. She was the wife of an Englishman who sold cloth on the island. She never asked, *Wie geht's?* in German. Instead she used the English, *How do you do?* That is why she was called Antje Howdjado.

In the settling darkness, Antje recognized the pastor only by his voice. She did not recognize Mr. Singer at all. So she asked, "With whom are you walking tonight, Pastor?"

"With Mr. Singer, the insurance agent, Antje!"

"Ah, with the Rubber-Nicholas! How do you do?"

"I beg your pardon?" cried Mr. Singer, beside himself. "Rubber-Nicholas?"

"Oh, please don't be offended by the name," said Antje Howdjado. "I meant no harm. I heard it from somebody else."

"But where did they get Rubber-Nicholas?" asked Pastor Rasmussen.

"That's easy, Pastor. It comes from his signature."

"From what?" asked Johann Jakob Singer.

"Well," said Antje Howdjado, "it says below your name on each one of your letters: 'Society for the Care of Lobsterfishermen's Widows, Agent.' That name stretches as long as a rubberband."

"But why do you say *Nicholas*?" asked Mr. Singer, embarrassed.

"Because all insurance agents are called Nicholas here."

"Aha," murmured the agent meekly. "That's why the street sweeper called me Nicholas Lemonfoot."

Pastor Rasmussen burst out in a real horselaugh and ended with a loud snort. "Serves you right, Singer, that they call you Rubber-Nicholas! How could anyone invent such a monstrous name! How does it go, Antje?"

" 'Society for the Care of Lobsterfishermen's Widows, Agent,' Pastor!"

"Hilarious!" cried the pastor.

Mr. Singer could only whisper, "Dreadful!"

115

Going home, Mr. Singer had to agree that he had completely lost the bet. He had gone down in shame. Instead of just one nickname, he had four of them. It bothered him so much that the pastor really felt sorry for him.

"You know what?" said Pastor Rasmussen. "I can make sure that you are only called Governor from now on. That name seems to please you most."

The agent nodded.

"All right. And when do you plan to row three times around the island, Mr. Singer?"

"Maybe on Saturday," mumbled the poor man.

"Very well, Mr. Singer! Saturday morning at nine o'clock a rowboat will be ready for you at the landing dock. I hope you don't mind if I go along for the ride."

The agent shook his head. Totally defeated, he said "Good night," and disappeared quickly into Widow Broders's house.

The next Saturday the islanders were astonished to see the Thunder Pastor and the new insurance agent climb into a rowboat and to see the spindly Mr. Singer strain at the oars and row awkwardly southward. Their astonishment grew as they saw from the edge of the cliff that the little rowboat was going around the entire island.

But everyone went completely wild when the rowboat, after three hours of circumnavigation, did not dock but went south for a second time, heading again around the rock. Now people came streaming out of their houses, and everywhere along the edge of the cliff, the curious gathered to watch the tiny boat down in the water.

The clever pastor had chosen a rowboat for the circular tour that belonged to the government and bore the name, *Governor*. This was cunning. Because as soon as Genever-Harry saw the boat from his tavern, "Joy of the North Sea," he shouted, "Hey, folks, look at that. The Governor is rowing the *Governor* around the island."

This quip flew from mouth to mouth, and in less time than it takes to tell, Johann Jakob Singer had the nickname he liked best. Rowing past the dock for the second time without stopping, everyone was already shouting, "Hello, Governor, are you trying to set an endurance record for rowing?"

Johann Jakob Singer nodded and was happy. This for two reasons: first, because they had called him Governor; and second, because he had now learned to row. He moved the oars almost as gracefully as a bird moves his wings, lightly and in rhythm, without even thinking.

Late in the afternoon, when he had finally rowed around the island three times and had fastened the boat at the little dock, he was immediately made an honorary member of the Rowing Club, "Heave-ho," and, together with the pastor, was taken to the tavern, "Joy of the North Sea."

For the next few days, the Widow Broders was almost overcome by the change in Mr. Singer. He no longer wore his yellow spats; he called his insurance business Nicholas Society; he often ate fish and liked it—even snails; he no longer shook hands with people ten times a day, but called "Hello" or "Hoi" when he met someone; and one day he even went to his office in a blue fisherman's sweater.

"You know, Governor," said the widow one Sunday during dinner. "It's getting hard to tell that you're not a Helgolander."

"That's right!" said Mr. Singer. And he pushed aside the pork chop the widow had put down and reached for the freshly smoked sharkbelly.

THE LITTLE HUMPBACKED HORSE

*Russian folktale
as told by Post Wheeler*

Across the wide sea-ocean, on the further side of high mountains, beyond thick forests, in a village that faced the sky, there once lived an old peasant who had three sons. The eldest, Danilo, was the most knowing lad in the place; the second, Gavrilo, was neither clever nor dull; and the youngest, who was named Ivan, was called a dullard, because while his brothers, after they had sowed their wheat and threshed it, drove to town and went merrymaking, he cared to do nothing but lie in the corner on the stove and sleep. So the whole neighborhood called him "Little Fool Ivan."

Now one morning when the peasant went to his stack, he found to his dismay that someone in the night had stolen some of the hay, so that evening he sent his eldest son to watch for the thief.

Danilo, accordingly, took his ax and his hayfork and went to the field. On this night there was a biting frost and heavy snow, and he said to himself, "Why should I freeze myself stiff to save a little worthless fodder?" So, finding a warm corner, he lay down, wrapped himself in his thick fur coat, and went to sleep.

In the morning he saw that some of the hay had been stolen. He rolled himself well in the snow, went home, and knocked at the door till his father let him in.

"Didst thou see the thief?" asked the peasant.

"I heard him prowling not far off," answered Danilo, "but I shouted and he dared not come nearer. However,

I have had a terrible night, thou mayst be sure! It was bitter cold and I am frozen to the marrow!"

His father praised him, calling him a good son, and the next night sent his second son to watch.

So Gavrilo took his hatchet and his long knife and went to the field. Now on this night it was raining, and he said to himself, "They say my brother is cleverer than I, but I am at least knowing enough to take care of myself, and why should I stand all night wet to the skin for the sake of a little dried grass?" So, having found a sheltered spot, he lay down, covered himself with his warm cloak and went to sleep.

In the morning he saw that more of the hay had been stolen. He went to a brook, poured water over his clothing so that it was drenched, went home, and knocked at the door till it was opened.

"Didst thou see the thief?" asked his father.

"I did," Gavrilo answered, "and laid hold of his coat and gave him such a beating that he will remember it. But the rascal tore away and ran so fast that I could not catch him. But I have had a night for my pains, I can tell you! The rain poured every minute and I am soaked to the bones!"

His father praised him likewise, calling him a brave fellow till he was as proud as a cock with five hens, and the next evening said to the Little Fool Ivan, "Now, my son, it is thy turn to watch, but thou art such a simpleton thou canst not even keep the sparrows from the peas. It will be small use for thee to go."

However, Little Fool Ivan climbed down from the stove, put a crust of bread under his coat, and went whistling off to the field. He did not lie down as his brothers had done, but went about the whole field, looking on every side, and when the moon rose he sat down under a bush, counted the stars in the sky, and ate his crust with a good appetite.

Suddenly, just at midnight, he heard the neigh of a horse, and looking out from the bush he saw a wonderful mare, as white as snow, with a golden mane curled in little rings.

"So," said Little Fool Ivan to himself, "thou art, then, the thief of our hay! Only come a little nearer and I will be on thy back as tight as a locust!" The mare came nearer and nearer and at last, choosing the right

123

moment, Ivan leaped out, seized her tail, and jumped onto her back, wrong side before.

The white mare's eyes darted forth lightning. She curled her neck like a snake, reared on her hind legs, and shot off like an arrow. She raced over fields, she flew like a bird over ditches, she galloped like the wind along mountains and dashed through thick forests. But run as she would, and rear and snort as she might, she could not throw off Little Fool Ivan. He clung to her tail and stuck to her back like a burr.

At last, just as day was beginning to dawn, the mare stopped and, panting, spoke to him with a human voice. "Well, Ivan," she said, "since thou canst sit me, it seems thou must possess me. Take me home and give me a place to rest for three days. Only, each morning, just at sunrise, let me out to roll in the dew. And when the three days are up, I will bear thee three such colts as were never heard of before. Two of them will be Tsar's horses, of brown and gray, and these thou mayst sell if thou choosest. But the third will be a little humpbacked stallion only three feet high, with ears a foot long, and him thou shalt neither sell for gold nor give as a gift to anyone whatsoever. So long as thou art in the white world he shall be thy faithful servant. In winter he will show thee how to be warm, and when thou dost hunger he will show thee where to find bread. In return for these three colts thou shalt release me and give me my freedom."

Little Fool Ivan agreed. He rode the white mare home, hid her in an empty shepherd's corral, whose entrance he covered with a horse cloth, and went home and knocked at the door till his brothers let him in.

When they saw him, they began to question him. "Well, no doubt thou didst see the thief! Perhaps thou didst even catch him! Tell us."

"To be sure I did," he replied. "I jumped on the thief's back and laid hold of the villain's tail, and we ran a thousand versts or more. My neck was nearly broken in the end, and ye may believe I am tired!" So saying he climbed onto the stove without taking off even his bark sandals, and went to sleep, while his brothers and his father roared with laughter at the story, not a word of which, of course, they believed.

Little Fool Ivan kept the white mare hidden from all other eyes. For three mornings he rose at daybreak and let her out to roll on the dewy meadow and on the fourth morning, when he went to the corral, he found beside her, as she had promised, three colts. Two were most beautiful to see; they were of brown and gray, their eyes were like blue sapphires, their manes and tails were golden and curled in little rings, and their hoofs were of diamond, studded with pearls. But the third was a tiny horse like a toy, with two humps on his back and ears a foot long.

Ivan was overjoyed. He thanked the white mare and she, released, curled her neck like a snake, reared on her hind legs, and shot off like an arrow. Then he began to admire the three colts, especially the little humpbacked one, which frisked like a dog about Ivan's knees, clapping his long ears together from playfulness and dancing up and down on his little hoofs. He kept them hidden, as he had the white mare, in the shepherd's corral, letting them out each morning at sunrise to roll in the dew and spending many hours petting them, talking to them, currying their coats till they shone like silver, and braiding their golden manes.

Time went on (but whether it was three weeks or three years that flew away matters little, since one need not run after them) till it befell, one day, that his eldest brother, Danilo, who had been to town for a holiday, returned late at night and, missing his way in the darkness, stumbled into the shepherd's corral. Hearing a sound, he made a light and to his astonishment saw the three young horses.

"So—ho!" he thought. "Now I understand why Little Fool Ivan spends so much time in this old corral!" He ran to the house and woke his brother Gavrilo. "Come quickly," he said, "and see what three horses our young idiot of a brother has found for himself!" And Gavrilo followed him as fast as he could, straight across a nettle field barefoot, since he did not wait to put on his boots.

When they came to the corral the two fine horses were neighing and snorting. Their eyes were burning like beautiful blue candles and their curling gold manes and tails and their hoofs of diamonds and pearls filled the two brothers with envy. Each looked at them so long that he was nearly made blind of one eye. Then Danilo said:

"They say it takes a fool to find a treasure. But where in the white world could Little Fool Ivan have got these marvelous steeds? As for thee and me, brother, we might search our heads off and we would find not even two roubles!"

"That is true," answered Gavrilo. "We should have the horses, and not Little Fool Ivan. Now I have an idea. Next week is the fair at the capital. Many foreigners will come in ships to buy linen, and it is said that even Tsar Saltan will be there. Let us come here by night and take the horses thither and sell them. They will fetch a great price, and we will divide it equally between us two. Thou knowest what a good time we could have with the money, and while we are slapping our full purses and enjoying ourselves our dolt of an Ivan will not be able to guess where his horses have gone visiting. What sayest thou? Let us shake hands upon it."

So the brothers agreed, kissed each other, crossed themselves, and went home planning how to spend the money they should get for the horses.

When the next week came round, accordingly, they said a prayer before the holy images, asked their father's blessing, and departed to the fair. When they had gone some distance, however, they returned to the village secretly after nightfall, took the two fine horses out of the corral, and again set out for the capital.

Next morning, when Ivan came to the corral, he found to his grief that the beautiful pair had vanished. There was left only the little humpbacked horse that was turning round and round before him, capering, clapping his long ears together, and dancing up and down from joy. Ivan began to weep salt tears. "O my horses, brown and gray!" he cried. "My good steeds with golden manes! Did I not caress you enough? What wretch—may he tumble through a bridge!—hath stolen you away?"

At this the humpbacked horse neighed and spoke in a human voice, "Don't worry, little master," he said. "It was thy brothers who took them away, and I can take thee to them. Sit on my back and hold fast by my ears, and have a care not to fall off!" So Little Fool Ivan sat on his back, holding up his feet lest they drag on the ground, and laid hold of his ears, and the pony shook himself till his little mane quivered, reared on his hind legs, snorted three times, and shot away like an arrow, so fast that the dust curled under his feet. And almost before Ivan had time to take breath, he was versts away on the highroad to the capital.

When his brothers saw Little Fool Ivan coming after them like the wind on his toy horse, they knew not what to do. "For shame, ye rascals!" shouted he as he overtook them. "Ye may be more clever than I, but I have never stolen your steeds!"

"Our dear little brother!" said Danilo. "There is little use denying. We took thy two horses, but we did so with no thought of wrong to thee. As thou knowest, this has been a poor season with our crops and a bad harvest, and for despair I and Gavrilo have been like to hang ourselves. When we came by chance upon these two steeds, we considered that thou hadst little knowledge of bargaining and trading, and doubtless knew not their worth, whereas we could get for them at least a thousand roubles at the fair. With this money we could help our little father, as thou wouldst wish, and we purposed to buy besides for thee a red cap and new boots with red heels. So if we have erred, do thou forgive us."

"Well," answered Little Fool Ivan, "thy words sound fair enough. If this was your thought, go and sell my two horses, but I will go with you." So, though they wished him well strangled, the two brothers had no choice but to take him with them, and thus they came to the capital.

Now when they reached the marketplace where the traders were assembled, so wonderful were the two steeds that the people swarmed about them, buzzing like bees in a hive, till for the press no one could pass either in or out, and there was great commotion. Perceiving this the head man sent a crier who blew on a gold trumpet and shouted in a loud voice, "O merchants and buyers! Crowd not, but disperse one and all!" But they would not move from the horses. Then the head man rode out himself, in slippers and fur cap, with a body of soldiers who cleared the way with their whips, so that he came to the middle of the market and saw the horses with his own eyes.

"God's world is wonderful!" he cried, rubbing his head. "What marvels doth it hold!" And bidding the crier proclaim that no buyer should buy them, he rode to the palace, came to the presence of the Tsar, and told him of them.

The Tsar could not sit still for curiosity. He ordered his state carriage and rode at once to the market, and when he saw the horses, tugging at their halters and gnawing their bits, with their eyes shining like sapphires, their curling golden manes, and hoofs of diamonds and pearls, he could not take his eyes from them. He examined them on both sides, called to them with caressing words, patted their backs, and stroked their manes, and asked who owned them.

"O Tsar's Majesty," said Little Fool Ivan, "I am their master."

"What wilt thou take for them?" asked the Tsar.

"Thrice five caps of full silver," answered Ivan, "and five roubles beside."

"Good," said the Tsar, and ordered the money given him. Then ten grooms, with gray hair and golden uniforms, led the pair to the royal stables. On the way, however, the horses knocked the grooms down, bit to pieces their bridles, and ran neighing back to Ivan.

Then the Tsar called him to his presence, and said, "It seems that my wonderful steeds will obey only thee. There is no help but that I make thee my Chief Equerry and Master of my Stables." And he ordered the crier at once to proclaim the appointment. So Little Fool Ivan called his brothers, Danilo and Gavrilo, gave to them the fifteen caps full of silver, and the five roubles beside, kissed them, bade them not neglect their father but to care for him in his old age, and led the two horses to the royal stables, while a great throng of people followed, watching the little humpbacked horse who went dancing after them up the street.

The telling of a tale is quick but time itself passes slowly. Five weeks went by, while Ivan wore red robes, ate sweet food, and slept his fill. Each morning at sunrise he took the horses to roll in the dew on the open field, and fed them with honey and white wheat till their coats shone like satin. But the more the Tsar praised him, the more envious many in the court were of him. As the saying is, one need not be rich only so he have curly hair and is clever; and because Little Fool Ivan had succeeded so easily people hated him, and the one who hated him most was the officer who had been the Tsar's

Master of Horse before his coming. Each day this man pondered how he might bring about Ivan's ruin, and at night he would creep to the stables and lie hid in the wheat bins, hoping to catch his rival in some fault.

When this failed, he went to all those court officials who were envious of the new favorite and bade them hang their heads and go about with sorrowful faces, promising, when the Tsar asked the cause, to tell him what would ruin Little Fool Ivan. They did so, and the Tsar, noticing their sad looks, asked:

"O boyars, why are ye cast down and crestfallen?"

Then he who had given this counsel stood forth, and said, "O Tsar's Majesty! Not for ourselves do we grieve, but we fear thy new Master of the Stables is a wizard and

an evildoer and familiar with Black Magic. For he doth boast openly that he could fetch thee, if he chose, in addition to thy two wonderful steeds, the fabled Pig with the Golden Bristles and the Silver Tusks, with her twenty sucklings, who live in the hidden valley of the Land of the South."

Hearing this, the Tsar was wroth. "Bring before me this wild boaster," he said, "and he shall make good his words without delay!" Thereupon they ran to the stables, where Little Fool Ivan lay asleep, and kicked him wide awake and brought him to the Tsar, who looked at him angrily, and said, "Hear my command. If in three days thou hast not brought hither, from the hidden valley of the Land of the South, the Pig with the Golden Bristles and Silver Tusks, together with her twenty sucklings, I will deliver thee to an evil death!"

Little Fool Ivan went out to the stable weeping bitterly. Hearing him coming, the little humpbacked horse began to dance and to clap its ears together for joy, but as soon as he saw his master's tears he almost began to sob himself. "Why art thou not merry, little master?" he asked. "Why does thy head hang lower than thy shoulders?"

Ivan embraced and kissed the little horse, and told him the task the Tsar had laid upon him. "Do not weep," said the pony; "I can help thee. Nor is this service so hard a one. Go thou to the Tsar and ask of him a bucket of golden corn, a bucket of silver wheat, and a silken lasso."

So Ivan went before the Tsar and asked, as he had been bidden, for the wheat, the corn, and the silken lasso, and brought them back to the stables. "Now," said the little humpbacked horse, "lie down and sleep, for the morning holds more wisdom than the evening."

Little Fool Ivan lay down to sleep, and next morning the pony waked him at dawn. "Mount me now," he said, "with thy grain and thy silken rope, and we will be off, for the way is far."

Ivan put the silver wheat and the golden corn into stout bags, slung them across the pony's neck, and with his silken lasso wound about his waist, mounted, and the little humpbacked horse darted away like an eagle. He scoured wide plains, leaped across swift rivers, and

sped along mountain ridges, and after running without pause for a day and a night, he stopped in a deep valley on the edge of a dreary wood, and said, "Little master, this is the Land of the South, and in this valley lives the Pig with the Golden Bristles. She comes each day to root in this forest. Take thou the golden corn and the silver wheat and pour them on the ground in two piles, at some distance apart, and conceal thyself. When the Pig comes she will run to the corn, but the sucklings will begin to eat the wheat, and while the mother is not by, thou mayest secure them. Bring them to me and tie them to my saddle with the silken lasso and I will bear thee back. As for the Pig, she will follow her sucklings."

Little Fool Ivan did all as the little horse bade him. He entered the forest, put the corn and wheat into two piles, hid himself in a thicket near the latter, and rested till evening, when there came a sound of grunting and the Pig with the Golden Bristles and Silver Tusks led her young into the forest. She saw the corn, and at once began to eat it, while the twenty sucklings ran to the wheat. He caught them, one by one, tied them with the silken lasso, and, hastening to the little horse, made them fast to his saddlebow. Scarce had he mounted when the Pig perceived them, and seeing her sucklings borne away, came running after them, erecting her golden bristles and gnashing her silver tusks.

The little humpbacked horse sped away like a flash back along the road they had come, with the Pig

pursuing them, and, after running without stop for a night and a day, they arrived after dark at the Tsar's capital. Little Fool Ivan rode to the palace courtyard, set down there the twenty suckling pigs, still tied by the silken lasso, went to the stables, and fell asleep.

In the morning the Tsar was greatly astonished to see that Little Fool Ivan had performed the task and was delighted to possess the new treasure. He sent for his Master of Horse and praised him and gave him a rich present, so that the envious ones thereat were made still more envious.

So, after some days, these came to the Tsar and said, "Thy Master of Horse, O Tsar's Majesty, doth boast now that the bringing of the wonderful Pig with her twenty sucklings was but a small service, and that he could, if he but chose, bring to thee the Mare with Seven Manes and her seven fierce stallions that graze on a green meadow between the crystal hills of the Caucasus."

Then, in more anger than before, the Tsar bade them bring Little Fool Ivan to his presence and said sternly, "Heed my royal word. If in seven days thou hast not brought hither from between the crystal hills of the Caucasus the Seven-Maned Mare with her seven stallions, I will send thee where the crows shall pick thy bones!"

Little Fool Ivan went weeping to the little humpbacked horse and told him of the Tsar's new command. "Grieve not, little master," said the other; "let not thy bright head droop. I can aid thee. Nor is this service too hard a one. Go thou to the Tsar and demand that he prepare at once a stone stable with one door opening into it and another opening out. Ask also for a horse's skin and an iron hammer of twelve poods weight."

Ivan obeyed. He demanded the stable, the horse's skin, and the iron hammer, and when all was ready the little horse said, "Lie down and sleep now, little master. The morning is wiser than the evening." Little Fool Ivan lay down and slept, and next morning at daybreak the pony waked him. Ivan tied the horse's skin to the saddlebow, slung the hammer about his neck, and mounted, and the little humpbacked horse darted away

like a swallow, till the dust curled about his legs like a whirlwind. When he had run three days and four nights without rest, he stopped between two crystal hills and said:

"Yonder lies the green meadow whereon each evening grazed the Mare with Seven Manes and her seven fierce stallions. Take now thy horse's skin and sew me within it, and presently the mare will come and will set upon me with her teeth. While she rends the skin from me, do thou run and strike her between her two ears with thy twelve-pood hammer, so that she will be stunned. Mount me then in haste, and thou mayest lead her after thee, and as for the seven stallions, they will follow."

So Little Fool Ivan sewed the little horse in the horse's skin, and when the mare with the seven stallions came, the stallions stood afar off, but the mare set upon him and rent the skin from him. Then Ivan ran and struck her with the iron hammer and stunned her, and instantly, holding by her seven manes, leaped to the back of the little humpbacked horse.

Scarce had he mounted, when the seven fierce stallions saw him, and came galloping after them, screaming with rage. But the little humpbacked horse was off like a dart back along the road they had come, and when they had traveled without stopping three nights and four days, they arrived at the Tsar's capital. Little Fool Ivan rode to the stone stable that had been built, went in at one door, and leaving therein the Mare with the Seven Manes, rode out of the other and barred it behind him, and the seven stallions, following the mare, were caught. Then Ivan went to his own place and went to sleep.

When they reported to the Tsar that this time also Little Fool Ivan had performed his task, the Tsar was more rejoiced than before and bestowed high rank and all manner of honors upon him, till, for hatred and malice the envious ones were beside themselves.

They conferred together and coming before the Tsar, they said, "O Tsar's Majesty! To bring the mare and the stallions, thy Master of Horse boasteth now, was but a small service, saying that, if he willed, he could fetch thee from across three times nine lands, where the little red sun rises, the beautiful Girl-Tsar, whom thou hast so long desired for thy bride, who lives on the sea-ocean in a golden boat, which she rows with silver oars."

Then was the Tsar mightily angered. "Summon this boaster again before me," he commanded, and when Little Fool Ivan was come in, he bade him bring him the lovely Girl-Tsar within twelve days or pay the forfeit with his head. So, for the third time, Ivan went weeping to the little humpbacked horse and told him the Tsar's will.

"Dry thy tears, little master," said the other, "for I can assist thee. This is not, after all, the hardest service. Go thou to the Tsar and ask for two handkerchiefs cunningly embroidered in gold, a silken tent woven with gold thread and with golden tent poles, gold and silver dishes, and all manner of wines and sweetmeats."

Ivan lost no time in obeying and when they were ready brought them to the stables. "Lie down and sleep now," said the little horse. "Tomorrow is wiser than today." Accordingly Little Fool Ivan lay down and slept till the little horse woke him at daybreak. He put all that had been prepared into a bag and mounted, and the little humpbacked horse sped away like the wind.

For six days they rode, a hundred thousand versts, till they reached a forest at the very end of the world, where the little red sun rises out of the blue sea-ocean. Here they stopped and Ivan alighted.

"Pitch now thy tent on the white sand," said the little horse. "In it spread thy embroidered handkerchiefs and on them put the wine and the gold and silver plates piled with sweetmeats. As for thee, do thou hide behind the tent and watch. From her golden boat the Girl-Tsar will see the tent and will approach it. Let her enter it and eat and drink her fill. Then go in, seize and hold her, and call for me." So saying, he ran to hide himself in the forest.

Ivan pitched the tent, prepared the food and wine, and lying down behind the tent, made a tiny hole in the silk through which to see, and waited. And before long the golden boat came sailing over the blue sea-ocean. The beautiful Girl-Tsar alighted to look at the splendid tent and, seeing the wine and sweetmeats, entered and began to eat and drink. So graceful and lovely was she that no tale could describe her, and Little Fool Ivan could not gaze enough. He forgot what the little horse had told him, and he was still peering through the hole in the silk when the beautiful maiden sprang up, left the tent, leaped into her golden boat, and the silver oars carried her far away on the sea-ocean.

When the little humpbacked horse came running up, Ivan too late repented of his folly. "I am guilty before thee!" he said. "And now I shall never see her again!" and he began to shed tears.

"Never mind," said the little horse. "She will come again tomorrow, but if thou failest next time we must needs go back without her and thy head will be lost."

Next day Little Fool Ivan spread the wines and sweetmeats and lay down to watch as before; and again the lovely Girl-Tsar came rowing in her golden boat and entered the tent and began to regale herself. And while she ate and drank Ivan ran in and seized and held her and called to the little horse. The girl cried out and fought to be free, but when she saw how handsome Little Fool Ivan was, she quite forgot to struggle. He mounted and put her before him on the saddle, and the humpbacked horse dashed away like lightning along the road they had come.

They rode six days and on the seventh they came again to the capital, and Little Fool Ivan—with a sad heart, since he had fallen in love with her himself—brought the lovely girl to the palace.

The Tsar was overjoyed. He came out to meet them, took the maiden by her white hand, seated her beside him beneath a silken curtain on a cushion of purple velvet, and spoke to her tender words. "O Girl-Tsar, to whom none can be compared!" he said. "My Tsaritsa that is to be! For how long have I not slept, either by night or in the white day, for thinking of thine eyes!"

But the beautiful Girl-Tsar turned from him and would not answer and again and again he tried his wooing, till at length she said, "O Tsar, thou art wrinkled and gray, and hast left sixty years behind thee, while I am but sixteen. Should I wed thee, the Tsars of all Tsardoms would laugh, saying that a grandfather had taken to wife his grandchild."

Hearing this, the Tsar was angry. "It is true," he said, "that flowers do not bloom in winter and that I am no longer young. But I am nevertheless a great Tsar."

Then she replied, "I will wed no one who hath gray hairs and who lacks teeth in his head. If thou wilt but grow young again, then will I wed thee right willingly."

"How can a man grow young again?" he asked.

"There is a way, O Tsar," she said, "and it is thus: Order three great caldrons to be placed in thy courtyard. Fill the first with cold water, the second with boiling water, and the third with boiling mare's milk. He who bathes one minute in the boiling milk, two in the boiling water, and three in the cold water, becomes instantly young and so handsome that it cannot be told. Do this and I will become thy Tsaritsa, but not otherwise."

The Tsar at once bade them prepare in the courtyard the three caldrons, one of cold water, one of boiling water, and one of boiling mare's milk, minded to make the test. The envious courtiers, however, came to him and said, "O Tsar's Majesty! This is a strange thing and we have never heard that a man can plunge into boiling liquid and not be scalded. We pray thee, therefore, bid thy Master of Horse bathe before thee; then mayest thou be assured that all is well." And this counsel seemed to the Tsar good, and he straightaway summoned Little Fool Ivan and bade him prepare to make the trial.

When Ivan heard the Tsar's command he said to himself, "So I am to be killed like a suckling pig or a chicken!" and he went sorrowfully to the stables and told the little humpbacked horse. "Thou has found for me the Pig with the Golden Bristles," he said, "the Seven-Maned Mare, and the beautiful Girl-Tsar; but now these are all as nothing and my life is as worthless as a boot sole!" And he began to weep bitterly.

"Weep not, little master," said the little horse. "This is indeed a real service that I shall serve thee. Now listen well to what I say. When thou goest to the courtyard, before thou strippest off thy clothes to bathe, ask of the Tsar to permit them to bring to thee thy little humpbacked horse, that thou mayest bid him farewell for the last time. He will agree, and when I am brought there I shall gallop three times around the three kettles, dip my nose in each, and sprinkle thee. Lose not a moment then, but jump instantly in the caldron of boiling milk, then into the boiling water, and last into the cold water."

Scarcely had he instructed him when the boyars came to bring Ivan to the courtyard. All the court ministers were there to see and the place was crowded with people, while the Tsar looked on from a balcony. The two caldrons were boiling hot and servants fed the great fires beneath them with heaps of fuel. Little Fool Ivan bowed low before the Tsar and prepared for the bath.

But having taken off his coat, he bowed again and said, "O Tsar's Majesty! I have but one favor to ask. Bid them bring hither my little humpbacked horse that I may embrace him once more for the last time!" The Tsar was in good humor thinking he was so soon to regain his youth, and he consented, and presently the little horse came running into the courtyard, dancing up and down and clapping his long ears together. But as soon as he came to the three caldrons he galloped three times round them, dipped his nose into each, and sprinkled his master; and without waiting a moment Little Fool Ivan threw off his clothes and jumped into the caldrons, one after the other. And while he had been good-looking before, he came from the last caldron so handsome that his beauty could neither be described with a pen nor written in a tale.

Now when the Tsar saw this, he could wait no longer. He hastened down from the balcony and, without waiting to undress, crossed himself and jumped into the boiling milk. But the charm did not work in his case, and he was instantly scalded to death.

Seeing the Tsar was dead, the Girl-Tsar came to the balcony and spoke to the people, saying, "Thy Tsar chose me to be his Tsaritsa. If thou wilt, I will rule this Tsardom, but it shall be only as the wife of him who brought me from mine own!"

The people, well pleased, shouted, "Health to Tsar Ivan!" And so Little Fool Ivan led the lovely

Girl-Tsar to the church and they were married that same day.

Then Tsar Ivan ordered the trumpeters to blow their hammered trumpets and the butlers to open the bins, and he made in the palace a feast like a hill, and the boyars and princes sat at oak tables and drank from golden goblets and made merry till they could not stand on their feet.

But Little Fool Ivan, with his Tsaritsa, ruled the Tsardom wisely and well, and grew never too wise to take counsel of his little humpbacked horse.

"Dear old man, do not be afraid."

ALI BABA AND THE FORTY THIEVES

from The Arabian Nights

Once upon a time there lived in a city of Persia two brothers. One was called Cassim and the other Ali Baba. Their father had died early and had left them only very little property. The brothers had divided it in halves and shared it equally. You would now think that their circumstances were similar. But fate had decided differently.

Cassim married the daughter of a rich merchant. After her father's death she inherited a well-stocked shop and large estates. Cassim had now become one of the richest men in the city. By skillful trading his property kept growing.

Ali Baba, however, had married a poor man's daughter who did not even bring a dowry to the marriage. So his small inheritance was used up quickly. Poverty and deprivation were the couple's daily companions. Ali Baba, his wife, and their only son lived in a miserable hut. He earned his livelihood by selling wood. For this purpose he used to journey to the mountains to fell trees. He then loaded the wood on his three donkeys and brought it down to the town, where he sold it.

One day he had gone to the wood again. He had just felled enough trees for loading the donkeys when he suddenly saw in the distance a cloud of dust which came nearer and nearer. He looked carefully, and when the cloud came closer, it turned out to be a group of riders, who came along on horseback at a fast pace. He saw also that they were wearing sparkling breastplates and shining weapons, and great terror befell him. True, nobody had ever heard of thieves in those parts, but the idea occurred to Ali Baba that they might be thieves all the same, and he was afraid they might murder him, and he wondered how he could save himself. He left the poor donkeys to their fate, climbed up a tall tree, and hid between its branches. In that way he could see everything that was going on without being seen himself. The tree grew at the foot of a sheer rock which was much higher than the tree, and so steep that nobody could climb it.

The riders, all young, tall men, dismounted at the foot of the rock. Ali Baba counted forty. After looking at their faces and their behavior he could not doubt that they were thieves. He was not mistaken; they were indeed thieves, but they did not carry on their trade in those parts. They did their thieving somewhere else. They came to this forest only to hold their regular meetings.

Each of the thieves unsaddled his horse, tied it to a tree, and threw a bagful of oats over its head. They had carried these sacks behind them on horseback. Then they took their saddlebags off, and these appeared to Ali Baba to be very heavy. He supposed they were full of gold and silver.

Now the tallest of the thieves, probably the leader, slung his saddlebag over his shoulder and approached the rock. Right above him in the branches of the tree, Ali Baba was sitting, trembling and looking down. The other thieves were following their captain. He stopped in front of a small door in the rock. It was so completely overgrown with thorny bushes that Ali Baba would never have noticed it. The leader now uttered the strange words:

"Open, Sesame!"

Hardly had he spoken them, when the small door opened. Now the thieves entered the rock. They all walked past the captain, who waited until the last one had gone in; then he followed. Noiselessly the door closed behind them.

For a long time the thieves remained inside. Ali Baba had to remain sitting in his tree and waiting. He was afraid they might come upon him just as he was descending. At last the door opened again. The captain stepped outside and let one after the other of the thieves walk past him. Ali Baba noticed that their saddlebags were now empty. When the last thief had come out, he heard the words:

"Shut, Sesame!"

and the door in the rock closed by itself again. Now each of the men went up to his horse, saddled it, hung his bag over the saddle, and swung himself up. Then they all rode away in the direction from which they had come.

Ali Baba followed them with his eyes until they had disappeared from sight. But still he did not dare descend from his tree. He was afraid one of the thieves might have forgotten something and would come back for it. At last, when everything had remained quiet for some time, he climbed down. He walked through the undergrowth up to the small door and studied it for a long time, thinking: Should I say the words the captain uttered? Ali Baba had kept the words in mind. He pondered about it for a long time, but as he wanted to find out what was behind the door, he eventually uttered the words:

"Open, Sesame!"

At once the door opened wide and Ali Baba could enter. Behind him the rock closed, but he was not worried about that. He knew how to open the door again.

He had expected to find a narrow, dark cave. Instead he saw a large, bright vault. It had been built by human hands and was paved with marble and adorned with high pillars. It received its light through openings in the ceiling. In this hall, everything you could wish for was stored. Large bales of cloth, valuable carpets, gold, brocade, and magnificent clothes were lying in heaps. Ali Baba, however, was especially attracted by the enormous quantity of silver and gold. It was lying about there in ingots and coins, partly heaped up like sand, partly packed in sacks. Numerous pearls and jewels sparkled in all the colors of the rainbow; like pebbles on the beach they were lying round the hall. It seemed to Ali Baba as though this cave had been the thieves' store for centuries.

He did not waste time. He gave no attention to the carpets and the silver. He walked straight to the bags with the gold. Of these he took as many from the cave as his donkeys could carry. Each time he wanted to enter or leave he called out:

"Open, Sesame!"

and the door duly opened. When he had carried out enough, he collected his donkeys. He loaded the sacks on their backs and put a layer of wood on top, so that nobody would notice what was underneath.

Hurriedly, Ali Baba drove his beasts of burden back to town. When he arrived home he pulled them into the yard quickly and locked the gate carefully behind him. Nobody must come upon him unawares! The few pieces of wood he put into the usual place. The sacks of gold, however, he carried into his house for his wife to see. One after another, he placed them in front of her. The woman watched what he was doing with increasing surprise. At last she lifted one of the sacks and felt it. She realized it was filled with gold. Now she grew suspicious and thought her husband had stolen it.

"Husband," she reproached him, "if you have been so wicked . . ."

Ali Baba interrupted her with the words: "Quiet woman, I am not a thief. I did not steal anything. I took this gold from thieves. Enjoy our good fortune and listen to what happened."

And he shook the sacks out. Their contents made a great heap of gold. The woman was dazzled by its splendor. Now Ali Baba told her the story from beginning to end. Finally he impressed on her that she must not breathe a word about it to anybody. By now the woman's terror had changed to pleasure. She was beside herself with joy. She wanted to count the gold, piece by piece, but Ali Baba stopped her impatiently.

"You are a fool," he said. "How long do you think it would take you to count it? I will dig a pit and bury the gold. We shall have to be quick; nobody must know of our secret."

"But I would like to know how much it is," said the woman. "I shall run over to our neighbor and borrow a measure. Then I can measure it while you are digging the pit."

"Woman," replied Ali Baba, "you had better leave that be. But I suppose you will not be deterred. All right, do as you like, only do not give our secret away."

In order to borrow a measure, Ali Baba's wife went to her brother-in-law, Cassim. But Cassim was out, so she asked Cassim's wife. The sister-in-law wanted to know if she wished to have a large or a small measure. Ali Baba's wife asked for a small one.

"Willingly," said the sister-in-law. "Just wait a minute. I will bring it along presently."

She went to get the measure, thinking: Those people have nothing. What do they want a measure for? She hit on the idea of sticking some wax on the bottom of the measure, to which some of whatever was to be measured would then stick. When she handed it to her sister-in-law, she apologized for the long time it had taken her to get it and explained she had had to search for it.

Ali Baba's wife thanked her and ran home unsuspecting. She put the measure on the heap of gold. Then she filled it with the gold and emptied it into the pit again and again, until the lot had been measured. She was very satisfied with the number of measures and reported it to her husband. He had, in the meantime, finished digging the pit; now he carefully heaped earth on the gold, so that nobody would see anything.

The woman, however, returned the measure to her sister-in-law. She had no idea that a gold piece had remained stuck to the outside.

"Sister," she said, "I am returning your measure. You see I have not kept it long. Many thanks for it."

Ali Baba's wife went home happily. Cassim's wife, however, turned the measure upside down and looked at the bottom. To her amazement she saw a piece of gold sticking to the wax. She thought her eyes were deceiving her. Then she examined the coin carefully and realized that it was a genuine gold piece.

"How is this?" she exclaimed. "Since when has Ali Baba got so much money that he has to calculate it by measure? Where did he get the riches from? How did he acquire so much gold?" And the devil of envy arose in her heart.

Cassim, her husband, was still not at home. He was busy in his shop and never returned before nightfall. She could hardly await his arrival. She was burning with impatience to tell him the news. At last he opened the door and entered.

"Cassim," she said to him, "you think you are a rich man! You are mistaken. Your brother Ali Baba is a thousand times richer than you. He does not count his money; he measures it."

In bewilderment Cassim asked her what she meant; so she told him of her ruse. Then she showed him the piece of gold that had remained stuck to the measure. It was very old. The name of the king and the inscription were completely unknown to him.

So Cassim, too, gained the conviction that his brother must be enormously rich. But he was not pleased about it. Envy seized him and caused him to lie awake all night. His avarice gave him no peace or rest.

The next morning, before daybreak, he betook himself to Ali Baba's house. Since his marriage he had not once paid a call on him. He did not want to count him as a brother. Even now, he did not call him that.

"Ali Baba," he said, "you pretend to be poor and needy. You behave as though you were a beggar. And yet you have so much money that you have to measure it."

"Dear brother," said Ali Baba, "explain yourself. What is the meaning of your words?"

"Do not make believe," replied Cassim, and produced the coin. "Have a look at this gold piece. My wife found it stuck to the bottom of the measure that your wife borrowed from her. How many such pieces do you possess?"

Now Ali Baba realized that his brother and sister-in-law had got to know of the matter which he had wished to keep an utter secret. But his wife's mistake could not be undone, so he swallowed his anger and confessed to his brother that by chance he had discovered a thieves' den. He also told him of the treasures that were stored there. Eventually he suggested to his brother that he would share the treasure fairly with him, but he would have to keep the secret. Since he knew the magic formula, he could always enter the cave.

"What you have told me is not enough," replied Cassim haughtily. "I want to know everything. Where is the treasure? How does one get in? I shall go to the cave myself and take what I please. If you do not tell me the magic formula, I shall lay information against you at court. Then you will even lose what you have already got, and I shall receive a reward for having revealed your guilt."

Ali Baba was not afraid of his brother's threats. But he was a good-natured man and told his brother everything. He indicated exactly where the treasure was. He even told him the magic formula which opened the secret door. That was all Cassim wanted to know; he rose and hurried home. He wanted to get a start on his brother and remove all the treasures for himself.

He at once prepared ten mules, loaded two large boxes on each of them, and got rope and saddlebags ready.

Next morning before daybreak, he started on the journey. He had made up his mind to fill all the boxes.

If he should not be able to get everything into the boxes, he would collect it later. He traveled the route Ali Baba had described to him and reached the rock. He recognized the tree in which his brother had hidden himself. Among the thorny bushes he saw the secret door. Loudly he pronounced the words:

"Open, Sesame!"

Immediately the door opened. Cassim entered the rock. Behind him the door closed.

His surprise grew every minute as he beheld the treasures. There were much greater riches than he had imagined. Dazedly he walked about. He felt and examined the bales of cloth, the gold, the jewels. He would have liked to stay all day and feast his eyes on the sparkle of the precious metals. But then he thought of his mules outside the cave, so he carried sacks full of gold to the entrance so as to have them handy for loading onto his beasts of burden. When he had finished collecting, he wanted to open the door, but the magic formula had escaped him. He called:

"Open, Barley!"

But the door remained shut. In his fright he called the names of other kinds of corn, but the door did not open.

Cassim had never expected anything like that to happen. He put down the sacks and sat on them in despair. Horror took hold of him. He racked his brain to recall the magic formula, but no matter how hard he thought, the word did not come back to him. He rose from his seat and paced up and down the cave. The treasures did not interest him any longer. He wrung his hands and plucked at his beard. His heart was filled with terror. He was afraid he was lost.

But let us leave Cassim bemoaning his fate. He does not deserve our pity.

Let us turn to the thieves. They had just attacked and robbed a caravan and were returning to their cave laden with treasures. By that time it was about midday. When they got near, they saw the mules with the boxes. They rode at them at full speed, and the animals were terrified and ran into the wood. Now the thieves wanted to find the owner of the mules. So they searched round the rock, pushed their way through the shrubs, and looked up all the trees. The captain, however, went to the door of the cave with a few of his comrades and uttered the magic formula.

Cassim in the cave had heard the trampling of hooves and realized that the thieves had returned. In his fear he thought of a way of escape. He stationed himself close by the door; as soon as it opened, he was going to rush out. Then he heard the word "Sesame" that had escaped him, and immediately the door opened wide. Cassim ran out with such speed that he knocked the captain over. He was able even to pass the second thief, but there were too many; he could not escape them all. One of them ran his sword into Cassim's chest, and he fell down dead.

The thieves now cautiously entered the cave; they wanted to make sure that there were no other people hidden inside. They returned the sacks which Cassim had taken to the door to their usual places. That there were several missing, they did not notice. They wondered how Cassim could have entered the cave. They were sure the secret of the door was safe, for he would have had to know the magic formula and nobody but they knew that. They had no idea that Ali Baba had been eavesdropping on them. The dead man could not have entered from the top: the openings in the ceiling were too small and too high up for that, and the rock itself was steep and slippery. Now they began to make their treasure secure. They decided to quarter Cassim's corpse and to hang up two pieces on the right and on the left close inside the door as a deterrent to anybody who might enter the cave. They themselves were going to leave the cave alone for quite a time, at least until the smell of the carrion had abated. Then they mounted their horses and rode away in order to continue their thieving on the busy caravan routes.

In the meantime, Cassim's wife had become very anxious. It was now pitch dark, and her husband had not returned. Full of fear, she ran to Ali Baba.

"Dear brother-in-law," she said, "I am sure you know that your brother has gone into the wood. So far he has not returned. I am terribly worried; I fear he has met with an accident."

Ali Baba had had similar thoughts. Therefore, he had refrained from going into the wood as usual, in order to avoid any cause for a quarrel with his brother. Now he, too, believed that some misadventure had befallen Cassim. But he remained calm and soothed his sister-in-law, saying that Cassim would certainly not return before the dead of night, so as to keep the matter as secret as possible.

This consoled Cassim's wife, and she went home and waited patiently until after midnight. When her husband had still not returned, she became restless again. When morning approached she was deeply worried, and she could not even relieve herself by crying, for the neighbors might have heard her. At daybreak she ran to Ali Baba again, and, sobbing wildly, she told him that her husband had not yet returned.

Now Ali Baba immediately set out with his three donkeys. He rode into the wood to the rock, looking right and left for his brother and seeing no sign of him. But near the entrance to the cave he discovered traces of blood; this seemed to him an ill omen and his heart sank. He walked toward the door and uttered the magic words:

"Open, Sesame!"

The door swung open. With a frightful shock he saw to the right and to the left of the door the bits of his brother's corpse, and he had to get a firm grip on himself not to scream loudly with horror and grief. However, he did not waste time. Despite Cassim's unbrotherly behavior, he had to pay him the honor of the last respects. Among the goods in the cave he found several valuable pieces of cloth. In these he wrapped the parts of the corpse and loaded one of the donkeys with the bundles. On it he put some brushwood so that nobody would see anything suspicious. The other two donkeys he hurriedly loaded with sacks of gold, and covered them, too, with dry wood. Then he ordered the door to shut.

He returned to town. At the edge of the wood he stopped; he did not wish to reach his home until nightfall. When darkness had fallen, he drove the donkeys with the gold to his house and requested his wife to unload them and bury the gold as quickly as possible. In a few words he told her of Cassim's fate. Then he led the third donkey to his sister-in-law's house.

Cautiously Ali Baba knocked at the door. It was noiselessly opened by Morgiana, his brother's maid, an extremely clever girl. When he had unloaded the bundle with the corpse in the yard, he drew Morgiana aside. "Listen to me, Morgiana," he whispered. "What I am going to tell you now you must never divulge to anybody. This bundle contains your master's corpse; he must be buried according to the prescribed rites. It must

165

look as though he has died a natural death. Now take me to your mistress, so that I can report to her. You, however, pay careful attention to what I am going to tell you."

Morgiana informed her mistress of Ali Baba's arrival, and the sister-in-law asked him in at once. She had been waiting for him with impatience. "What sort of news do you bring me?" she asked him. "Your expression bodes no good."

"Sister-in-law," replied Ali Baba, "you must listen to me quietly from beginning to end, and you must never tell anyone a single syllable of our conversation. Promise me that. It is as important for you as it is for me."

She promised everything. Stricken with profound grief she listened to her brother-in-law's report.

"A terrible misfortune has befallen you," he concluded, "but there is nothing we can do. What Allah ordains, we must take upon us. For consolation I have a suggestion: When you have mourned your husband long enough, I shall marry you; then I can join my property with yours. My wife will not be angry or jealous. She is sensible and does as she is told. In that way we can remain one family. We shall be able to live well on our property, for we have now ample money and possessions. But first we must pretend that Cassim died a natural death. Here you can rely on Morgiana. She will find ways and means to arrange everything satisfactorily."

Cassim's widow did not need long to consider Ali Baba's suggestion. In addition to her fortune, she was going to have a second husband, and he was richer than she would ever be. Therefore she did not refuse the proposal, and it helped her to get over her first husband's death. So she refrained from the usual loud lament. Ali Baba now knew that she would accept his offer, and he left her house somewhat less worried. Before he went home, however, he instructed Morgiana in the part she was to play.

Morgiana left the house immediately after Ali Baba. She ran all the way to the chemist's shop and arrived there out of breath and very agitated. She ordered a medicine that one gives to people who are dangerously ill. The chemist gave her what she had ordered and asked sympathetically who was ill in her master's house. "Oh," she said, "it is the master himself. He is fatally ill."

With these words, she took the medicine which, of course, could not now be of any use to Cassim, and hurried home.

Next morning, Morgiana turned up at the chemist's shop again. With tears in her eyes she requested the chemist to give her an even stronger medicine, which is given to the sick only when their condition is desperate. "My poor master," she cried, "even this medicine will not help him. What a good master he was! And now I am to lose him!"

People noticed how Ali Baba and his wife kept running to Cassim's house all day with misery on their faces, and so the rumor of his illness quickly spread all over the city. It therefore came as no surprise to them when Cassim's wife and Morgiana broke into loud lament. It simply informed them of the fact that Cassim had died.

Early next morning Morgiana went to see a venerable old cobbler in the market square. He was wont to open his shop long before the other shopkeepers. She bade him good morning especially politely. At the same time she pressed a piece of gold into his hand. The cobbler was a cheerful, witty old fellow, known all over the town as Baba Mustapha. As there was not yet much daylight, he examined the coin carefully and realized that it was gold.

"A fine piece of money!" he exclaimed. "What would you like me to do? I will do anything you want."

"Baba Mustapha," Morgiana said, "take your mending gear and come with me straightaway. I shall lead you. When we arrive near our destination, you will have to let yourself be blindfolded."

"No, no," protested Baba Mustapha, "you are asking something of me which is against my honor and my conscience."

"Heaven forbid," said Morgiana, and pressed another piece of gold into his hand. "I am not asking anything of you that would be wrong. Come along and do not worry."

Now Baba Mustapha gave up his resistance. When they had arrived in the vicinity of Cassim's house, Morgiana blindfolded him. It was only when they had arrived inside her master's room that she took the bandage off. There was the quartered corpse. When the cobbler saw it, he paled. Terror overcame him.

"Dear old man, do not be afraid," said Morgiana soothingly. "Nothing is going to happen to you. All you have to do is to sew the parts of this corpse together. Hurry up with your work. When you have finished, I shall give you another piece of gold."

When Baba Mustapha had finished the job, Morgiana gave him the promised piece of gold. Then she blindfolded him again and conducted him back. On the way, she impressed on him that he must keep strictly silent about the matter. At the point where she had blindfolded him on the way to the house, she took the bandage off again. She stopped and asked him to go home alone from there. She watched him carefully to make sure that he did not follow her to find out where she lived.

Morgiana had prepared hot water, so that Ali Baba could wash his brother and anoint him. With the usual ritual he wrapped him in the shroud. The carpenter brought the coffin as ordered, but the family placed the corpse into it so as not to arouse the carpenter's suspicions. Then they ceremoniously mounted the coffin in the middle of the sitting room. After the lid had been nailed on the coffin, Morgiana went to the mosque to inform them that everything was ready for the funeral.

At once the imam arrived with the other servants of the mosque. Four neighbors took the coffin on their shoulders and carried it along behind the imam. Later, other neighbors took turns in carrying the coffin. The imam murmured prayers all the way. Morgiana and the lamenting women followed; they cried loudly and beat their breasts. Ali Baba and many citizens of the town made up the funeral procession. At last they arrived at the cemetery and buried the dead man. Then people dispersed and went their separate ways.

Cassim's wife had stayed at home. She had raised loud wails of lament. The neighbors' wives joined in, as was the custom, so that the whole district echoed with laments during the funeral. Cassim's miserable way of dying remained a secret from everybody. Nobody, apart from the widow, Ali Baba, his wife, and Morgiana, knew what had really happened.

A little while after the funeral, Ali Baba brought his possessions and his money to the widow's house. He intended to live there in the future with his first wife. At the same time, he also announced his marriage to the widow, as was the custom. Such marriages were not at all unusual, and nobody was surprised about it.

Ali Baba's son had to take charge of Cassim's shop. The boy had just finished his apprenticeship to a merchant and had extremely good references. As soon as he showed himself capable of running the shop well, his father would marry him off to a girl of good standing.

Let us now leave Ali Baba in the enjoyment of his new-found happiness and turn to the forty thieves again. When the appointed time had elapsed, they returned to their hideout in the wood. They were greatly surprised that they could not find Cassim's corpse anywhere. Their surprise turned into anger when they realized that a large number of sacks containing money was missing. They were certain now that the dead man must have had accomplices who knew the secret. This thought disturbed them deeply.

"We are certainly discovered," said the captain. "We shall have to take precautions against our enemies at once, otherwise the treasure that our fathers started to collect will be lost in no time. The thief we found knew the magic formula, but there must be someone else who knows it too. That is proved by the removal of the corpse and the missing sacks of gold. We shall therefore have to kill the second man as well, and this will have to be done as quickly as possible. What do you think, men? Or have any of you any better advice?"

The entire gang approved of the captain's suggestion. They agreed that the thief must be found.

"I expected this reply because of your courage and intelligence," the captain went on. "Now, we shall need a bold, clever man. He is to disguise himself as a merchant and go into the nearby city, where he must find out if there is talk about a citizen's strange death recently. Then he will have to ascertain where that man lived, and who his relatives are. That our enemy comes from the city seems fairly certain to me. Our man must, however, be clever and cautious, otherwise he might disclose our hideout. If the messenger should bring an incorrect report, he will be punished by death."

At once one of the thieves volunteered and said, "Let me go to the town and explore the situation. Upon my honor I promise to risk my life. If my mission should fail, I will willingly submit to any punishment."

The captain and all his comrades praised him highly and wished him every success. He disguised himself so well that nobody would have taken him for a thief. At dawn he arrived in the city. He went to the market square where only a single shop was open—that of Baba Mustapha, the cobbler.

Baba Mustapha was already sitting on his cobbler's stool, his awl and leather punch by his side. He was just about to begin his cobbling when the thief entered his shop. He bade the old man a kindly good morning. Then he started to talk.

"Tell me, my good old man," he began, "is it light enough for your work? By this half-light, even a younger person could not see well enough, but at your age your eyes must be weak. I wonder that you can pull the threads through the eye of the needle."

"You seem to be a stranger in this town," replied the cobbler, "or else you would know that despite my age my eyes are very good indeed; that is why everybody wants my services. Only the other day, I had to sew up a corpse, and he was lying in a room which was a great deal darker than this one is. Nevertheless I completed my job to the entire satisfaction of my employer."

The thief pricked his ears. He had met the right person already. But he wanted to know more.

"A corpse?" he asked. "How was that? Why should you have to sew up a corpse? You mean to say, do you not, that you had to mend the shroud?"

"No, no," said the cobbler, "I meant nothing of the sort. But I realize you want to pump me, and you have hit on the wrong man. I will not say another word."

But the thief needed no further proof. He knew he was on the right track, and he had to get more information from that quarter. He therefore drew a piece of gold from his pocket and pressed it into Baba Mustapha's hand.

"I will not pry into your secrets," he said, "but I am very discreet. Perhaps the dead man was one of my relations or friends. In that case it would be my duty to offer my condolences to the sorrowing relatives. I would ask you, therefore, to show me the house where the dead man used to reside."

Baba Mustapha weighed the piece of gold in his palm hesitatingly.

"My good man," he said with regret, "even if I wanted to, I could not comply with your wish. A maid came to collect me; at a certain spot she blindfolded me. That is how she took me to the room where the dead man was lying. It was there that I did my job. Afterward she conducted me in the same manner back to the same place. From there I went home. So you will see that I cannot tell you anything of value. I just do not know the way to that house."

But the thief began anew, "Surely you will remember part of the way. Please come with me. Take me to the spot where she blindfolded you. I shall do the same there. Then I shall take you round all over the place. Perhaps in that way we shall find the house where you did the job. Now every piece of work merits its reward, so I will give you yet another piece of gold. Come along and do me this favor."

The cobbler took the second coin. He examined it carefully and pocketed it. He chuckled and got up.

"All right," he said to the thief, "we will do as you said. But I cannot promise you that I shall find the place."

They set out immediately. Baba Mustapha did not have to lock up his shop; there were no valuables in there. So they went together to the spot where Morgiana had blindfolded the old man.

"It is here that she put the bandage over my eyes," said Baba Mustapha. "I recognize the spot exactly."

The thief now tied his kerchief over the cobbler's eyes. Then he took him by the hand and let himself be led. The old man first walked straight along the road. Then he turned off to the left and then to the right again. At last they came to a narrow passageway. Here the old man suddenly stopped in front of a small house.

"I did not get any farther before," said Baba Mustapha. "At least that is what I think."

Indeed, he was standing just in front of Cassim's house, but now Ali Baba was living there. Before the thief removed the kerchief from the old man's eyes, he hurriedly took from his pocket a piece of chalk and made a sign on the front door. Then he asked the cobbler whether he knew whose house it was.

"No," said the old man, "this house is too far away from my shop. I do not know the people who live in this district."

The thief now realized that he could get no more information out of the cobbler, so he allowed him to go home. He himself quickly returned to his companions in the wood.

Soon after the thief and Baba Mustapha had gone, Morgiana left the house to go shopping. When she returned, she noticed the chalk mark on the door. She stopped and looked at it in surprise. She was disquieted and thought: What is the meaning of this sign? Of course it is possible that it was made by playing children. On the other hand it is also possible that an enemy of

175

my master has something evil in his mind. So she got a piece of chalk and made the same mark on all the neighbors' doors. Then she went back to her work. Neither to the master nor to the mistress did she breathe a word of the matter.

Meanwhile, the thief had arrived back in the wood. Cheerfully he approached his comrades and immediately reported to the captain about the success of his mission. He praised the good luck that had taken him straightaway to the right person. They were all pleased to hear it. The captain most of all praised his skill and his devotion.

"Comrades," he addressed the members of his gang, "we will take up arms and go to the city at once. But take good care to hide the weapons. It will be best if we go one by one. In town we will meet in the market square. Our scout will lead me to the right house, where I shall make arrangements. I shall tell you of my further plans when we have met in the market square."

They all assented to the captain's orders, and soon they were ready to go. In twos and threes, their weapons concealed under their clothes, they reached the town without causing any sensation. The captain and the scout were the last; they straightaway went to the thoroughfare where Ali Baba's house was situated. When the scout saw a mark on the first door he passed, he thought this was the house. The captain went on a little to avoid making himself conspicuous. When he arrived at the next house, he saw the same mark again; so he asked the scout whether it was this or the previous house. That confused the poor fellow; he did not know what to say. As they proceeded, they noticed that there were the same signs on every house door. Now the captain grew angry.

"You scoundrel," he thundered, "which of these houses did you mark?"

The thief earnestly assured his captain that he had put the chalk mark on one door only. He had no idea who could have put the other marks; but now he was so confused that it was impossible for him to be sure which was the correct door. One house was exactly like the others. He had seen no distinguishing mark on the right one in the morning.

The captain realized that his plan had gone awry. So he went to the market square with his companion to meet the other thieves. He ordered them to return to the wood; the day's journey had been of no avail. He preceded them. The others followed at intervals. In front of the rock cave they gathered again. There the captain explained to them why their plan had failed. Then they sat in judgment on the clumsy scout. Unanimously they condemned him to death. Willingly the scout bent his head, which was chopped off there and then.

Now another of the thieves volunteered to scout. He was sure he could do better than his predecessor. It was most important for the gang to eliminate as soon as possible the man who knew their secret. So the offer was accepted, and he knew that he forfeited his life if the mission should fail.

The thief immediately set out on his way to town. Just like the first scout, he bribed Baba Mustapha. In the same way as his predecessor had done, he got to Ali Baba's house. There he marked the door in an unobtrusive spot, but this time he used red chalk. He was sure he would be able to tell it from the doors with the white signs. But again Morgiana, whose suspicions had now been aroused, saw the mark when she got home from shopping, and again she marked all the neighboring doors with the same red sign.

Cheerfully and contentedly, the thief returned to his comrades in the wood. He boasted that he had marked the house with an unmistakable sign; this time it could not be missed. Thereupon the whole gang went back into town again and collected in the market square. This time they were going to carry out the plan that had misfired on the day before.

The captain and the scout went straight to Ali Baba's street. There they noticed with horror that this time many doors bore red marks; again one could not tell the right house. The captain was seized by a terrible fury, but he had to contain himself, or he would have aroused suspicion in the town. He ordered his men to return to the wood and there explained to them why the mission had again failed. The boastful scout, nevertheless, was beheaded as agreed.

Now the captain had lost two valuable members of his gang and had achieved nothing. He thought: I shall only lose more men if I entrust this task to them. My men are brave and courageous in battle. They are suited to plunderings and bloodshed. But when it comes to fraud and ruses, they are helpless.

So he decided he himself would undertake this difficult job. He, too, approached Baba Mustapha and asked him to lead him to the house in question. But he put no mark on it; rather, he looked at it carefully. He walked past it several times and impressed on his memory what it looked like and where it was situated.

When he had done this, he returned to the wood. There he assembled the gang.

"Comrades," he said, "nothing shall come between us and our revenge now. I know exactly which is the house of the scoundrel who stole from us. On walking back I thought of ways and means to manage the matter so cunningly that nobody will get to know anything of our cave and our treasure, which would be disastrous for us. So listen to my plan; but if any of you can think of a better one, he may let me know. Go to the villages and markets in the vicinity and buy nineteen mules and thirty-eight large leather jars for carrying oil. Fill one of them, and leave the others empty. Then bring everything here. You will creep into the jars but take

179

your weapons. I shall get you all into town unseen. The rest leave to me."

Within a few days everything had been supplied. The empty jars were somewhat tight at their necks, so the captain had them made a little wider. Every man now crept into a jar with his weapons. The captain sewed up the openings, apart from a small gap which was to serve as an air hole. Every man should think that these were real oil jars. The captain also painted their outsides with oil, and that made the deception complete. Then he loaded two jars each on a mule. Toward the evening he traveled to town, disguised as a merchant.

He arrived there about one hour after sunset and went straight to Ali Baba's house with his whole train. He wanted to ask for night quarters there for himself and his mules. He did not have to knock. Ali Baba was sitting comfortably in front of his house, enjoying the cool evening air after dinner. The captain halted his mules. Modestly and courteously he bade the time of day.

"Master," he then said, "I have brought all this oil from afar. Tomorrow I will sell it in the market. But I do not know where I can find accommodation at so late an hour. I do not wish to be a burden to you, but could you possibly give me lodging for the night? I should be most grateful to you. Also, of course, I would pay you well."

True, Ali Baba had seen the captain of the thieves in the wood and had also heard his voice. But he did not recognize him in his disguise as an oil merchant.

"Be welcome," said Ali Baba. "You may spend the night at my house."

He made room for him, and the captain drove his mules into Ali Baba's yard. Ali Baba ordered his slaves to unload the animals and feed and tie them up. He himself went to the kitchen and ordered Morgiana to prepare a good supper for the late guest. Also she was to get a bed ready for him in one of the rooms.

Ali Baba then returned to his guest. When he saw that the stranger had unloaded the mules and was looking for a place to sleep in the yard, he took him by the hand and wanted to lead him into the sitting room. But the thieves' captain refused. He said he did not wish to become a nuisance to his host. The truth was, he wanted to remain near his men. But Ali Baba asked him so politely and pressingly that he did not dare refuse any longer. Then the captain partook of a hearty meal and his host kept him company. At last the guest rose.

"I will now leave you alone," Ali Baba said to him. "If you should require anything, just call. Everything in the house is at your service."

The master of the house went to the kitchen to discuss tomorrow's breakfast for the guest with Morgiana. In the meantime the guest wandered into the yard, pretending he wanted to have a look at his mules in the stable.

Ali Baba instructed the maid to look after the guest well. "Also," he added, "I want to go to the bathhouse tomorrow morning. Get the bath towels out and hand them to Abdullah, the slave, and do not forget to cook a nourishing soup for me. I shall be hungry after the bath."

Then he went to his room and got into bed.

Meanwhile, the captain had left the stable and had given instructions to his men. For this purpose he walked slowly past the jars.

"As soon as you hear small stones fall in the yard," he said in a low voice, "cut the jars with your daggers, creep out, and wait for me. I shall be with you in no time."

After that he returned to the house. Morgiana led him into a well-appointed room. She asked him if he wanted for anything, but the stranger needed nothing, so she left him alone. He extinguished the light and lay down on his bed fully dressed, in order to wait a little longer.

Morgiana did not forget the master's orders. First she got the bath towels out and handed them to Abdullah. Then she went to the kitchen to make preparations for the soup and to light a fire.

While she was working, the light of her lamp grew smaller and smaller, and in the end the lamp went out; the oil in it was finished. She turned to the oil jug to refill the lamp and found that the jug was empty, too. She had no candles either and did not know what to do, because she urgently needed light for her work. So she asked Abdullah.

"Do not worry," said the slave, "there is plenty of oil in the house. The whole yard is full of the oil jars that belong to the strange trader. Help yourself to as much oil as you need; he is sure not to mind. Besides, tomorrow we can pay him the price of the oil."

This seemed reasonable advice to Morgiana, and she thanked Abdullah. He went to bed, and she took her oil jug to the yard for filling. When she approached the first jar she came to, the thief inside thought his captain had come. He was impatient to get out of his narrow confines; it was so uncomfortable, all his bones ached.

"Has the time come?" he asked in a low voice.

Any other woman would have been terrified to death. Morgiana, too, was considerably upset. She had expected to find oil in the jar, not a man. But she got a grip on herself at once. She realized how important it was to keep the matter secret. Without showing her disquiet, she said in a deep man's voice:

"Not yet, but soon."

Then she turned to the next jar, and the same thing happened there. And so she went on, until she came to the last jar. That one did contain oil enough to fill her jug. Swiftly she returned to the kitchen, where she cleaned the lamp and refilled it.

While she was lighting the lamp, she gave the matter anxious thought. So her master's guest was not an oil trader, but a thieves' captain! The thirty-seven thieves within the jars were probably about to commit a despicable crime. Something had to be done about it! She went to the yard with a huge kettle and filled it with the oil out of the last of the jars. She returned to the kitchen with the full kettle and put it on the fire, on which she had laid an extra supply of good, dry wood to obtain a powerful flame. It did not take long for the oil to boil and to bubble. She took the seething oil into the yard and poured enough into every jar to kill the man inside.

This deed was a credit to Morgiana. She had shown a great deal of courage and ingenuity. After having attended to the matter quite noiselessly, she went back to the kitchen. She banked the fire just enough to keep her master's soup simmering, then she extinguished the light, bolted her kitchen door, and sat down by the window. She wanted to observe from that vantage point anything else that might occur.

For a quarter of an hour she sat by the window without anything happening. The thieves' captain had waited until everybody in the house was asleep. Now he went to his window and looked down into the dark yard. Nothing stirred; no light was to be seen anywhere. So he dropped some small stones as the signal they had arranged. Some of the stones even hit the jars, but nothing moved; the men did not emerge from the jars. That puzzled him. He threw stones again and even a third time, but all remained quiet. In great alarm, he ran silently into the yard. When he approached the first jar, the smell of hot oil mixed with a horrible odor assailed his nostrils. The same happened when he neared the second jar. He knew at once that his plan had failed. His intention of murdering Ali Baba and plundering his house had come to nothing. He saw that all his men had lost their lives in the same manner. A great quantity of oil was missing from the last jar; with that oil his men had been killed. In despair he saw his hopes destroyed. Now all he could do was to save his own life as quickly as possible. So he jumped over the wall into the neighbor's garden; from there he fled over the fences and hedges until he reached the open country and ran into the wood.

Morgiana heard no more noise, neither did she see the thieves' captain return, so she felt sure that he had fled through the gardens. The front door had been locked and bolted; he could not have escaped through it. She was satisfied that her action had succeeded and went to bed at peace. She had saved her master and the whole house from a gang of thieves.

Early next morning Ali Baba got up and went to the bath with his slave. He had no idea of the happenings of the past night. Morgiana had told neither him nor Abdullah, so that they should not worry.

When Ali Baba returned from the bath, the sun was already high in the sky. In surprise he saw that the oil jars were still in his yard. He thought the strange trader would have gone to the market long ago. So he asked Morgiana why the man was still in the house.

"My master," said Morgiana, "may Allah protect you and your entire house. You are destined for a long life. Last night Allah's benevolence protected you from certain death. Your enemies, however, have perished miserably. Come with me into the yard and see with your own eyes."

Ali Baba followed the maid into the yard. She pointed to the first jar. "Have a look," she said, "at the oil inside!"

Ali Baba bent down to see better. When he noticed a man inside with a bare dagger he retreated with a scream.

"Do not be afraid," said Morgiana. "The man can do no harm to anybody. He is dead."

"Morgiana," exclaimed Ali Baba, "what is the meaning of this?"

"I shall tell you in a minute," replied Morgiana, "but drop your voice. The neighbors need not know our secret. First take a look at the other jars."

Ali Baba looked into every jar, one by one. In each was a dead, burned man with a dagger in his hand. There were thirty-seven men in all. Only the last jar contained some oil. Ali Baba stopped in confusion. He looked at Morgiana and at the jars. At last he regained enough control over himself to be able to speak.

"But what has become of the strange merchant?" he asked.

"That merchant," replied Morgiana, "is no more a merchant than I am. But come to the house. I would rather tell you the whole story inside. There you can sit down comfortably and strengthen yourself with some meat soup."

Ali Baba betook himself to his room and Morgiana brought him the soup.

"Come, come, tell me," he said impatiently. "Tell me the whole story in all particulars. I can hardly wait."

Morgiana complied, and began:

"My master, last night I got the bath towels out as you had ordered and handed them to Abdullah. Then I began to prepare the soup, but the lamp went out, because the oil had come to an end. I could not find any in the jug either, and there were no candles at all in the house. Then Abdullah drew my attention to the oil jars in the yard. So I took the jug to get some oil from them.

"A voice called from the first jar:

" 'Has the time come?'

"I got a shock, but soon composed myself again. It was clear to me that some evil deed was about to be perpetrated. So I disguised my voice and replied:

" 'Not yet, but soon.'

"Then I went from one jar to another, and from each came the same question, and I gave the same answer. That is how I became aware that there was a man hidden in every single jar except the last. That contained oil; with it I filled my jug. Now I knew that there were thirty-seven thieves in your house, and that they were all waiting for a sign to attack you. So I took a large kettle, filled it with oil, and brought it to the boil; with it I scalded the thieves in the jars. Then I went back to the kitchen, bolted the door, and turned the light off. I sat down by the window to watch what our guest would do next. After a while I heard how he threw little stones on the jars. When nothing stirred, he did it a second and then a third time. Then he sneaked down into the yard and went from one jar to the next. As it was so dark I lost sight of him. I believe he must have fled over the garden wall.

"This is the story," she went on, "that you wanted to know. But I can tell you even more. A few days ago I noticed a white chalk mark on our door. I had no idea what it was for. So I went round the neighborhood and made the same marks on all the other doors in the vicinity. The following day I saw a red mark on our door, so I went round chalking red marks on the other doors. Now think that over. I realized all this was connected with the forty thieves in the wood. Why there were only thirty-eight here is not quite clear to me. Anyway, it proves that the thieves are after your life. There are now only three left, but you must take care. As long as there is only one alive, it is dangerous for you. I shall do what I can to watch over you."

Ali Baba now realized what an enormous service Morgiana had done him.

"You have saved my life," he said in gratitude. "From this hour I give you your freedom, and I will look after you in future as much as I can. I, too, am convinced that these men were the forty thieves. Praised be Allah! Through your hand he has saved me from dire peril. I implore him that he may continue to care for me. Now we first have to dig a trench and throw the corpses of these thieves in. We will do it quietly; nobody must hear anything. Abdullah will help me."

Ali Baba's garden was very long; at the bottom it was bordered by tall, old trees. Here, with the help of his slave, Ali Baba dug a long deep trench. As the ground was soft, the work proceeded smoothly.

Then they pulled the corpses from the jars and threw them into the trench one by one. On them they heaped earth and stamped on it to make it firm. On top they spread some loose soil, so that the ground looked just as it had looked before. The oil jars were hidden in the house. The mules were sold one by one, at different times, in the market. In this way Ali Baba did everything he could to keep the secret of his wealth hidden.

Meanwhile the thieves' captain had arrived at his rocky cave, his heart full of anger and grief. Inside the cave he sat down and mourned the fate of his men. Their lives had ended horribly. Never again would he be able to gather around him such a band of courageous comrades. He decided he would avenge their deaths. And his enemy was not to get the treasures in the cave either! By and by he quieted down. In the end, sleep overcame him.

Next morning he put on an exquisite suit, went to the town, and took a room in a fine hotel. He was sure the events at Ali Baba's house must have become known in the town. So he asked the landlord about recent happenings. The man told him of a number of insignificant events, but nothing of the matter about which the thief expected to hear. He saw from this that Ali Baba must have acted cautiously. He probably did not wish to disclose the origin of his wealth. The thief therefore decided to remove Ali Baba by some secret method.

He bought a horse and rode several times to the cave in the wood. Each time he brought with him bales of fine cloth, suits, carpets, precious jewels. In the town he rented a shop where he stored his goods and began a lively trade. Opposite his shop was the late Cassim's business, which was now run by Ali Baba's son.

The thieves' captain now called himself Cogia Houssain. As a new trader he paid calls on the neighbors, as is the custom, and exchanged polite conversation with them. He was obliging and behaved in a dignified manner, and so he soon gained esteem and repute.

Ali Baba's son sought his acquaintance, and soon these two became firm friends. The boy was intelligent and well educated. The thief liked to chat with him. Now and then Ali Baba came to see his son, and Cogia Houssain recognized him as the owner of the house where his comrades had lost their lives. Then the youth told him that Ali Baba was his father, and now the thief became even more amiable. He gave him small presents and invited him occasionally for meals.

The young man did not wish to accept so many courtesies without repaying the kindness, but he could not invite the trader to his own place, as it was small and uncomfortable. So he talked it over with his father. Ali Baba was only too pleased to be host to his son's friend.

"My son," he said, "it is Friday tomorrow. On that day all the traders keep their shops closed. Invite your neighbor for a walk through the town. Arrange for the two of you to pass my house on the way back. Then invite him to come in. I will not issue a formal invitation, but I shall instruct Morgiana to prepare a tasty supper."

And so, on Friday afternoon, Ali Baba's son and Cogia Houssain went for a walk together. On their way back, the son arranged that they happened to pass through the street where Ali Baba lived. When they reached the front door the youth stopped.

"This is our house," he said. "Please enter, and do me the honor of having a meal with my father."

Cogia Houssain at first refused the invitation. He made a number of excuses, but the young man asked him more and more urgently to add this one more favor to all the others he had already bestowed on him. True, the thieves' captain had already made up his mind to gain access to Ali Baba's house and kill him, but he went on refusing for a while to keep up the pretense. In the end, a slave opened the door. The young man seized his friend's hand and led him courteously into the house.

Ali Baba welcomed Cogia Houssain with a friendly gesture. He thanked him for the honor of his visit and wished him happiness and well-being.

"I am greatly indebted to you," he said. "You are an experienced man, but you do not think it beneath you to contribute to my son's education."

Houssain answered with a few well-chosen words and then wanted to take his leave. But Ali Baba kept him and asked him to do him the honor of being his guest for supper.

"Sir," replied Cogia Houssain, "I thank you for your kind invitation. But forgive me; I cannot accept. Do not consider this as a slight or an impoliteness. There is a special reason for it. You would understand if you knew."

"May I know the reason?" asked Ali Baba.

The merchant replied, "Yes, I can tell you. I must not eat meat or anything else with salt. That would look odd at table, and I wish to avoid it."

In the Orient, if a man eats salt with another, the other man becomes his friend and brother and must never be harmed by him. This is important to know.

"That is no reason to deprive me of the honor of your visit," was Ali Baba's answer. "There is no salt in my bread. And there will be no salt put into any of the other dishes that will be offered to you. So, please stay. I shall go to the kitchen to give instructions to this effect."

Ali Baba went to the kitchen to tell Morgiana not to add any salt to the meat today. Also she was to prepare some other unsalted dishes. Morgiana, who had already made her preparations, and had just been about to put the finishing touches to the meal, grew annoyed.

"Who is that obstinate fellow?" she asked. "Why does he not want to eat any salt? If I have to get fresh dishes now in a hurry, they will not be very good."

"Do not be angry, Morgiana," begged Ali Baba, "do as I tell you."

Morgiana obeyed reluctantly. She was curious to see the strange man who would not eat any salt. When Abdullah had laid the table, she helped him carry the dishes in. Despite his disguise, she at once recognized the guest as the thieves' captain. She also noticed that he was carrying a dagger hidden under his suit. Aha, she thought, now I can see why this scoundrel will not eat any salt with my master. He wants to murder him. Well, I shall prevent that.

Back in her kitchen, Morgiana wondered how best she could carry out her plan. While the guest was eating with her master, she made her preparations. Just when Abdullah called for the fruit for dessert, she had completed them. She herself carried the fruit in, and placed it on a small table by the side of Ali Baba. On leaving the room, she pulled Abdullah along with her, pretending she was going to leave her master alone with his guest.

Now, thought the thieves' captain, the time has come to kill Ali Baba.

"I shall make use of this favorable opportunity," he said to himself. "I shall make them both drunk, father as well as son. Then I will push the dagger into the old man's heart; the son may live, if he does not hinder me. I, however, shall flee over the garden wall, as I did the other day. Only I shall have to wait just a little longer, until the slave and the maid are having their meal."

Morgiana, however, had seen what was in the scoundrel's evil mind; she did not give him time to carry out the wicked deed. Instead of having her meal, she put on a charming dancing dress, a silver head ornament, and a sparkling belt. A dagger encrusted with diamonds was hanging from the belt. When she had finished dressing, she turned to Abdullah.

"Abdullah," she said, "take your bell-drum. We will go into the dining room to entertain our master and his guest."

The slave fetched the bell-drum, banged on it, and walked into the dining room in front of Morgiana, who followed in his footsteps. She bowed low with natural grace. Then she asked for permission to show her prowess in dancing.

"Come in, Morgiana," Ali Baba called to her. "Let our guest see how well you know this art." And turning to his guest, he said, "You see I have everything in the house; I do not have to get strange dancers. My maid and my slave provide that pleasure for me. I hope you will like it."

Cogia Houssain was annoyed about the delay and secretly cursed the two dancers. Again a favorable opportunity had been missed. But he could not very well refuse, so he said he was pleased to have this unexpected pleasure.

Now Abdullah began to beat his bell-drum and sing a dancing tune. Morgiana danced with incomparable grace that would have done credit to a professional dancer. But the fake merchant had no eyes for the girl's charming movements; he gazed angrily into space. Ali Baba and his son, however, gave the two performers whole-hearted applause.

One dance followed another. The steps became quicker and more complicated. At last Morgiana took the dagger out of her belt. Swinging the sparkling blade in her hand, she whirled round the room in leaps and turns. Now she thrust the dagger forward, now sideways. Now she aimed it at Ali Baba, now at the son, now at the guest. At last she seemed to have lost her breath. She tore the bell-drum from the slave's hand with her left, while she was still holding the dagger in her right. Now she held the concave side of the drum toward Ali Baba, as though she were collecting money.

Ali Baba threw a gold piece into the drum, and so did his son. Cogia Houssain was about to do the same; he had already pulled out his money bag. Just when he was drawing out a coin, Morgiana, with the courage of her resolution, thrust the dagger into his chest. The merchant sank back lifelessly.

Ali Baba and his son shrieked with horror simultaneously.

"Wretched girl," exclaimed Ali Baba, "what have you done? Do you want to ruin me and my family?"

"No, master," replied Morgiana quietly. "I did it to save you. Look what I shall show you."

With these words she opened the false merchant's suit and showed her master the dagger he was carrying.

"Do you realize now," she went on, "who the man was? Just look a little more closely, and you will recognize him as the supposed oil merchant. In reality, of course, he was the captain of the forty thieves. He was always after your life. Now you will understand why he did not want to eat salt with you; that is what made me suspicious straightaway, and I was right, as you can see now."

Deeply moved, Ali Baba embraced the girl. She had now saved his life for the second time.

"Morgiana," he said, "I have given you your freedom. That, however, is not enough to express to you my great gratitude. I promised you more to come. Now is the time to fulfill my promise. I will tell you how I am going to reward you for your loyalty and devotion. I am going to give you in marriage to my dear only son."

And he turned to the young man.

"My dear son," he said, "you heard what I have decided. I hope you will bow to your father's wish. You owe Morgiana no less gratitude than I do. Cogia Houssain sought your friendship only for the purpose of killing me. Perhaps he would have made you, too, a victim of his revenge. Morgiana will always be a credit to our family; to you, however, she will be a support until the end of your days. That is why I shall marry you to her."

The young man had not the slightest objection. Marriage to Morgiana was greatly to his liking.

Then they buried the captain's corpse next to his henchmen. It was done quickly and quietly. It was only many years after that the matter leaked out, and then nobody concerned was alive any longer.

A few days later, Morgiana's wedding to Ali Baba's son was celebrated. There was a splendid, lavish meal, accompanied by song, dance, and the usual festivities. Ali Baba was especially pleased, as all the guests praised Morgiana's virtues, although they had no idea of the real motives underlying the marriage.

The last time Ali Baba had been to the cave was when he had found his brother's corpse. For a long time he refrained from going there again. Only thirty-eight thieves had been accounted for. What had happened to the remaining two, he did not know. He thought they might be lying in wait for him in the cave.

But for more than a year everything was quiet. Now Ali Baba was seized with curiosity. One fine morning he mounted a horse and rode into the wood. When he arrived at the rock cave he looked round cautiously. But he did not see any traces either of humans or of horses. The thorny bushes in front of the secret door had become almost impenetrable. That told him that for a long time nobody had been in the cave. So he tied his horse to a tree, crept through the shrubs to the secret door, and spoke the magic words:

"Open, Sesame!"

At once the door swung open, and he entered. He saw that the goods and treasures had not been touched. So nobody had been in the cave since Cogia Houssain's death! Evidently none of the forty thieves was alive any longer, and Ali Baba was the only person in the world who knew of the treasures. He was the master of the immeasurable wealth in the cave. But he filled only one sack with gold, so as not to overburden his horse, and returned to town, serene and contented.

From that time on, Ali Baba lived in peace. Highly esteemed by all his fellow citizens in the town, he enjoyed his wealth in comfortable serenity. Later, he let his son into the secret of the cave and the magic formula. His son, in turn, confided it to his children. They all disposed wisely and modestly of their fortune, so they were loved by the poor and held in esteem by the rich. And so they spent their lives in happiness and joy.

ACKNOWLEDGMENTS

All possible care has been taken to trace ownership and secure permission for each selection in this series. The Great Books Foundation wishes to thank the following authors, publishers, and representatives for permission to reprint copyrighted material:

Shrewd Todie and Lyzer the Miser, from WHEN SHLEMIEL WENT TO WARSAW AND OTHER STORIES, by Isaac Bashevis Singer. Translation copyright © 1968 by Isaac Bashevis Singer and Elizabeth Shub. Reprinted by permission of Farrar, Straus and Giroux, LLC.

The Goldfish, from THE LITTLE BOOKROOM, by Eleanor Farjeon. Copyright © 1955 by Eleanor Farjeon; renewed 1983 by Gervase Farjeon and M. S. H. Jones. Reprinted by permission of Harold Ober Associates, Inc.

The Great Blackberry Pick, from FAMILIAR AND HAUNTING, by Philippa Pearce. Copyright © 1972 by Philippa Pearce. Published by Greenwillow Books, 2002. Reprinted by permision of Laura Cecil Literary Agency and the author.

The Story of Wang Li, from CASTLES AND DRAGONS, by Elizabeth Coatsworth. Copyright © 1932 by Elizabeth Coatsworth. Reprinted by permission of Paterson Marsh, Ltd. on behalf of the Estate of Elizabeth Coatsworth.

The Hemulen Who Loved Silence, from TALES FROM MOOMINVALLEY, by Tove Jansson. Copyright © 1962 by Tove Jansson. Reprinted by permission of Moomin Characters.

THE ENCHANTED STICKS, by Steven J. Meyers. Copyright © 1979 by Steven J. Meyers. Reprinted by permission of the author.

Mr. Singer's Nicknames, from MY GREAT-GRANDFATHER AND I, by James Krüss. Translation copyright © 1964 by Atheneum Publishers. Reprinted by permission of Atheneum Books for Young Readers, an imprint of Simon & Schuster Children's Publishing Division.

Ali Baba and the Forty Thieves, from TALES OF THE ARABIAN NIGHTS, translated by Charlotte Dixon, edited by Hedwig Smola. Copyright © 1964 by Verlag Carl Ueberreuter Gesellschaft. Reprinted by permission of Verlag Carl Ueberreuter Gesellschaft.

ILLUSTRATION CREDITS

Brock Cole prepared the illustration for *Mr. Singer's Nicknames*.

Donna Diamond's illustration for *The Enchanted Sticks* is from the book of the same name. Illustration copyright © 1979 by Donna Diamond. Reprinted by permission of the illustrator.

Leo and Diane Dillon prepared the illustrations for *The Goldfish* and *The Little Humpbacked Horse*.

Olga Dugina's illustration for *Ali Baba and the Forty Thieves* is reproduced with the permission of Esslinger Verlag and the artist.

Tove Jansson's illustrations for *The Hemulen Who Loved Silence* are from TALES FROM MOOMIN-VALLEY. Illustrations copyright © 1962 by Tove Jansson. Reprinted by permission of Moomin Characters.

Rosalind Charney Kaye prepared the illustration for *Shrewd Todie and Lyzer the Miser*.

Rudyard Kipling's illustration for *The Elephant's Child* is from JUST SO STORIES, by Rudyard Kipling, first published in 1902.

Jane Tattersfield prepared the illustration for *The Great Blackberry Pick*.

Ed Young prepared the illustration for *The Story of Wang Li*.

Cover art by Louise Brierley. Copyright © 2006 by Louise Brierley.

Text and cover design by William Seabright & Associates.

Interior design by Think Design Group.

W9-CQL-943

The Cruise of the *Janet Nichol*

edited by Roslyn Jolly

The Cruise
of the
Janet Nichol

among the
South Sea Islands

A DIARY BY
MRS ROBERT LOUIS STEVENSON

University of
Washington Press
Seattle

University of
New South Wales Press
Sydney

A UNSW Press book

Published by
University of New South Wales Press Ltd
University of New South Wales
Sydney NSW 2052
AUSTRALIA
www.unswpress.com.au

Published in the United States of America by
University of Washington Press
PO Box 50096 Seattle WA 98145-5096
www.washington.edu/uwpress

© Arrangement, introduction and notes Roslyn Jolly 2004

This book is copyright. Apart from any fair dealing for the purpose
of private study, research, criticism or review, as permitted under the
Copyright Act, no part may be reproduced by any process without
written permission. Inquiries should be addressed to the publisher.

U.S. Cataloging-in-Publication data is available from the Library of Congress
ISBN 0-295-98370-1

National Library of Australia
Cataloguing-in-Publication entry:

Stevenson, Fanny Van de Grift, 1840-1914.
The cruise of the Janet Nichol among the South Sea Islands :
a diary by Mrs Robert Louis Stevenson.
ISBN 0 86840 606 6.
1. Stevenson, Fanny Van de Grift, 1840–1914. 2. Stevenson, Robert Louis,
1850–1894. 3. Stevenson, Robert Louis, 1850–1894 – Journeys – Oceania.
4. Oceania – Description and travel. I. Jolly, Roslyn. II. Title.

919.604

Cover photo Reproduced by permission of The Writers' Museum, Edinburgh.
Design Di Quick
Printer Everbest Printing, China

Contents

Acknowledgments   9

List of illustrations   10

Introduction
by Roslyn Jolly   13

Note on the text   45

Note on the photographs   47

Preface
by Fanny Van de Grift Stevenson   49

**The Cruise of the
Janet Nichol
among the South Sea Islands**   51

Explanatory notes   198

Further reading   204

For Simon and Alice,
my
travelling companions
R.J.

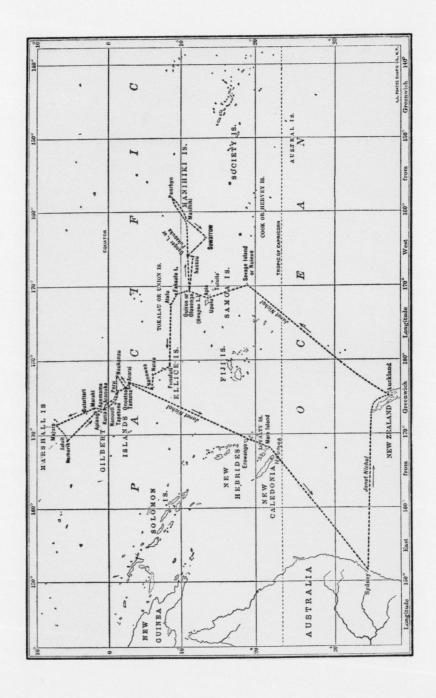

Acknowledgments

ll photographs in this book are reproduced by permission of The Writers' Museum, Edinburgh. Quotations from Fanny Stevenson's manuscript diary of the *Janet Nicoll* cruise, and from her recipe book, are by permission of the Robert Louis Stevenson Silverado Museum, St Helena, California. I am grateful to the University of New South Wales for allowing me to undertake a Special Studies Program in 2000, and for providing a University Research Support Program Grant in 2002, which enabled me to carry out the research for this book. An Australian Research Council Small Grant in 1999 also assisted the project.

I would like to thank Elaine Greig for her help in supplying the photographs, and Roger Swearingen and Ernest Mehew for generously sharing their knowledge of the Stevensons. I am grateful for the assistance given me by Ann Kindred (Associate Curator/Museum Archivist) and Edmond Reynolds (Curator) at the Robert Louis Stevenson Silverado Museum, St Helena, California; Kris Quist and staff at the Stevenson House Museum, Monterey, California; Susan Snyder and staff at the Bancroft Library, University of California, Berkeley; and staff at the National Library of Scotland. Thanks also to Sandra Knowles and Rebecca Sheehan for research assistance.

My deepest thanks are to Simon Petch, who encouraged and supported this project from beginning to end.

Illustrations

PAGE 2 Fanny Stevenson with two Pacific Islanders,
date and location unknown.

PAGE 8 Map of the *Janet Nicoll*'s voyage (11 April–26 July 1890).

PAGES 10–11 (BACKGROUND) AND 197
The *Janet Nicoll* at anchor off Penrhyn Island.

PAGE 12 Penrhyn Island.

PAGE 48 The *Janet Nicoll* with ship's company.

PAGE 52 AND COVER The Stevensons
on the bridge of the *Janet Nicoll*.

PAGE 55 The Stevensons with Nan Tok and Nei Takauti
at Butaritari, 1889.

PAGE 56 Nan Tok and Nei Takauti, 'the baron and
baroness', Butaritari, 1889.

PAGE 65 Boy from Niue.

PAGE 70 Women and children photographed on the
Janet Nicoll cruise, location unknown.

PAGE 83 Manihikians with adopted white man.

Penryn Island.

PAGE 85   King of Manihiki in centre, with the Island Judge on his right, Tin Jack seated on his left, and a beachcomber in the foreground.

PAGE 86   Manihiki dancers.

PAGE 93   Penrhyn Island.

PAGE 97   Figurehead from a wrecked ship on the trader's veranda, Penrhyn. The figurehead later featured in Robert Louis Stevenson's novella, *The Ebb-Tide*.

PAGE 100   Little girls singing, Penrhyn.

PAGE 113   Girl in Tokelau Islands.

PAGE 127   Fanny Stevenson and a local woman, hand in hand.

PAGE 128   On board the *Janet Nicoll:* Fanny is seated front left, and Stevenson (in striped jacket) is at the far right.

PAGE 141   Apaiang: Fanny Stevenson being carried ashore, 1889.

PAGE 142   Tom Day, the 'flower of the Pacific'.

PAGE 164   Majuro: Marshall Islands canoe, with the *Janet Nicoll* in the background.

PAGE 167   'Topsy' with her husband and her pet monkey, Majuro Island.

PAGE 172   One of the kings of Majuro.

PAGE 175   King Tembinoka's harem and little son (centre) on board the *Janet Nicoll*.

PAGE 179   Landing Tembinoka's court at Apemama.

PAGE 183   Islanders in traditional and 'missionary' dress.

PAGE 193   Crew setting sail on the *Janet Nicoll*.

Penryn Island

Introduction

n 1946 the *Reader's Digest* asked the playwright Austin Strong to contribute an essay on 'The Most Unforgettable Character I've Met'. He chose to write about his grandmother, Fanny Van de Grift Stevenson.

> I can see her now — a small woman in a blue dress, sitting barefoot on the roof of the after-cabin of a trading schooner in the South Seas. Her Panama hat, set at a rakish angle, shades a face of breath-taking beauty. She is holding a large silvered revolver in each hand, shooting sharks with deadly accuracy as they are caught and hauled to the taffrail by excited sailors.

The anecdote has all the hallmarks of family legend. Although it is true that Fanny Stevenson was a crack shot and did once help catch sharks from a trading schooner in the Pacific, Austin Strong could never have witnessed precisely this scene. Nor does he claim to have: he sees it 'now' in the present tense of imagination, a composite of memory, observed traits and hearsay. The picture conveys an authentic sense of vividness, force and glamour that had clearly taken hold of him in his youth, and remained with him. What kind of woman would impress her grandson in this way?

Fanny Vandegrift (she later changed the spelling of her name to make it look more aristocratic) was born on 10 March 1840 in Indianapolis, Indiana. It was not the frontier — to the west lay the states of Illinois and Missouri and the Iowa and Wisconsin territories — but a society making the rapid American transition from wilderness to civilisation. The cowboys were moving westwards and the farmers were settling in; Indianapolis, the state capital, was developing as a commercial and industrial centre, and had aspirations to culture, which the young Fanny shared. The Vandegrifts owned a farm, but they lived in town. (Fanny's father was a successful real estate agent and lumber merchant.) Subsequent experiences would reveal Fanny's many quintessentially 'frontier' qualities: she was physically courageous and adaptable, 'handy and inventive' as Robert Louis Stevenson later observed. But these traits seem to have been more innate than evolved, for Fanny always overstated the 'pioneering' background to which she ascribed them. She was certainly a tomboy, and was also noted for her skill in cooking, sewing and gardening. But the idea of a frontier childhood was personal mythology, as important to her later sense of self as the family tradition that she was descended from Captain Cook.

At the age of 17 she married Sam Osbourne from Kentucky, private secretary to the Governor of Indiana. By all accounts he was charming, generous, restless and utterly unreliable. After some service in the Civil War he decided to prospect for silver in Nevada, and in 1864 Fanny, with their young daughter Belle, went out to join him. There was no railroad to the West in those days, and they travelled to California via Panama; the last part of the journey, from San Francisco to Austin, Nevada, was by stagecoach. Fanny was one of only seven women among the men of the mining camp. There she kept house in the primitive conditions of the camp, and learned to roll and smoke cigarettes and shoot a revolver. Sometimes Indians came and stared through the cabin windows of the miners who had encroached their land.

Osbourne's mine failed, and the family moved to Virginia City, Nevada, described by Mark Twain in *Roughing It* as 'the "livest" town, for its age and population, that America had ever produced', a place of 'wildcat' mines and 'wide-open gambling palaces', with 'a whiskey mill every fifteen steps'. Sam, who had proved an unfaithful husband, left to go prospecting with a friend in Montana. Fanny moved to San Francisco, where she supported herself and Belle by dressmaking after hearing that Sam had been killed in an Indian massacre. It proved a rumour: Sam returned, and there followed a pattern of separations and reconciliations that lasted many years. Two sons, Lloyd and Hervey, were born, but the marriage continued to fall apart. Finally, sick of her husband's philandering, Fanny decided to make a break: she would take her family to Europe, where she and her daughter Belle (now aged seventeen) would study art. Both had been students at the school of the artist Virgil Williams in San Francisco, whose social circle of artists and writers Fanny also joined. In 1875 (funded by her husband) she and her three children crossed the Atlantic, heading first to Antwerp, then to Paris, where mother and daughter enrolled at the Atelier Julian. Fanny, however, was increasingly occupied in looking after her younger son, Hervey, who was seriously ill with the painful and disfiguring disease, scrofulous tuberculosis. After he died in April 1876, aged only four years, Fanny broke down emotionally and physically. The doctor warned her that her other son needed country air, and an artist friend suggested that she try the Hôtel Chevillon at Grez, on the edge of the Fontainebleau forest. Fanny and her children spent most of the summer there. Over this time the hotel gradually took on its character as an artists' colony, filling with painters and writers, including the young Scotsman Robert Louis Stevenson.

Stevenson was born in Edinburgh on 13 November 1850, the only child of a civil engineer, Thomas Stevenson, and his wife Margaret, a minister's daughter. The family was solidly middle-class and religious. Stevenson was a misfit, preferring the company of working men and prostitutes to the genteel social circles his parents approved. His early twenties were dominated by a bitter religious dispute and simmering vocational struggle with his father. Stevenson abandoned his training for the family profession, engineering, and, as a compromise with his father's wishes, studied law while privately planning to be an author. At the same time, he rejected the strict Calvinism in which he was raised. In these psychological dramas of his youth, Stevenson's father was the consistent antagonist, while his cousin Bob Stevenson was his confidant and intellectual companion. Both young men affected bohemian manners and aspired to a life of art — Bob as a painter, Louis as a writer. It was Bob who first introduced Stevenson to the artists' colony at Grez in 1875, and they were there together again in 1876. Stevenson had completed his law studies the year before, but was making no serious attempt to practise; rather, he was taking his first steps into the profession of authorship. He came to Grez directly from a canoe trip in Belgium, which would provide the material for his first book, *An Inland Voyage*. At twenty-five, he was much concerned with his art and his chances of earning a living from it. The most important emotional attachment of his youth, his platonic devotion to an older, married woman, Mrs Frances Sitwell, had resolved into a close friendship, and the young man was ready for a new romantic adventure.

Stevenson's attraction towards Fanny seems to have been immediate. The family legend that he fell in love with her at first sight may be an exaggeration, but there is little doubt that he did so over the three weeks they were together at Grez in the autumn of 1876; in November he wrote to a friend that he was 'damnably in love'. Her feelings for him took longer to develop — she was originally much more interested in his cousin Bob — but the relationship was consolidated during his visits to her in Paris over the winter. They spent the summer of 1877 together again at Grez, painting, talking, boating, lounging in the sunny garden of the Hôtel Chevillon, and seem to

have reached some sort of understanding. Certainly they were estab-
lished lovers by December 1877, when Stevenson wrote confidently
to his friend W. E. Henley, 'do I not love? and am I not loved?' and
expressed his loneliness, back in Scotland, without Fanny: 'I'll hate to
go to bed, where there is no dear head upon the pillow.' A description
of Fanny's physical appearance by Stevenson's friend Sidney Colvin
conveys her somewhat androgynous beauty and her sexuality:

> In spite of her squareish build she was supple and elastic in
> all her movements; her hands and feet were small and beau-
> tifully modelled, though not meant for, or used to, idleness;
> the head, under its crop of close-waving thick black hair,
> was of a build and character that somehow suggested
> Napoleon, by the firm setting of the jaw and the beautiful-
> ly precise and delicate modelling of the nose and lips: the
> eyes were full of sex and mystery as they changed from fire
> or fun to gloom or tenderness …

The fact that she was ten years older than Stevenson probably only
increased the attraction; his feelings for his childhood nurse, Alison
Cunningham, and his devotion to the beautiful Mrs Sitwell showed
his tendency to be drawn to older women. The fact that Fanny was
American was also appealing. A few years after they met, Stevenson
wrote of his own youthful feelings about America:

> It will be hard for an American to understand the spirit. But
> let him imagine a young man, who shall have grown up in
> an old and rigid circle, following bygone fashions and
> taught to distrust his own fresh instincts, and who now sud-
> denly hears of a family of cousins, all about his own age,
> who keep house together by themselves and live far from
> restraint and tradition; let him imagine this, and he will
> have some imperfect notion of the sentiment with which

spirited English youths turn to the thought of the American Republic. It seems to them as if, out west, the war of life was still conducted in the open air, and on free barbaric terms; as if it had not yet been narrowed into parlours, nor begun to be conducted, like some unjust and dreary arbitration, by compromise, costume, forms of procedure, and sad, senseless self-denial.

Fanny Osbourne must have seemed a personification of this spirit of American freedom and wildness. As Henry James later commented to Owen Wister (author of the first 'Western' novel, *The Virginian*), 'If you like the gulch & the canyon you will like *her*.' And what attracted Fanny Osbourne to the eccentric, often sickly young writer? Undoubtedly the flavour of Bohemia that surrounded him, and behind it the solid value of access to high culture he promised. She had also made her choice between 'the two mad Stevensons' (Bob and Louis) who were 'so filled with the joyousness of mere living that their presence is exhilarating'. Why Louis rather than Bob? Perhaps the simple fact is that she chose the one who chose her.

Their affair continued over the next year, more or less openly, mainly in France. The relationship was never hidden from Fanny's children, nor (after a while) from Stevenson's parents and circle, although only a few of his friends had met her. But in August 1878 Fanny decided to return to America; it seems likely that Sam Osbourne had withdrawn his financial support for the European enterprise, leaving her little option but to go home. Attempts at reconciliation were short-lived, for although Fanny initially rejoined her husband at Oakland, she soon moved down the coast to Monterey, while he returned to San Francisco with the latest girlfriend. She began, hesitantly, to consider divorce. After her departure from Europe, Stevenson had set off almost immediately on the walking tour of the Cévennes that would become *Travels with a Donkey*. His first considerable literary success, and still one of his most popular works, it has a secret emotional history; as Stevenson told his cousin Bob, 'lots of it is mere protestations to F., most of which I think you will understand. That is to me the main thread of interest.' It was a love letter disguised as a travel book. 'For to F. I never write letters' he told another friend. This is factually inaccurate (they did exchange letters during this year of separation) but his explanation rings emotionally true: 'All that people want by letters has been done between us. We are acquainted; why go on with more introductions? I cannot change so much, but she would still have the clue and recognise every thought.'

At the end of July 1879 came a telegram from Fanny, contents unknown — still — to all but its writer and recipient. A summons, a plan, a plea, a cry of despair? — whatever it contained, the telegram unlocked all the emotional energy Stevenson had accumulated during that year of waiting. He acted immediately and decisively, defying family and friends to join her in America. It was a sentimental journey, but an arduous one: the guiding idea so romantic, the material conditions so squalid. Stevenson's family was well-off, but without their backing, and with no professional income of his own to speak of, he travelled as a poor man, sailing second-class from Glasgow to New York, and going on by emigrant train to California. The rail trip was particularly harsh physically and Fanny's detractors held, and hold, this journey against her for its disastrous and permanent effects on Stevenson's already precarious health. He arrived in Monterey looking shabbier and more eccentric than ever, a stone lighter in weight, his skin covered in an off-putting 'blister, blain, blight and itch'. Fanny was still unsure whether she wanted to divorce Sam and marry him, and with 'a broken heart' the exhausted Stevenson took off to camp in the Carmel Valley, where he collapsed and nearly died. After being nursed by 'two rancheros', an Indian and a veteran from the Mexican war — his genius for the picturesque did not desert him even in such extremities — he returned to Fanny, who had finally made up her mind. She began negotiating for a divorce, which was granted quickly, in December 1879, but in consideration of her ex-husband's and the Stevenson parents' sense of decency, the couple waited another five months to marry. During most of this time, ill and poor, unbelievably thin, Stevenson was harassed by his parents and friends from home, who were prepared to use every claim and subterfuge to separate him from his chosen partner, yet his purpose never wavered: 'I want to be married,' he wrote in February 1880. Stevenson believed that all the delays had proven the relationship: 'Few people before marriage have known each other so long or made more trials of each other's tenderness and constancy,' he wrote to his friend Edmund Gosse. 'I do not think many wives are better loved than mine will be.' On 19 May 1880 the two were finally married in San Francisco. It is often remarked that in the marriage register Fanny described herself as 'widowed' rather than divorced, but owned up to her forty years of age; what is less often noted is that Stevenson chivalrously kept the age gap to a single decade by claiming to be thirty: he was twenty-nine.

Fanny's character, the tenor of the marriage, and the taste of adventures ahead, were all indicated by the Stevensons' very unusual honeymoon. The state of Stevenson's lungs demanded that they go high into the mountains to escape the sea-fogs of the Bay area. Accommodation needed to be cheap, and they hit on the plan of 'squatting' at a deserted silver mine with a romantic name: Silverado. Here the newlyweds, together with Fanny's son Lloyd, passed the better part of June and July. (The area is now the Robert Louis Stevenson State Park.) They were quite aware that 'the neighbourhood of an old mine is a place beset with dangers': the platform might collapse or the mine dump might shift and bury them; moreover, the place was infested with poison oak and, they later realised, alive with rattlesnakes. (Stevenson had heard the noise, but didn't know what it was.) Yet it offered the life in nature Stevenson always craved, and a fulfilment of the desire he had expressed in *Travels with a Donkey*: 'To live out of doors with the woman a man

loves is of all lives the most complete and free.' They could live as they
pleased — like kings, he thought, and this became the shaping conceit
of his book *The Silverado Squatters*. For Fanny it was a weird transfor-
mation of her experiences in the mining camps of Nevada during her
first marriage. Now there was solitude instead of rough company, and
ruin and decay replaced Indian raiders as the chief dangers, but there
was the same need for practical expedients as she cooked and kept
house in primitive conditions. It was a 'world of wreck and rust, splin-
ter and rolling gravel', but Fanny used the wood and nails scattered
about to knock together some rudimentary furniture. The results were
recorded by Stevenson in *The Silverado Squatters*:

> The house, after we had repaired the worst of the damages,
> and filled in some of the doors and windows with white
> cotton cloth, became a healthy and a pleasant dwelling-
> place, always airy and dry, and haunted by the outdoor per-
> fumes of the glen. Within, it had the look of habitation, the
> human look. You had only to go into the third room, which
> we did not use, and see its stones, its sifting earth, its tum-
> bled litter; and then return to our lodging, with the beds
> made, the plates on the rack, the pail of bright water behind
> the door, the stove crackling in a corner, and perhaps the
> table roughly laid against a meal — and man's order, the lit-
> tle clean spots that he creates to dwell in, were at once con-
> trasted with the rich passivity of nature. And yet our house
> was everywhere so wrecked and shattered, the air came and
> went so freely, the sun found so many portholes, the gold-
> en outdoor glow shone in so many open chinks, that we
> enjoyed, at the same time, some of the comforts of a roof
> and much of the gaiety and brightness of *al fresco* life.

Of course, the order created was not so much man's as woman's, and
Stevenson admitted that his household duties ended at breakfast time:
'Thenceforth my wife laboured single-handed in the palace, and I lay

or wandered on the platform at my own sweet will.' If Silverado became a palace in Stevenson's imagination, it was Fanny's work that made it so.

In August 1880 the Stevensons, with Fanny's son Lloyd, returned to England. For the next seven years they lived in a variety of places, including the Scottish Highlands, the Swiss Alps, the south of France, and Bournemouth on the south coast of England. During this period Stevenson wrote the books that made him famous: *Treasure Island*, *Kidnapped*, *Dr Jekyll and Mr Hyde*. His parents had now accepted Fanny and indeed treated her as a daughter. (Thomas Stevenson even bought her a house, 'Skerryvore', at Bournemouth.) But the marriage was resented and attacked by many of Stevenson's friends, and has remained controversial. Biographers have presented wildly contrasting portraits of Fanny Stevenson. She was a skilled and devoted nurse who repeatedly saved her husband's life; she was a hypochondriac who self-ishly competed with him for the attention given to invalids. She protected him from the social demands made by his London literary circle; she was jealous of the friends of his youth and bachelor days and deliberately set out to alienate him from them. She was a wonderful emotional and professional support; she was a terrible emotional and financial drain. Stevenson's own testimony after four years of marriage was unequivocal. He called his marriage 'the most successful in the world' and said of his wife: 'I love her better than ever and admire her more; and I cannot think what I have done to deserve so good a gift ... She is everything to me: wife, brother, sister, daughter and dear companion; and I would not change to get a goddess or a saint.' Stevenson had a somewhat combative view of marriage, preferring interesting counterpoint to perfect harmony; this is clear in his famous definition, 'Marriage is one long conversation, chequered by disputes.' The Stevensons were in many ways an odd couple, not just because of the differences of age and nationality, but in appearance: as she grew stouter and he remained preternaturally thin, pictures of them inevitably bring to mind the rhyme of Jack Sprat and his wife. But they were also alike in their oddity. According to the writer J. A. Symonds, who saw a great deal of them in Switzerland in the early 1880s, 'Stevenson and his wife were a curious ménage, being the most unconventional people in the world.' Edmund Gosse said of her: 'She was one of the strangest people who have lived in our time, a sort of savage nature in some ways, but very lovable — extraordinarily passionate and unlike everyone else in her violent feelings and unrestrained way of expressing them — full of gaiety, and with a genius for expressing things picturesquely, but not literary. I think R. L. S. must have caught some of his ways of feeling from her.'

My own impression is that Fanny must have been a very difficult woman in many respects. She could be self-dramatising, greedy and possessive, with a strong need to dominate and control. A sense of her sometimes intrusive and overbearing influence on Stevenson's friendships and writings is suggested by the disturbing image Jekyll uses for Hyde, 'knit to him closer than a wife, closer than an eye'. There is no doubt that her family, with their extraordinary incapacity to provide for themselves as adults, became a financial burden to Stevenson, and the mental illness she suffered in the early 1890s brought enormous stress and distress to their last years together. Yet, as Stevenson's friend Colvin wrote, 'She was to him a perfect companion, taking part keenly and critically in his work, sharing all his gipsy tastes and love of primitive and natural modes of life.' Such modes of life brought out her best qualities, those seen in the Silverado honeymoon: resourcefulness, a capacity for improvisation, the ability to meet practical challenges, a willingness to try strange experiments and defy social convention. Contending with nature, the world of men, or the challenges of a vastly different culture, she revealed the quality almost everyone, friend and foe, has attributed to her: she was 'game'. I cannot imagine any of the other women Stevenson knew — the majestic Mrs Sitwell, the nice young Edinburgh ladies his parents might have favoured, or the

Englishwomen his literary friends loved and married — undertaking the kinds of journeys, adventures and enterprises that Fanny shared with him in the second half of their marriage.

In August 1887 Stevenson and Fanny, her son Lloyd, Stevenson's mother, and their Swiss maid, Valentine Roch, left England for America. Stevenson had been restless and depressed since his father's death earlier in the year, his health was as poor as ever, and his doctors recommended a change of scene and climate. It was believed that cold, dry air in high places would benefit his lungs, so the party settled for the winter at Saranac Lake in the Adirondacks, not far from the Canadian border. With the night temperature at forty degrees below zero, waking up in the flimsy board cottage to find their clothes frozen and their ears frostbitten, venturing outside swathed in buffalo coats and fur hats Fanny had picked up on a visit to Montreal, Louis and Lloyd began to dream of a yachting trip in a tropical climate. The enterprising editor-publisher, S. S. McClure, who was a frequent visitor at Saranac, turned the idea into a business proposition, offering to use his extensive syndication contacts to sell any travel 'letters' Stevenson might write describing such a yacht cruise. When Fanny left for California in March 1888 to visit her daughter Belle, she was enjoined to look out for a suitable vessel, and in May she secured the sea-going yacht *Casco* for a seven-month Pacific cruise. The rest of the party, including Stevenson's mother and Valentine Roch, travelled west a few weeks later, and the *Casco* sailed from San Francisco on 28 June 1888 for the Marquesas, Paumotus (now Tuamotus) and Tahiti, finishing the voyage in Honolulu on 24 January 1889.

The trip was, as Stevenson anticipated, 'the dream of a life realised'. The travellers saw the archetypal Pacific coral atolls of the Paumotus and the more majestic high-island scenery of the Marquesas and Tahiti. In the Marquesas they met cannibals and a tattooed queen, whom Fanny taught to roll cigarettes. They bathed in the lagoon at Fakareva in the Paumotus and listened to local legends by moonlight under the palm trees. At Tautira in Tahiti they made friends with a local sub-chief, Ori a Ori, who exchanged names with Stevenson in a kind of ceremony of brotherhood, and with the beautiful Princess Moë, who brought the sickly author dishes of raw fish in coconut milk, lime juice, sea water and chilli. The voyage had its dangers: the *Casco* was not really fit for some of the ocean conditions they encountered, and they once became lost in the waters around the Paumotus (at that time also aptly named 'the Dangerous Archipelago'). Yet it takes nothing away from their adventure to suggest that, on this first Pacific voyage, the Stevensons' path was prepared and their experience shaped by the writings of previous travellers. The cruise of the *Casco* was wholly within Polynesia, that area of the Pacific which had been part of the European imagination for over a hundred years, thanks to the writings of eighteenth-century explorers and the philosophers who interpreted their observations. Their Arcadian, primitivist voices can be heard in Fanny's letters back to Colvin in England: 'Oh, that you and a few — a very few friends were with us in these enchanted Isles to stay for ever and ever, and live and die with these delightful miscalled savages'; 'I write you from fairyland, where we are living in a fairy-story, the guests of a beautiful brown princess.' Ready-made structures of thought and feeling were also provided by nineteenth-century American writers, Charles Warren Stoddard, a friend of Fanny's from San Francisco and the author of *South-Sea Idyls*, and Herman Melville, whose *Typee* and *Omoo* the *Casco* voyagers had read with relish. And on the ground the rawness of the encounter with foreign cultures was softened by a succession of hosting, guiding locals, both indigenous and European — priests, government officials and high-born Marquesans and Tahitians, some of them educated in England or France, who took the Stevensons under their wing, introducing, translating, explaining and arranging.

By the end of the *Casco*'s voyage, the Stevensons were hooked on the Pacific, but ready for a bigger challenge. They declared Honolulu too 'civilised' and rented a cottage and some shacks on the beach at Waikiki to rest, write and watch for an opportunity to make a second, more adventurous, cruise. All the places they had visited on the *Casco* were under French administration, while Hawaii was economically and politically dominated by the Americans, who would take over the government a few years later. Now the Stevensons wanted to see the independent kingdoms of the western Pacific, what Fanny called 'the "unregenerate" islands'. At first it seemed their only option was to take places on the missionary ship *Morning Star* as it toured the American mission stations on remote western islands, but Louis, Lloyd and Fanny reacted with exaggerated horror to the idea of conforming to a missionary regime of no drinking, smoking or swearing. Fortunately an alternative emerged: Stevenson chartered a schooner, the *Equator*, from a San Francisco trading firm for a four-month voyage through Micronesia. The ship would sail from island to island pursuing its usual business of taking on board copra (dried coconut-meat) in exchange for European trade goods such as sewing-machines, cloth and tinned foods; within the framework of the firm's normal trading routes, the passengers could request extra stops or longer visits ashore as they wished. Stevenson's mother did not come on this voyage, which was considered too rough and wild for her, and she returned to Scotland instead. Valentine Roch had left the family soon after they arrived in Honolulu. The two women were replaced by two new members of the party: the artist Joe Strong, husband of Fanny's daughter Belle, and Ah Fu, the Chinese cook who had joined the Stevensons in the Marquesas, where he had been marooned as a boy. The *Equator* left Honolulu on 24 June 1889. Calms and squalls disrupted all plans in these seas, and in fact the cruise lasted nearly six months instead of four, during which time the Stevensons visited Butaritari, Mariki, Apaiang and Apemama, all in the Gilbert Islands (also then known as the Kingsmills, now Kiribati).

This second Pacific cruise was very different from the first, especially for Fanny. On the *Casco* there had been three white women;

on the *Equator*, Fanny was the only woman among fifteen men. The *Casco* was a luxury yacht; the *Equator* was a working trading vessel which, though new, was extremely uncomfortable to travel in, for it was overcrowded, offered little protection against either rain or heat, and was inhabited by some very aggressive cockroaches. While Fanny anticipated more serious dangers, she balanced them against the prospective benefits of the voyage: 'Of course there is the usual risk from hostile natives, and the horrible sea, but a positive risk is so much more wholesome than a negative one, and it is all such a joy to Louis and Lloyd. As for me, I hate the sea, and am afraid of it ... but I love the tropic weather, and the wild people, and to see my two boys so happy.' In fact there were quite specific problems associated with the *Equator*'s itinerary. In these islands under native rule, where traditional authority had often been subverted by the people's contact with white traders or missionaries but had not been replaced by European government, law and order was far less secure than in the Polynesian islands the Stevensons had previously visited. This became especially apparent in Butaritari where, after the lifting of a *tapu* (taboo) on alcohol, the entire town went on a drunken spree. Racial tensions simmered and the travellers faced the threat of riots and even assassination attempts: the Stevensons felt obliged to get out their revolvers and do some ostentatious target practice in view of the locals. At a more mundane level, on these 'low' coral islands the diet was monotonous and food could become scarce; the lack of fresh fruit and vegetables was a particular health problem, which Fanny tried to solve in Apemama by growing salad vegetables (quite successfully). In addition, the travellers faced a more subtle but pervasive challenge, in that the region as a whole was simply harder for the European imagination to accommodate than Polynesia. There had been fewer precursors to smooth their path.

Of course, this was the whole point of the trip, and the gamble paid off particularly well in relation to Apemama and its king. Tembinoka, the much-feared and many-wived 'Napoleon of the

Gilberts', despot, schemer, man of parts, was an extraordinary character, described thus by Stevenson:

> Now he wears a woman's frock, now a naval uniform; now (and more usually) figures in a masquerade costume of his own design: trousers and a singular jacket with shirt tails, the cut and fit wonderful for island workmanship, the material always handsome, sometimes green velvet, sometimes cardinal red silk. This masquerade becomes him admirably. In the woman's frock he looks ominous and weird beyond belief.

Tembinoka had held onto his power against the determined incursions of the white man. He dealt warily with traders, whom he classified in three groups: "'He cheat a litty" — "He cheat plenty" — and "I think he cheat too much.'" Missionaries he sent away, rightly divining that they would undermine his authority. All foreigners he regarded with deep suspicion, and the Stevensons scored a major coup when they won permission to stay on the island. As Fanny wrote afterwards, 'no one has had such experiences. All the South Sea books speak, by hearsay only, of the terrible Tembinok', but we threw ourselves into his arms, and went and lived with him for months, and learned to love him almost as much as we admired him.' Tembinoka not only allowed them to stay, but had a special compound built for them — Equator town — where they lived for six weeks under his special protection. He shed tears when they left.

The Stevensons were justly proud of their connection with Tembinoka. Stevenson made the Apemama visit the climax of his Pacific travel book, *In the South Seas*. Fanny refers to it often in *The Cruise of the 'Janet Nichol'*.* It offered them a unique and privileged

---

* Fanny always misspelt *Janet Nicoll* as *Janet Nichol*. Throughout this introduction I refer to the ship by its correct name, the *Janet Nicoll*, but retain the book title as it was written by Fanny: *The Cruise of the 'Janet Nichol'*.

insight into a world normally closed to whites, an insight that became even more valuable when that world suddenly vanished; as Stevenson wrote five years later, it was 'a real curiosity, a thing that can never be seen again, now the group is annexed and Tembinoka dead'. Yet in many ways it was their experiences in the other Micronesian islands — Butaritari, Mariki and Apaiang — that gave them their best understanding yet of the contemporary Pacific. As Stevenson said, Tembinoka's vigilance made Apemama a sort of 'social quarantine', but elsewhere in the Gilberts, where traders, missionaries and beachcombers had settled, a vigorous cross-contamination between indigenous and white cultures was occurring, and the travellers witnessed the complex social interactions and power relations that resulted. These would feed into Stevenson's Pacific fiction, particularly 'The Beach of Falesá' and *The Ebb-Tide*, and become a major theme of *The Cruise of the 'Janet Nichol'*.

As the *Equator* approached Samoa and the end of its charter, Stevenson wrote to his mother: 'Fanny has stood the hardships of this rough cruise wonderfully; but I do not think I could expose her to "another of the same".' The last leg of the journey was particularly difficult, a devilish mixture of violent squalls, dead calms, and 'p.d.' (position doubtful) reefs. They finally arrived at Apia, Samoa, on 7 December 1889. It was a relief to gain dry land and decent food, and after six months of atolls the travellers were captivated by the grand high-island scenery. In a little over a month the Stevensons had bought 300 acres of land in Samoa and decided to make their home there, although they still intended to return to England to see their friends and organise their affairs. With this in mind they sailed for Sydney in February, and there booked their passages home by steamer, via Colombo and Naples. But the weather in Sydney was dreadful and Stevenson fell seriously ill at the end of March, suffering his first lung haemorrhage since Tahiti. He had been so well on the *Equator* voyage that another island cruise seemed the only remedy, but the normally

bustling port of Sydney was closed down by a dock strike. Fanny started hanging about the waterfront trying to learn of any ship that might
be setting out for the islands in defiance of the unions. She discovered
that the Auckland trading firm of Henderson and Macfarlane was
preparing to send the steamer *Janet Nicoll* on a four-month Pacific
cruise using a non-unionised 'Kanaka' crew, mostly from the Solomon
Islands. She applied for passages and, as Stevenson's biographer
J. C. Furnas tells it, 'the firm refused — understandably — to book a
dying man and an eccentric woman who kept repeating stubbornly
that it was a matter of life and death and neither of them would be any
trouble'. Eventually, somehow, Fanny managed to persuade Henderson
to let them on board: she was good at persuading people. The maritime
unions did not let the *Janet Nicoll* go without a struggle, however; they
detained the ship in port for a day beyond its scheduled departure,
demanding the instatement of a union crew, then boycotted the vessel
and threatened a labour enquiry. The captain was unmoved and the
Janet Nicoll left Sydney on 11 April 1890 with Louis, Fanny and Lloyd
on board. The union trouble followed them to Auckland, as Fanny
recorded, but the controversial voyage was underway.

So, suddenly, unexpectedly and dramatically, the Stevensons found
themselves on their third Pacific cruise. Stevenson's health immediately picked up, although not as much as he had hoped; there were
episodes of blood-spitting throughout the voyage. The *Janet Nicoll*
rolled terribly and the steam engines made the cabins very hot, but
conditions overall were much better than on the *Equator*. The travellers
enjoyed plenty of space, good meals and 'a most agreeable ship's company', three of whom would see their names in print as the dedicatees
of Stevenson's collection of short stories, *Island Nights' Entertainments*,
published in 1893. Harry Henderson was the partner in the trading
firm whom Fanny had persuaded to take them on as passengers. Ben
Hird, the supercargo, was a well-known figure in the central Pacific,
with a vast acquaintance among islanders and traders and a knowledge

of the islands unmatched by any white man. The Stevensons esteemed him for his genial manners and firm character, his wide experience and his story-telling abilities. Fanny often cites him in her narrative as a source of information. Jack Buckland or 'Tin Jack', the only other passenger on board, was a real South Sea character. The archetypal remittance man, he spent his income in an annual spree in Sydney lasting a few months, then passed the remainder of the year trading copra in the Gilbert Islands. He was handsome, high-spirited, careless, improvident and childish; the maker and butt of jokes; generous, but with a dubious moral sense; in appearance a cross between gentleman-beachcomber and island dandy; like Ben Hird, an excellent repository of anecdotes and spinner of yarns. Stevenson portrayed him as the character 'Tommy Haddon' in *The Wrecker* (co-authored with Lloyd Osbourne) and he features as a lovable but exasperating clown in Fanny's account of the voyage. In addition to the captain and engineer, there was a ship's crew of around forty 'Kanakas'. Fanny liked the 'boys' very much and her depiction of them is consistently positive. She praises their industry, piety, grace and good nature, and writes with pleasure of their love of music, dance and all forms of merriment and play. Stevenson took them as the basis for the gentle, hardworking, good-natured crew in his novella *The Ebb-Tide*, where one of them, Sally Day, even appears by name.

The *Janet Nicoll* sailed from Sydney with 'sealed orders'; that is, its itinerary was secret, and the passengers neither knew nor had any say in which islands they would visit. As it turned out, one of the early stops was at Apia, so the Stevensons were able to catch up with friends made on their earlier visit to Samoa, and check the progress that had been made clearing and building on their property, 'Vailima'. From here the *Janet Nicoll* made a convoluted journey through the central and western Pacific, stopping for copra and shell at around thirty-five islands. Some of the islands on the trading route were, as Stevenson said, 'old acquaintances, and pleasant to revisit'. Butaritari, Apemama and Mariki in the Gilbert Islands were all familiar from the *Equator* cruise, and Fanny includes in her *Janet Nicoll* narrative substantial notes on the previous visits to each (spelling the last 'Maraki'). But most of the islands were entirely new: the independent Polynesian kingdom of Niue (Nuieue in Fanny's spelling), also known as Savage Island; Danger Island or Pukapuka, Manihiki, Suwarrow and Penrhyn (also called Tongarewa) in the Cook Islands, which had very recently (in 1888) been made a British Protectorate; the Tokelau group, also newly declared a British Protectorate (in 1889); the Ellice Islands, now Tuvalu, still independent at the time of the *Janet Nicoll*'s visit, but brought under British Protection two years later; Majuro, Jaluit and Namorik in the Marshall Islands, at that time under German government; and many other tiny islands, some of them uninhabited or privately owned. The last stop was at Noumea in the French colony of New Caledonia, the only Melanesian island the Stevensons visited in their three cruises.

In the end, the voyage did not benefit Stevenson's health as much as he had hoped, and he complained that 'as you go westward, the charm of the people wanes and at last dies'. He did not include a narrative of this cruise in his travel book, *In the South Seas*, which recounts only the *Casco* and *Equator* voyages. (As part of the original commission from S. S. McClure, he did write up one travel 'letter' on Penrhyn, which may be compared with Fanny's account of the island.) But the *Janet Nicoll* voyage is repeatedly invoked throughout *In the South Seas*, where Stevenson's experiences in Majuro, Noumea, Manihiki, Niue, Namorik, Funafuti, Arorai and Jaluit, together with information and anecdotes gleaned from Ben Hird, are introduced as reference points in comparative discussions of Pacific customs, manners, language, belief and environment. The influence of the cruise on Stevenson's Pacific fiction was even more significant. The beachcomber looking for a 'soft job', the burial alive story, the trader who refused to leave his Polynesian wife and half-caste children, the magic tricks with coins performed by Mr Henderson, the conspiracies and poisonings carried out by rival traders — all found their way into 'The Beach of Falesá'. The strange figurehead at Penrhyn, the pearl atolls, the ghost-settlement at Suwarrow with its romantic jumble of salvage, and the penal colony at Noumea all appear in *The Ebb-Tide*.

Fanny's narrative of the cruise gives us the background to these Stevenson stories, but it also does much more. The book has considerable historical value as a report on the central and western Pacific in 1890, a space subject to varying kinds and degrees of formal and informal colonisation, and marked everywhere by traces of the nefarious 'labour' trade. This was the practice of collecting islanders and relocating them to other parts of the Pacific to work in commercial enterprises owned and controlled by whites. The trade began in the 1860s and 1870s, was at its height in the 1880s, and continued until the early twentieth century. The British and Australians recruited labour for their cotton, and later sugar, plantations in Fiji and Queensland; the French for their nickel mines in Noumea, and the Germans for their coconut plantations in Samoa. American and Peruvian labour traders were also active in the Pacific in the second half of the nineteenth century, and were responsible for some of the most devastating assaults on island communities with their raids on Penrhyn and various of the Tokelau and Ellice islands in the 1860s. At Funafuti a local trader told Fanny that, as late as 1886, American slavers sailing under the Peruvian flag took two-thirds of the population by trickery: they were never seen again. By 1890, though, most 'labour' was recruited from the western islands, first the Gilberts and Marshalls, then increasingly Melanesia. The practice was given many names: 'the labour trade' and 'recruiting' were euphemisms for what others called 'blackbirding', 'kidnapping' or simply 'slaving'. In many instances it represented a virtual revival of the slave trade, for force and deception were regularly employed to get islanders on board the labour ships. This was particularly disturbing to the British, who prided themselves on the abolition of slavery within the British Empire almost sixty years earlier, and the history of the British political presence in the Pacific in the nineteenth century is largely the history of British attempts to control the labour trade by legislation: the first Pacific Islanders Protection Bill was passed in 1872, and led directly to the annexation of Fiji, the setting up of the Western Pacific High Commission, and the establishment of more and more British Protectorates in the region. But although it was increasingly regulated, the labour trade — which employed some of the most violent and degraded white men in the Pacific — continued to give rise to outrages against native people, as well as having more insidious long-term effects. It led to increased hostility and distrust between whites and islanders. Many labourers died from disease or ill-use during their period of service or on the labour ships. Families and communities were broken up by the recruitments. Individuals and even large groups were displaced, sometimes permanently, as many labourers found it difficult to return to their homes at the end of their period of service; many were carelessly 'returned' to the wrong island or settlement, where they could expect to be robbed and murdered, and some chose a further period of labour in preference to this fate. When they did return home, the social and power structure of their communities was often radically altered by the European weapons, trade goods and manners they brought with them.

Fanny Stevenson's narrative testifies repeatedly to the social displacement and psychological damage sustained by individuals and communities because of 'recruiting' or 'kidnapping'. The *Janet Nicoll* returned parties of labourers to Niue and Pukapuka, and Fanny records the emotional homecomings that ensued, including that of an 'eight-year exile' who, having signed to work five years, had waited a further three for a passage home. She observes the differences in manners between Manihiki in the Cook Islands, where the locals displayed almost overwhelming trust and affection towards the European visitors, and Natau in the Ellice Islands, where the depredations of slavers had rendered the people fearful and suspicious. Here, watching a schooner fill with islanders bound on an excursion around the group, she recalls the recent violent past: 'It was just so, not very long ago, that slave-ships used to carry them away.' The sense of a threat not fully dispelled is reinforced by Tin Jack's chilling remark: 'What a haul that would be for labour!'

Although the 'labour' theme forms a sinister undercurrent to the narrative, it does not set the pattern for the politics of cross-cultural encounter recorded in *The Cruise of the 'Janet Nichol'*. In Fanny's account, indigenous people, beachcombers, traders, missionaries and visitors assume surprisingly various positions of power and subjection in their negotiations, accommodations and dialogues with each other. Central to all these relationships is trade. Trade was the *Janet Nicoll's* business, but it was also the mode of almost every interaction between the travellers and the local people. Like all European visitors to the Pacific since the voyages of Bougainville and Cook, at every island the passengers on the *Janet Nicoll* found themselves caught up in a round of gift-giving, reciprocity, purchase and exchange, and were often uncertain of the distinctions between them. Fanny was a determined and sometimes aggressive collector. Her persistence was rewarded, although her travelling companions had some doubts about the results; as Stevenson recorded near the end of the voyage, 'The ship wallows deep with barbaric trumpery collected by Mrs Stevenson, twopenny spears are triced up in the rigging; whenever the ship rolls, I look to have a shark's tooth scimitar discharged upon my dead head; and as I walk about the cabin dictating to Lloyd, my path is impeded by a Manihiki drum, vainly sprinkled on the outside with buhac powder, but supposed internally to be one clotted bolus of cockroaches.' One has the sense that in trading Fanny generally got what she wanted, although in some cases her unswerving pursuit of her object may not have been appreciated by the local people involved, and in one encounter, at Penrhyn, the trading process broke down completely amid mutual mockery and contempt.

More often, though, trade is shown to connect rather than alienate islanders and visitors. As a veteran of two previous Pacific voyages, Fanny knew what was likely to please, and came supplied not only with the universal currency, tobacco, but also with articles to trade specifically with women: dresses, pieces of 'print' cotton cloth, wreaths of artificial flowers, combs, necklaces and gold rings. Her resulting interactions with indigenous women form one of the most fascinating and distinctive aspects of her narrative. There are very few Pacific travel texts written by women, and Fanny's is all the more remarkable for her genuine interest in the possibilities of human contact across radical cultural divides. The narrative shows her consistently seeking out, and being sought out by, the women on the islands she visited. Her usual phrase is that the local women 'took possession' of her: white women were rare sights on these far-flung islands, and the native women were fascinated by Fanny's clothes, skin, body and the goods she had to trade. In one episode, at Nanomea in the Ellice Islands, the cry of '*Fafine! Beretani fafine!*' (Woman! White woman!) signals the beginning of a women-only trading scene in which, after the exchange of various items of clothing and jewellery, Fanny herself is imagined as the ultimate trade object: 'One woman was most anxious that I should stop on the island with her. I really think she had some hope that she might keep me as a sort of pet monkey.' In this and other scenes with local women, commonality and difference, sympathy and alienation, are in constant interplay, but mostly Fanny believed that the bond based on sex would override, or at least balance, differences based on race and culture. At Natau, where slave-raids had destroyed the locals' trust of all white men, a young girl, terrified of the *Janet Nicoll's* captain, turned to the '*Beretani fafine*' for help: 'Plainer than words her smile said: "You are a woman, too; I can trust you; you will protect me, will you not?"' Of course, this is only the white woman's interpretation of the other's gestures and expressions but Fanny often presents the sympathy between women as a force that transcends racial and linguistic barriers.

Everywhere in *The Cruise of the 'Janet Nichol'* we find a focus on women's experiences in the islands. There is Mrs Lawes, the missionary's wife at Niue, despairing when — after months without European female company — two ships with white women on board arrive on a single, rushed day and are gone in a few hours. There is Topsy, the Micronesian wife of an English trader at Majuro, a young girl 'greatly given to dress', sorting through her chests full of clothes and ornaments, and delightedly donning Fanny's gift of a red silk bodice. Fanny was interested in the details of these women's material, social and domestic lives — what they wore and owned, where they lived and how they entertained — and she was eager to adopt island ways. The recipe book she used when housekeeping in Samoa bears the signs of her Pacific travels in its eclectic mix of cultural influences. Instructions 'To make a South Sea Oven' and for 'Butaritari Pudding', 'Butaritari Potato Cake', 'Ginger Beer — Apemama', 'Cocoanut Miti Sauce', 'Ah Foo's Pig's Head' and various recipes 'For Ship's Use' sit next to entries for tortillas, salsa and enchilladas (legacies of the Mexican influence from her Californian days) and conventional English cooking.

The same cultural mix is apparent in Fanny's dress and demeanour. When the missionary William Clarke saw her for the first time in Samoa in December 1889 (four months before the *Janet Nicoll* voyage), she 'wore a print gown, large gold crescent earrings, a Gilbert-island hat of plaited straw, encircled with a wreath of small shells, a scarlet silk scarf round her neck, and a brilliant plaid shawl across her shoulders; her bare feet were encased in white canvas shoes, and across her back was slung a guitar'. He assumed that she and her husband and son were a group of poor travelling players. In October 1890, two months after the cruise ended, the visiting American historian Henry Adams met Fanny in Samoa and declared her 'a wild Apache'. He was scandalised that she went without stockings and shoes and that her loose dresses seemed unwashed: 'Her complexion and eyes were dark and strong, like a half-breed Mexican.' This impression of racial difference, suggested throughout Fanny's life by her unusually dark skin, can only have been strengthened when, as she records several times in *The Cruise of the 'Janet Nichol'*, she borrowed island women's clothes. According to her husband, her appearance during the voyage overstepped class as well as racial boundaries: 'The whole ship's company ... are dressed like beggar men (and in the case of Mrs Stevenson like a beggar woman); all go with bare feet, all are in rags and many partly naked.' Occasionally we glimpse the Victorian lady traveller, distressed when carried to a canoe by an islander 'before I had time to arrange my skirts', crying when her bare arms and legs were exposed to the curious gaze of local men. More often though, the impression is of something more modern and relaxed; the photographs in this book show the short hair, bare feet and loose clothes that were the hallmarks of Fanny's practical, unconventional style of dress on the *Janet Nicoll* cruise. How far she had drifted from European norms is shown in the wonderful last sentence of the book: 'We all don the clothes of civilisation to go on shore, looking very strange to each other.'

Age was a liberating force here: at fifty, Fanny had little concern with appearances or propriety (she frequently slept on deck with other male passengers rather than in her own cabin), and although she travelled with her husband and grown-up son, she did not go about under their chaperonage. As the 'Note on a previous visit to Butaritari' shows (page 57), on the *Equator* cruise when 'it was thought unsafe' for her to go out alone at this turbulent island, she 'broke bounds' and went anyway: the adventure led to the Stevensons' friendship with Nan Tok and Nei Takauti (see page 55). Her *Janet Nicoll* diary records only two instances where she allowed her independence to be curtailed by questions of safety. At Majuro, in the Marshall Islands, prowlers approached the hut where she was sleeping; after that 'they all seemed to think' that she should not sleep alone on shore and Lloyd was despatched to keep her company. At Nassau 'the landing was thought to be too dangerous for me to attempt' because of the rough surf, and 'to my great disappointment, the men went without me'. Here and at Atafu, where she felt too unwell with rheumatism to go ashore, she relied on her husband's accounts of the islands. These, and Stevenson's record of their arrival at Niue, are published in her book, just as Stevenson included a long extract from Fanny's *Equator* diary (her description of a Gilbertese 'opera' performed at Butaritari) in his travel book *In the South Seas*.

But the relation between husband's and wife's travel-writing was not always collaborative; it could be combative, and even competitive. Fanny claimed that her diary was originally 'only intended to be a collection of hints to help my husband's memory', but in assisting she was also (characteristically) trying to influence him. The two disagreed about how Stevenson ought to write up his Pacific travels. As Fanny wrote to Sidney Colvin in May 1889:

> Louis has the most enchanting material that any one ever had in the whole world for his book, and I am afraid he is going to spoil it all. He has taken into his Scotch Stevenson head, that a stern duty lies before him, and that his book must be a sort of scientific and historical impersonal thing ... leaving out all he knows of the people themselves. And I believe there is no one living who has got so near to them, or who understands them as he does. Think of a small treatise on the Polynesian races being offered to people who are dying to hear about Ori a Ori, the making of brothers with cannibals, the strange stories the_____old, and the extraordinary adventures that befell us_____at a thing it is to have a 'man of genius' to deal with.____ke managing an overbred horse. Why with my own feeble hand I could write a book that the whole world would jump at.

Before they set off on the *Janet Nicoll*, Fanny wrote again to Colvin: 'Of course this cruise will give additional interest to the book. I am very glad you spoke of the historical and scientific question. It has been rather heavy on my mind. If I were the public I shouldn't care a penny what Louis's theories were as to the formation of the islands, or their scientific history, or where the people came from originally — only what Louis's own experiences were.' On the *Janet Nicoll*, Fanny's selection of incidents and experiences to record in her diary reflects her sense of what her husband should have been writing about, but throughout the cruise Stevenson held to his own alternative vision. As Fanny's diary records, at Arorai, in the Gilberts, instead of accompanying her and Lloyd to the village, Stevenson nearly made himself ill chipping bits of coral off the reef in the midday sun as part of his 'scientific' work. Later she wrote an exaggerated and distorted, but very funny, account of the incident for Colvin, to make the point that Stevenson had missed 'having some odd adventures and seeing many curious things' because of what she considered his wrong-headed attitude to his travel-writing. 'Never had any man such enchanting material for a book, and much of the best is to be left out. "Very well," I say, "if you will not, then I shall. I'll gather together all my letters, and publish them with my diaries wherever they will fill up a gap you have wantonly left."' In the end, Stevenson pleased neither his wife nor himself; *In the South Seas* offers little of the kind of personal narrative Fanny favoured, while Stevenson felt that he had not been able to write the authoritative, anthropological study of the Pacific he had planned: 'I'll never be allowed for Fanny has strong opinions and I prefer her peace of mind to my ideas.' As for publishing her own travel diary, Fanny waited nearly a quarter of a century before she did so.

The Cruise of the 'Janet Nichol' ends with arrival at Noumea on 26 July 1890. While Stevenson remained a week in what he called 'this town of convicts at the world's end', Fanny and Lloyd stayed only one night and sailed on with the *Janet Nicoll* for Sydney. It was an unpleasant and dangerous trip, for they ran into a storm and were nearly shipwrecked off the Australian coast. The family were reunited in Sydney in August, and in early September they went on to Samoa to begin the work of establishing their home on the Vailima estate. On spare pages in her *Janet Nicoll* diary Fanny had compiled a 'List of things needed for Vailima' — farm tools and seeds, ice machines and water filters, books on mechanics and gardening — which shows the scale of their preparations and their plans. For they intended not only to build a house, but to try to support themselves with a small farm of livestock, fruit and vegetables, and eventually to have a paying plantation of cacao or coffee. To start from largely uncleared bush was a daunting task, but it appealed to Fanny's 'pioneering' sense of herself, and she, who had always loved and excelled at gardening, was soon experimenting with different seeds and crops. This became a typically combative activity: Stevenson describes her going out each morning 'with the industry of a bee or a devil ... to prowl and wrestle in her garden'. She kept a diary (published in 1956 as *Our Samoan Adventure*), which provides a vivid record of her daily life at Vailima, her struggles with the farm, and her relationships with the Samoans who worked on the estate. Understandably, the diary is silent about the mysterious psychotic illness that befell her, severely testing her marriage, in the years 1892–93.

At this time Stevenson wrote a memorable description of his wife, 'The Weird Woman' of Vailima:

> Infinitely little, extraordinary wig of gray curls, handsome waxen face like Napoleon's, insane black eyes, boy's hands, tiny bare feet, a cigarette, wild blue native dress usually spotted with garden mould. In company manners presents the appearance of a little timid and precise old maid of the days of prunes and prism; you look for the reticule. ...

Hellish energy; relieved by fortnights of entire hibernation.
Can make anything from a house to a row, all fine and large
of their kind. ... Doctors everybody, will doctor you, cannot be doctored herself. The Living Partizan: A violent
friend, a brimstone enemy. ... Is always either loathed or
slavishly adored; indifference impossible. The natives think
her uncanny and that devils serve her. Dreams dreams, and
sees visions.

On 3 December 1894 Fanny was in the grip of such dreams and
visions: for several days she had had a strong premonition of disaster
close to the family. That evening her husband collapsed with a cerebral haemorrhage, and died the same night. For a few years Fanny
tried, with the help of her son and daughter, to keep the Vailima
estate running, but in 1897 she gave up battling the encroachments
of the jungle and left Samoa; the house and land, except for
Stevenson's grave, were later sold. (In the twentieth century,
Vailima became the official residence of Samoa's colonial governors
and, after independence, of the Samoan Head of State. It is now a
museum.)

Fanny spent most of the rest of her life in California, first in San
Francisco and then at Santa Barbara. She bought several properties and
built several homes, and made money in Californian real estate, as well
as receiving royalties from Stevenson's literary estate. She worked to
preserve her husband's fame (and the income it generated), overseeing
the publication of his biography by his cousin Graham Balfour in
1901, and writing prefaces for new editions of his work. As Stevenson's
widow she was both guardian and relic of a literary legend. 'She is like
an old grizzled lioness — or resigned captive South Sea Chieftainess,'
Henry James said. Fanny did not remarry, but she adopted a series of
young male protégés: the artist and humourist Gelett Burgess, novel-
ist Frank Norris, and writer Ned Field. The last, forty years her

junior, became her constant companion and member of her household. In her old age Fanny continued to travel, in Europe and increasingly in Mexico, but never returned to the Pacific islands. She did, however, revisit them in imagination when she finally decided to publish her diary of the *Janet Nicoll* cruise. She finished reading the proofs only a few days before she died, on 18 February 1914 — like Stevenson, of a cerebral haemorrhage. In 1915 her daughter Belle and Ned Field took her ashes to Samoa to be placed in Stevenson's grave; the occasion was marked by a procession, ceremony and Samoan feast. A panel was added to the tomb, quoting Stevenson's poem 'My Wife', in which he called Fanny 'A fellow-farer true through life'.

The Cruise of the 'Janet Nichol' was published posthumously in 1914 and seems to have attracted little notice at the time. Through the twentieth century it was known mainly as a resource for Stevenson scholars. But the book is much more than a supplement to the Pacific oeuvre of the writer's famous husband. As the Stevensons' friend Sidney Colvin said of Fanny, 'all her moods, thoughts, and instincts were vividly genuine and her own, and her daily talk, like her letters, was admirable both for play of character and feeling and for choice and colour of words'. These qualities are evident in her diary, as is the spirited personality that led her into scenes and situations few Europeans, and even fewer European women, had experienced. Her narrative and the photographs that accompany it (some published in 1914 with *The Cruise of the 'Janet Nichol'*, others selected from the Stevensons' photo album from the cruise) offer a unique glimpse of life in some of the last independent Pacific kingdoms and societies just passing under colonial rule. It was a world made up of kings and chiefs, missionaries, traders and beachcombers and, as Fanny constantly reminds us, of an immense variety of women and girls, each offering an insight into the traditional and transitional ways of island life memorialised in her book.

NOTE ON SOURCES

Fanny Stevenson's recipe books, and her manuscript diary from the *Janet Nicoll* cruise, are at the Robert Louis Stevenson Silverado Museum in St Helena, California. Some of Fanny's letters are included in the eight-volume *Letters of Robert Louis Stevenson*, edited by Bradford A. Booth and Ernest Mehew, and published by Yale University Press (1994–95). Others were published by Sidney Colvin as 'More Letters of Mrs R. L. Stevenson: Ocean Travels in the Pacific' in *Scribner's Magazine* for 1924, and by E. V. Lucas in *The Colvins and their Friends* (1928).

Austin Strong's account of Fanny as 'The Most Unforgettable Character I've Met' is in the *Reader's Digest*, volume 48 (1946). Colvin's descriptions of her are from *Memories and Notes of Persons and Places, 1852–1912* (1921), and from his entry on Stevenson for the *Dictionary of National Biography*. Henry James's letter to Owen Wister, and the comments by Gosse and Symonds, are quoted by Margaret Mackay in *The Violent Friend: The Story of Mrs Robert Louis Stevenson* (1968). William Clarke's portrayal of Fanny appears in the Stevenson *Letters* (vol. 6). Henry Adams's reactions to Fanny may be found in *Robert Louis Stevenson: Interviews and Recollections*, edited by R. C. Terry (1996), and in volume 7 of the Stevenson *Letters*.

Stevenson writes of the appeal of America in *The Amateur Emigrant* (1895), and his definition of marriage appears in the essay 'Talk and Talkers: Second Paper' in *Memories and Portraits* (1887). His portrait of King Tembinoka is in Part IV of *In the South Seas* (1896). These works by Stevenson, and indeed all of his writings that have been cited in the Introduction, are readily accessible, having been reprinted in many editions. All other Stevenson quotations are from the *Letters*.

Note on the text

he Cruise of the 'Janet Nichol' was first published in New York by Charles Scribner's Sons in 1914; an identical edition was published in London by Chatto & Windus in 1915. The published text prepared by Fanny Stevenson was a version, sometimes abridged, sometimes expanded, of the diary she had kept on the voyage. The manuscript diary, written in a Letts's Australasian Diary and Almanac for 1890, is now at the Silverado Museum at St Helena, California.

This book follows the text of the first edition, except that the footnotes (many of them quite long) have been brought into the main text. These notes, added when Fanny was preparing the book for publication, are in some cases merely explanatory; in some cases they introduce information and perspectives gained after the voyage, and in some cases they reproduce material from an earlier diary, of the Stevensons' *Equator* cruise of 1889. Portions of the text that appeared as footnotes in the first edition are the three sections discussing the *Equator* cruise — 'A note on a previous visit to Butaritari', 'A note on a previous visit to Apemama' and 'A note on a previous visit to Maraki' — and the following passages:

Page 62   'This flag ... to the shark.'

Page 63   'Very few flowers ... almost necessities.'

Page 63   'I have seen ... coveted possessions.'

Page 64	'(As all mine ... civilised appearance.)'
Page 71	'(He used this ... let it stand.)'
Page 77	'Sitione was suffering ... shattered shoulder.'
Page 79	'(The "labour boys" ... died of homesickness.)'
Page 115	'(We forgot it ... belated celebration.)'
Page 121	'(two somewhat ... rest of the world).'
Page 123	'(We made ... trading schooner.)'
Page 124	'(This must ... flourish.)'
Page 130	'The *ridi* ... active service.'
Page 137	'At this island ... tumbler.'
Page 140	'when we were ... former cruise.'
Page 154	'Butaritari had lapsed ... King and all.'
Page 156f.	'We were forced ... in Samoa.'
Page 163	'a political refugee from Samoa'
Page 168	'(Fresh palm toddy tastes ... another thing.)'
Page 177	'(retainers)'
Page 184f.	'Raw fish may seem ... been boiled.'
Page 185f.	'Tin Jack came to ... wherever he went.'

A few further emendations have been made. On page 61 I have changed the possessive form of 'Louis' to 'Louis's', consistent with Fanny's usual practice, and on page 158 I have altered 'ingenuously' to 'ingeniously', as the sense requires. The spelling of the island name written sometimes 'Piru' and sometimes 'Peru' by Fanny has been regularised to 'Piru'. Foreign words have been italicised, and a very small number of obvious errors in punctuation have been corrected.

Throughout the text stars have been used to indicate the presence of explanatory notes, which may be found on pages 198–203.

Note on the photographs

Thirteen of the photographs in this book, including the cover illustration, were published in the first edition of *The Cruise of the 'Janet Nichol'*. Two of these were taken during the Stevensons' cruise on the *Equator* in 1889, the rest on the *Janet Nicoll* cruise in 1890. A further twelve photographs from the Stevensons' *Janet Nicoll* album and one from their *Equator* album are published here for the first time. The circumstances in which the frontispiece was photographed are unknown; it appears to be the work of a commercial photographer.

Not every photograph in the book can be attributed with certainty, but most, if not all, of them (other than the frontispiece) were taken by Fanny's son, Lloyd Osbourne. Osbourne photographed all three of the Stevensons' Pacific voyages, intending to provide illustrations for Robert Louis Stevenson's Pacific travel book, *In the South Seas*. Fanny's reference to her husband and son as 'the photographers' makes clear that Stevenson worked closely with Osbourne in selecting the subjects of the pictures, although he may not have operated the camera. Fanny's diary shows that she was involved with the photography too, although painting was her preferred method of visually recording her travels.

Stevenson's plan for an illustrated edition of *In the South Seas* fell through, and it has been *The Cruise of the 'Janet Nichol'* that has provided a setting for the publication of some, at least, of the Stevensons' Pacific photographs.

Preface

It is always necessary to make certain elisions in a diary not meant for publication at the time of writing. For many reasons *The Cruise of the 'Janet Nichol'* has been pruned rather severely. It was, originally, only intended to be a collection of hints to help my husband's memory where his own diary had fallen in arrears; consequently, it frequently happened that incidents given in my diary were re-written (to their great betterment), amplified, and used in his. I have deleted these as far as possible, though not always completely; also things pertaining to the private affairs of other persons, and, naturally, our own. I fear the allusions to the *Devil Box* may seem obscure. It happened that my husband wrote a complete description of the purchase of the *Devil Box* in his own diary, so it seemed necessary for me to note further references to it, but nothing more. In the minute description, almost like a catalogue, of the articles in the different buildings in the island of Suwarrow, I must appear to have gone to the opposite extreme. At that time my husband had an idea of writing a South Sea island romance where he might wish to use such pathetic and tragic flotsam and jetsam from wrecked ships and wrecked lives. At the risk of tedium I have let it stand, hoping that some one else may see the intangible things I beheld.

One reason I have hesitated a little to give for publishing this diary, is the extraordinary number of books now being printed purporting to give accurate accounts of our lives on board ship and elsewhere, by persons with whom we were very slightly acquainted, or had never consciously met. I have read, among other misstatements, of the making of the flag for Tembinoka, by the writer and my daughter on the beach at Apemama. The flag was designed by me, on board the schooner *Equator*, and made, in the most prosaic manner, by a firm in Sydney. No one, outside our immediate family, sailed with us on any of our cruises. All the books 'With Stevenson' here, and 'With Stevenson' there, are manufactured out of 'such stuff as dreams are made on', and false in almost every particular. Contrary to the general idea, my husband was a man of few intimate friends, and even with these he was reticent to a degree.

This diary was written under the most adverse conditions — sometimes on the damp, upturned bottom of a canoe or whaleboat, sometimes when lying face down on the burning sands of the tropic beach, often in copra sheds in the midst of a pandemonium of noise and confusion, but oftener on board the rolling *Janet* (whose pet name was the *Jumping Jenny*) to the accompaniment of 'Tin Jack's' incessant and inconsequent conversation — but never in comfortable surroundings. For such inadequate results the labour required was tremendously out of proportion, giving my diary a sort of fictitious value in the eyes of my husband, who wished to save it from oblivion by publication. The little book, however dull it may seem to others, can boast of at least one reader, for I have gone over this record of perhaps the happiest period of my life with thrilling interest.

FANNY V DE G STEVENSON
California 1914

The Cruise
of the
Janet Nichol
among the
South Sea Islands

The *Janet Nichol* was an iron-screw cargo boat, topsail schooner rigged, of some six hundred tons gross. Her large, airy saloon and cabins were placed amidship on the main deck, with ports opening forward, the 'trade room' being at the extreme aft. There was a comfortable bathroom and space enough on deck for exercise; but, for that matter, we might walk, sit, or sleep where we would. I have slept in the chart room and on the platform of the captain's bridge; though the after hatch, over which a great awning was spread, was the place chosen by the most of us for permanent night quarters. Here some swung in hammocks, some lay on mats, while the more luxurious carried blankets and pillows back and forth each night and morning. For me four mats were hung in a square; the mats, being loosely woven, did not cut off the current of air that usually swept over the hatch nor, unfortunately, the terrible groans of one of the mates who slept near me and was subject to nightmares.

Our mess consisted of Mr Henderson, a member of the company that owned the vessel; Captain Henry, sailing-master; Mr Hird, supercargo; Mr Stoddard, engineer; Mr Buckland, commonly called Tin Jack (Tin being the island equivalent for Mr), a trader of the company returning to his station, my husband, my son Lloyd, and myself. The *Janet* carried a crew of about nine white men and some forty-odd black boys from the different islands of the Solomons and the New Hebrides.

We left Sydney on the 11th of April with a head wind and heavy seas until we arrived at Auckland, making seven days from port to port.

18 April 1890

At Auckland in time for dinner. Went on shore and dined at a hotel with the supercargo and Tin Jack. Louis and I slept at the hotel with the understanding that Tin Jack and Lloyd should meet us in the morning with a shopping list. Immediately on our arrival in Auckland a strange cat jumped through a port-hole and now remains on board.

19 April

Bought a broadcloth coat for Maka and a good black silk dress for Mary. As the *Janet* was bound for 'the South Seas' and nothing more definite, we thought it better to carry presents in case we found ourselves in the neighbourhood of Butaritari. I came back to the hotel in advance of Tin Jack and Lloyd, who stopped to buy fireworks for the entertainment of Tin Jack's native retainers. Besides the fireworks, which included ten pounds of 'calcium fire', Tin Jack has also purchased cartridges, grease-paints, a false nose, and a wig.

Lloyd was a little doubtful about the calcium fire and questioned the man at the chemist shop rather closely, particularly as to its inflammability, explaining that it was to be carried on board ship. The man declared that it was perfectly safe, 'as safe', said he, 'as a packet of sugar,' adding that fire from a match would not be sufficient to ignite it. 'Will you have it with or without fumes?' he asked as he turned to make up the parcel. The thrifty trader thought that he might as well get all he could for the money expended, therefore took it with fumes.

ON BOARD
IN THE
AFTERNOON

A little trouble with the trades-union, but nothing serious. Mr W—, a bookseller, who had recognised Louis from a published portrait, called in the evening. He kindly offered to get pistol cartridges for us, and after a few minutes' conversation ran away after them, returning just as we were about to leave, with a couple hundred or thereabouts. The fireworks were sent aboard with other parcels, and, having no distinguishing marks, Lloyd put them all, along with our cartridges, on his bunk until Tin Jack, whose cabin he shared, should come below and sort them out. Among them should be a pistol Tin Jack had taken to have mended, belonging to Louis.

ho Louis Stevenson in company with Nantoki and Natakauti. Butari

ntoki and Natakauti — Two strong friends of the party when in Brit

A NOTE
ON A
PREVIOUS VISIT
TO
BUTARITARI

We had met the Hawaiian missionary Maka and his wife Mary on our second South Sea cruise at Butaritari, one of the low islands belonging to the Kingsmill group. Maka and his wife being away at the time, by the advice of the resident trader we had burglariously entered and taken possession of the missionaries' comfortable little wooden house, where we made ourselves at home while we complacently awaited the arrival of our involuntary host. Having thus identified ourselves with the missionary party, and laid ourselves under such heavy obligations to them, we felt bound to forego many amusements and friendships, otherwise interesting, that would have been objectionable to Maka. However, during the time of the great festival, when the neighbouring islanders of Little Makin (called by the traders 'Little Muggin') came over, in answer to a challenge from the Butaritaris to dance against them for what sportsmen would call 'the championship', Maka retired into discreet obscurity, giving us an opportunity to become acquainted with the King of Little Makin and to attend the heathen dances. But Maka and Mary remained our most real friends in spite of our momentary defection toward Makin. When we left Butaritari we could find nothing suitable to offer them as parting gifts, in the island fashion, and to show our gratitude for their many almost overwhelming kindnesses; hence the silk dress and clergyman's frock coat. Two other friends, consistent converts to Christianity, to whom we also carried presents, we left behind us with regret, Nan Tok and his wife; but they were of a different sort from Maka and Mary, being natives of Butaritari and, from Maka's point of view, quite uncivilised, as, in ordinary life the lady (there are only ladies in the South Seas, woman being a word that is tapu★ *in all society, high or low), a rich, high chief* woman, wore the ridi* only, while for full dress she appeared in a white chemise fresh from the trader's shelves with the marks where it had been folded still showing. My first meeting with Nan Tok and his wife was rather alarming. The King had raised the tapu *from* drink, consequently, the entire island, including his dull majesty, was wildly drunk on 'sour toddy' (the fermented sap of the flower-stalk of the cocoanut), which is the most dangerous intoxicant in the world, as it incites in its users a frenzied desire to shed blood. During this period of licence I accidentally came upon two women fighting together like wild beasts, their teeth sunk into each other's faces, which were streaming blood. 'Oh, what is the matter?' I cried. 'Sour toddy,' replied the woman to whom I spoke, casting a contemptuous glance over her shoulder as she passed on.

In the circumstances it was thought unsafe for me to leave our own small premises, but one quiet afternoon I broke bounds and went over to the weather side of the island to hunt for shells. Here a strange man and woman joined me; they were not reassuring companions, judging from outer appearances, as they were unkempt, clad in nothing but a small fragment, each, of dirty, old gunny sack, and their faces were haggard and anxious. At first they walked with me as I went about my business of gathering shells, but presently, seeming to tire of this amusement, they began to crowd me off the beach toward the land; then seizing me by the arms, one on either side, they boldly marched me into a narrow, crooked path that led through the clustering cocoanut-trees with which the island was heavily wooded. As I reluctantly moved along beside my captors, the lady, evidently with a kindly feeling for my comfort, drew a clay pipe from out an enormous hole in her ear, stuffed it with strong, coarse tobacco, lighted it, puffed a moment, and then placed it in my mouth. As I could not guess whether their intentions were hostile or otherwise and all the warnings I had received flashed through my mind, with sublime courage I accepted the situation. But it was a solemn experience. We emerged *from the palms to find the town in a turbulent uproar, the street in front of our house filled with a howling, fighting, drunken mob. It was a great relief to find we were just in front of my own door; the two natives held me fast until we were safely on the little veranda, when, to my astonishment, the man fell on his knees and offered up a fervent prayer.*

So began our friendship with Nan Tok and his wife (my husband always called them the 'baron and baroness'). They told us afterward with what anxiety they had watched me wander through the woods alone; then how, after a heated argument as to the proper means to pursue, they concluded to force me back to safety. The incident of the pipe was an attempt to conciliate me because of a supposed fiery gleam in my eyes that disconcerted them. The prayer was one of thanks for the outcome of their adventure and a petition that this should prove the beginning of a new friendship that should be blessed to us all.

20 April

We left Auckland last evening at about eight, the streaming lights from the town following us a long way. A small, half-grown dog has joined the ship's company.

Between ten and eleven Louis was lying in his cabin very tired and glad to rest. Tin Jack and Lloyd were in Mr Henderson's cabin drinking coffee and discussing 'land booms'. I sat at the saloon table eating brown bread and butter. Suddenly, from the cabin occupied by Tin Jack and Lloyd, came a spitting puff, almost immediately followed by gorgeous flames and the most horrible chemical stench. The calcium fire that was as safe as a packet of sugar had gone off and ignited the rest of the fireworks. Only Lloyd and I knew of the cartridges in their midst, but we discreetly held our tongues, though every moment we expected to hear the ping of flying bullets. I ran into our cabin and snatched a heavy red blanket. At the same time Mr Henderson was fetching a large, handsome woollen rug from his cabin. I felt for a hand to put the blanket in, for the place was so full of suffocating vapour that one could see nothing but the many-hued flames darting through it. Fortunately, it was the captain's hand I delivered my blanket into. Rid of my blanket, I ran back and thrust my head out of a port to get a breath of air; the ports, although they were the means of fanning the flames, could not be shut on account of the strangling fumes. Here Mr Henderson, who had been for some minutes lying on the stairs quite insensible, came to fetch me out; so, catching his hand, I ran through the saloon to the companionway and up to the deck.

Louis, who knew nothing of the fireworks having been brought on board, was thunderstruck by the vivid changing colours of the spouts of flame, and stood for some time gazing at the extraordinary scene and inhaling the poisonous vapours. 'Why', he thought with wonder, 'should a fire at sea look like a Christmas pantomime?' His amazement was so great that he was hardly conscious of the fumes.

The captain, from the bridge, had seen heavy vapour pouring upward and was both puzzled and angry, thinking the engineer was letting off steam for purposes of his own. The stuff must, therefore, have been smouldering for a considerable time before it burst into flames, the draught carrying the smoke out of the open port instead of into the saloon, so that our first knowledge of anything amiss came from the bursting of rockets into the saloon. As the captain was looking at the supposed column of steam there suddenly shot through it, rising high into the air, a shaft of blue, green, and red fire. Ordering the donkey-engine to pump water and the hose to be put on, he ran below and crawled into the very centre of the fire with the blanket, rug, and hose, and succeeded in smothering the flames none too soon for the safety of the ship; he said afterward that had the wind come from a different quarter, or had the cartridges exploded, nothing could have saved us.

There was no panic among our black boys, who worked swiftly and obediently; I rather suspect they enjoyed the excitement of the affair. Talking it over, the captain said how lucky it was that he had a man at the wheel that he could trust. Lloyd and I said nothing, but we both knew there had been no man at the wheel; the trusted one ran below with the rest. It was a rather dangerous moment to leave the ship drifting, for we were not nearly out of the harbour, being just opposite the lighthouse when the fire broke out. A steamer passed us quite closely when the scene was at its wildest. Coloured fire and thick white vapour belching from our ports must have given us a very strange and alarming aspect. Lloyd looked over the opposite side of our ship and saw the ports there, also, vomiting vapour like a factory.

To our surprise the cartridge-boxes were only slightly scorched. Our personal loss, however, has been very severe. About ninety photographs were destroyed and all of Lloyd's clothes except those on his back. Neither he nor I have even a tooth-brush left. The annoying thing is that Tin Jack has lost nothing whatever. Lloyd is very bitter about the discrimination shown in the matter of trousers by the fire. I stopped a couple of black boys just in time to prevent them throwing overboard a blazing valise containing four large boxes of Louis's papers. A black bag, its contents at present unknown, is burned, and innumerable small necessaries that conduce to comfort on shipboard are lost. I have ever since been in a tremor lest Louis have a haemorrhage. If he does I shall feel inclined to do something very desperate to the chemist, who, for the sake of a few shillings, put us all in such deadly peril. A horrid smell still hangs about the place and every one feels ill. Though I hardly breathed in the room, I have a heavy oppression on my chest, and my throat and lungs burn as though I were inhaling pepper. From the time we left Auckland the water has been as smooth as glass, and there has been no jarring or knocking about; the stuff must have gone off by simple spontaneous combustion. Had it taken place a very little later, Tin Jack must have been sleeping in the berth above, and should undoubtedly have been suffocated.

21 April

Still drying the remains of Lloyd's clothes, burned and wet in the fire, and discovering more and more losses. Fortunately, the flag I had made for King Tembinoka was not injured at all (a royal standard I invented for him). The flag for the island I had already sent, and the cartridge-belt Lloyd is taking to him for a present is only a little smudged. Both our cameras escaped as by magic.

This flag was designed on a former cruise after we had left Apemama, the principal of the three islands comprising the group under King Tembinoka, the last of the absolute monarchs of the South Seas. The King had asked that we send him a flag, so one evening, on board the schooner *Equator*, we each drew and coloured a flag. These were voted on by the ship's company. It happened that mine was unanimously chosen. The three cross-bars, red, yellow, and green, were intended to stand for the three islands, while the black shark lying across the bars was meant to be typical of Tembinoka's ancestry. The King's line was not lost in obscurity; he gave us almost embarassing details of the first of his forebears, who sprang from a liaison between a beautiful lady and a shark. The drawings I made on the *Equator* were taken to a firm in Sydney that did such work; they turned out a couple of very gorgeous flags that were quite to the taste of his majesty. The house flag had a white crown over the head of the shark (a little different shape from that on the island flag). I chose for the motto 'I bite triply', which referred not only to the King's three islands, but to the three rows of teeth peculiar to the shark.

Louis has been playing chess with the captain, who has not played before for many years. I have been making wreaths of artificial flowers for presents to the natives. I bought in Sydney several large boxes of old-fashioned artificial flowers, perfectly fresh and pretty, also green leaves unwired. For one pound and three shillings I got enough for twenty full wreaths and eighteen more to be worked up with coloured feathers. I do not think the natives will enjoy getting the wreaths any more than I enjoy making them. Very few flowers are found in the atolls, wherefore the natives, who use wreaths for every festive occasion, are forced to devise all sorts of makeshifts for the garlands that are considered almost necessities. (One of our sailors appeared on duty in a garland and necklace of orange-peel.) I have seen only two flowers that seem indigenous to the true atoll, one quite insignificant, that looked like the blossom of the male *papaia*, the other a sort of 'spider lily'; both these were of a whitish colour, and, as far as I could see, were worn only by people of position, and not by the common herd, who contented themselves with imitations made from some part of the cocoanut-tree. I wish those artistic souls, who so scorned my purchases at the milliner's, could have seen with what frantic joy they were received. Many times staid matrons burst into sudden hysterical weeping when I offered them my wreaths, while kings, chiefs, and even white traders intrigued to gain one of these coveted possessions.

The sea is smooth and the weather perfect.

22 April

The weather still lovely. Saw a small island called Curtis Island, and at half past ten sighted Sunday Island. The captain kindly took us very close in that we might get a good photograph. A puff of smoke appeared on the horizon, supposed to be a steamer; great excitement. I ran to write letters and found Mr Henderson doing the same; but alas, the ship, which looked like a man-of-war, moved away from us nearer to the island, and it was too late to venture to chase her, so our letters must wait. Sunday is the island where an American family once took up their residence, remaining until it began to blow up. Some settlers have lately gone there. Lloyd reminds me that this was the place Louis and he once proposed to try and get possession of, and I refused to hear of the plan because of the volcano and the hordes of rats that infest the place. I repented when I saw it, and my heart is now set upon owning an island. It grows warmer daily, and I hope soon to be able to put away my shoes and stockings. (As all mine and most of Louis's were burned, except what I had on my feet, I wished to pre-serve these for such times as it might seem necessary to make a civilised appearance.) Mr Henderson is looking for an island about the existence of which there is some doubt. Lloyd tells me that Mr Low, the artist in New York,* once said that he had a friend who had actu-ally been upon this very island.

26 April

I have not been able to put away my shoes and stockings, for the sun disappeared soon after my last entry; for several days we have been knocking about in a gale of wind with almost continuous rain. The air is thick and breathless, hot, and at the same time chill. To my discom-fort, I caught a cold and developed a smart attack of rheumatism. The captain has also been unfortunate; he, too, took cold, and in addition had a heavy door slam upon one of his fingers, crushing the nail. Some time ago a cinder blew into one of his eyes, causing an inflammation, and now the other is as bad in consequence of the poisonous fumes of our involuntary firework display.

To-day we came to anchor off Savage Island, or Nuieue, having on board some eight natives of the place who were being returned home by the company. It was pleasant to see the happy, excited faces of the 'boys' as we drew near their native land. They were all dressed for the occasion in new clothes, every man with a pair of strong new boots on his feet. A couple of dandies wore velvet smoking-caps with tassels, and red sashes. It is a smaller and lighter-coloured race than we have been accustomed to, their features and expression reminding one of pretty, sweet-faced Chinamen. Before we had anchored, neatly made outriggers were circling round the ship and cries of greeting arose from all sides. When the steam-whistle sounded a joyful answering shout ran along the beach. No women came out to us. To them a ship is *tapu*, but numbers of small boys accompanied the men. Soon they

Boy from Niue or Savage Island.

were all wandering over the ship, marvelling at the strange sights, but also cannily ready to make an honest or dishonest penny. I bought a couple of sticks of sugar-cane for a stick of tobacco and ordered a hat from a man for which I am to pay two shillings. The man had a hat with him but charged four shillings for it on account of its trimming, a small bit of red flannel laid round the crown. I also bought a couple of little model canoes (one for Tin Jack) for two shillings.

Our sailors are 'black fellows', some from the New Hebrides, some from the Solomons and various other places. They seem to find it easier to speak to one another in English than in their own tongues; I heard one say: 'I wouldn't like to go across that water in that fellow's canoe.' The men from Nuieue looked at those black fellows with great curiosity and asked in what island did they find men like that. One of these black sailors has his name signed as Sally Day. To-day I heard one of the others politely call him Sarah. Savage Island is a high-low island; that is, it is a coral atoll with a soil, raised more or less unevenly, some two hundred feet above the sea-level. It produces copra, bananas, cotton, breadfruit, *bêche-de-mer*, and fungus, and is governed by a king with the assistance of four chiefs and four sub-chiefs. Food trees and plants are carefully cultivated, and the people have the reputation of being industrious and willing to work. Captain Henry wished to take a little girl home to his wife, but was not allowed, it being against the law that a female should leave the island.

In at least one of the villages of Nuieue a singular custom prevails. One day in the year is fixed as a day of judgment. Every soul, man, woman, and child, gathers together on the village green. Votes are cast for a whipper, and a jury, composed of half Christians and half heathens, is chosen. One by one the people come forward and publicly confess their sins, while the jury fixes the punishment, which is whipping or an equivalent fine. The fines may be paid in goods of any sort, the value of the article offered being rated at the price originally paid for it. For instance, a man fined a dollar may bring the unwearable remains of a tattered hat that cost him a dollar the year before. The elected officials do not escape punishment by virtue of their position. After the jury has confessed and fixed its own punishment, the whipper must do the same, and, if whipping is his doom, must proceed to whip himself. So, next day, every soul starts afresh with consciences sponged clean, ready for a new record of sins. The confessions seem to be genuine and sometimes cause the utmost surprise and consternation to those who have been sinned against.

The desire to own an island is still burning in my breast. In this neighbourhood, nearer Samoa, is just the island I want, owned, unfortunately, by a man in Tahiti. It is called Nassau and is said to be uninhabited.

Last night an immense rat ran over me in bed, and Mr Henderson had the same unpleasant experience. In the hold of the *Janet* are a number of pure white rats with red eyes, which appeared of themselves quite mysteriously. The captain will not allow them to be harmed, which I think is very nice and sentimental of him. It was amusing to see our dog's perplexity when we came to anchor, and he put his head out of a port-hole to have a look at Auckland. His very tail expressed alarmed surprise. Our second steward (a white man) is in a state of wild delight. He took his 'billet' under the head steward from a romantic hope of seeing Samoa, of which he had once read a description in a newspaper. Every little while I hear his voice, quivering with excitement: 'What do you think of it, Mrs Stevens?' One moment he is thrusting sugar-cane into my hand: 'Taste it, Mrs Stevens, it's sugar stick! I never saw it before!' and the next is: '*Cocoanut! cocoanut!* It's *green cocoanut*, Mrs Stevens; I never saw it before in my life!' It is of no use to tell him that it is all an old story to me; he hears nothing but babbles on with shining eyes. I have just overheard this from a white stoker who had also never been in the tropics before: 'He's been and swindled me, that native! There's nothing inside this green cocoanut but some kind of water.'

Mr Henderson has just told us as a secret that our next island will be Upolu, Samoa, and we are now as wildly excited as the second steward. On Wednesday afternoon, at four o'clock, we shall arrive at Apia, and the next morning, at break of day, off we fly to Vailima. As we were discussing the subject, the captain called out that there was a white rat in his cabin and he wished to catch and tame it, so I ran to help him. It was under his bed, he said, and the loveliest rat in the world. As he was dilating on its beauty, out it flashed, jumping on him and rebounding against my breast like a fluff of white cotton wool. The captain laughed and screamed with shrill, hysterical cries, in which I joined, while the loveliest rat in the world scurried away.

27 April

The weather really abominable, so cold that I have had to put on a flannel bodice. Tin Jack and Lloyd went to the station last night and returned with the white trader, a thin, pallid man, with a large, hooked nose and soft, frightened brown eyes. For very dulness I was about to go to sleep, when Mr Henderson ran up crying: 'Sail ho!' Sure enough, there was a large vessel wallowing in the great seas. Captain Henry thought her an American driven in by the heavy weather. Round the point of the island the breakers were rising, he said, some forty feet high. While we were watching the strange craft she turned about and sailed away, to our great disappointment, no doubt having only come up to take her bearings. After I had closed my diary last night Mr Henderson got out the chart and showed us his own islands and the supposed location of Victoria Island which he is looking for. I offered to toss him for the latter, to which he agreed. Louis threw up a piece of money and I won. I have yet, however, to find Victoria.

Nuieue has not yet recovered from the effects of last year's hurricane, and we shall not get many delicacies here. There are no ripe cocoanuts, few bananas, and no breadfruit. Some one said that I could get spring onions. 'How do they grow them?' I asked; meaning did they sow seeds or plant sets. 'On the graves,' was the rather startling answer.

Last night Mr Henderson pulled off a rat's tail. He thought to pull the rat from a hole from which the tail protruded, but the tail came off, and the rat ran away. The captain tells me that there is generally a plague of flies in Nuieue. It is too cold for them now, but usually when the natives come out in their canoes their backs, especially, are black with flies. Some one has sent me a basket of bananas almost too sweet and rich; also some excellent oranges. I have mended the bellows of our camera, where it has been eaten by cockroaches, with sticking-plaster.

28 April

Steamed round to the other side of the island to the missionary station, carrying with us the trader and a young Irishman named Hicks; also a native woman and a boy. Here, to our surprise, we saw the vessel we had sighted and lost; she proved to be the *John Williams*.

We watched her plunging to and fro, now close under the cliffs, now skirting the *Janet*, now fetching our hearts in our mouths as she stayed, and forereached in staying, till you would have thought she had leaves on her jib-boom. We actually got up the camera to take a photograph of the expected shipwreck. We were told afterward that it was only Captain Turpie showing off his seamanship.

The *John Williams* is a missionary ship on her way to Samoa with an English missionary and his family and a German lady who is going to open a school for Samoan girls. Mr Lawes is the Nuieue missionary, a dark, foreign-looking man. We heard nothing but good of him from traders and natives.

We landed and climbed up the part path, part stairs of the cliff, our boys already trailing down it with copra sacks, the ship's boat slamming away at the jetty with a couple of black fellows holding on to it like grim death. The missionary natives were ranged in bodies on the path to meet us. First the men pressed forward, giggling, and shook hands; then the women, whose many-coloured garments we had remarked even from the ship, glowing on the cliff like a bank of flowers. The children who followed after pretended alarm and fled, but laughed as they ran. I was some distance from Louis, who has written the following in my diary: 'They closed in on me like a sea; I was in the close embrace of half a dozen outstretched hands, with smiling faces all round me, and a perfect song of salutation going up. From the sirens I escaped by means of a present of tobacco, which was the cause of my ruin, later on, when Lloyd and I went out to photograph. A bevy of girls followed, hugging and embracing me, and going through my pockets. It was the nearest thing to an ugly sight, and still it was pretty; there was no jeering, no roughness, they fawned upon and robbed me like well-behaved and healthy children with a favourite uncle. My own cut tobacco and my papers they respected; but a little while after, on making a cigarette, I found my match-box gone. There was small doubt in my mind as to the culprit; a certain plump little maid, more like a Hawaiian, with a coquettish cast of face and carriage of the head, and conspicuous by a splendid red flower stuck in her ear, had visited me with a particular thoroughness. I demanded my matches. She shook her head at first; and then from some unknown receptacle produced my box, drew out a single match, replaced the box, and with a subtle smile and considerable grace of demeanour, something like a courtly hostess, passed me on the match!' (He used this afterward, but as it seems to belong to my diary I thought I might let it stand.)

Tin Jack was shown some spies who were taking names of women who had, against rules, been aboard ship. They will all be fined tomorrow.

Levity of conduct, they tell us, is not allowed and is met by fines. I should imagine the public funds to be in a plethoric condition.

Before I knew where I was the trader had swept me up to the mission house, well built of coral, with a high, wide roof of cocoanut thatch beautifully braided together and tied with cocoanut sennit. In an inner room we found the passengers from the *John Williams*, Mr and Mrs Marriott and the German teacher. The Marriotts had with them the loveliest little twins imaginable, two years old, and almost exactly alike. Louis and Lloyd disappeared at once in search of photographs. The king, who seems to be liked and respected, was off in the bush, so they were disappointed in his likeness. After a reasonable time of worship before the twins, I started to follow the photographers, the trader conducting me, the *John Williams* party and Mr Lawes (the resident missionary) following. We passed a cow, a bull, and two horses, strange sights for these latitudes. There were a great many flowers blooming in the underbrush — jasmine, the flamboyant, and a yellow blossom like a 'four-o'clock' — and where a space had been cleared grass was growing. There is no running water, but through small fissures in the rock brackish water is found at the depth of seven fathoms. I was told of one great fissure, into which stone steps had been cut, where a subterranean stream gushes out in a waterfall.

The trader, who had already sold us three *tappa* (native bark-cloth) table-cloths at an exorbitant price, clung to me pertinaciously, taking me into his house, where he showed me a mat he wished a pound for, whereas it was worth but a couple of dollars. I refused to buy it, whereupon he presented me with two small rather pretty mats. I thought he owed them to me, so I accepted them without compunction. The young Irishman, who had followed us in, opened his box and took out an immense yellow shell necklace, a cocoa-shell basket, and a strange, very heavy, carefully shaped stone, which the natives use in fighting. All these articles he insisted on my accepting. I was greatly pleased with the fighting stone. The trader promised to get me a couple of 'peace sticks' when we return to his side of the island. These are used by the women when they think a fight has lasted long enough. They rush between the combatants, waving their 'peace sticks', and the affair ends. These peace sticks are made of dark, almost black ironwood, are about three feet long, shaped like spears, and ornamented, where the hand naturally holds them, with cocoa-fibre sennit and yellow bird feathers. The feathers looked to be the same as were used in Hawaii for the royal cloaks. As I write Tin Jack appears in a hat of Nuieue manufacture, braided pandanus, in shape an exact reproduction of the civilised high silk hat, and indescribably comic.

Returning to the mission house, we stopped at the king's newly built palace for a piece of ironwood that I wanted to mend the camera stand. The queen, a pretty, smiling, young woman, stood in the doorway directing us where to look. Arriving at the house, I examined the house dog's ear, and found he was suffering from canker. Louis and I, together, remembered the remedy for him, and told it to Mr Lawes. I begged that Louis and Lloyd might see the twins. The little fairies were heavy-eyed from the knocking about and the close air of the *John Williams*. Each had had a convulsion during the last two days. I thought they looked rather too much like little angels. I tried, without success, to make our party refuse Mrs Lawes's invitation to high tea. It did seem very hard; month after month passes in the most deadly monotony. Suddenly here are two ships at her door, each, incredible fact, with white women on board, and she has almost no time to speak to either, and in an hour or two they are gone. Poor Mrs Lawes had wild eyes when the two sets of passengers and most of the officers gathered in a great circle round her board. It was an excellent meal, which I should have thoroughly enjoyed had I not felt like a cannibal and that I was eating Mrs Lawes. But this it is to be a missionary's wife. I am sure she must have had a nervous fever after we were gone. She found a moment to bewail her fate to Louis; if only we had come piecemeal, as it were, and not all at once, like a waterspout, she would have been so happy. We shall leave behind us only a memory of hurry and flurry and confusion worse confounded. While we were at table the *John Williams* ran so close inshore that we were frightened, and Mr Marriott very anxious, as all his worldly goods were on board. The *John Williams* left Sydney on Friday the 11th, the same day we did, and now we meet here and possibly may meet again in Samoa. We had just finished our meal when the steam-whistle blew for us, and away we all trooped to the boat. The *John Williams* was leaving also.

We had some trade stuff to be landed at the other side of the island. There Lloyd went ashore and got my peace sticks for which he paid two shillings the pair. A great many natives came aboard, among the rest the handsome sister and daughter of a chief. I gave them both a wreath, to their great pride and joy. Tin Jack dressed up in his wig and whiskers and false nose. The natives at first were much alarmed and some of the women inclined to cry.

29 April

Squally all night, but this morning the sun has come out and it really looks hopeful. The captain has been working all day until four o'clock at my device for mending the camera with Nuieue ironwood. I hardly slept last night for the heavy rolling and pitching of the *Janet*. A black cat has appeared, brought on board from Nuieue. It was proposed to have a rat hunt with the Auckland dog. I meanly intended to inform the captain, but I need not have troubled myself, for when a rat was shown to the dog he nearly went into a fit with terror. I have all my things ready packed to go on shore at Samoa.

30 April

Passed Tutuila in the morning. Almost despair of reaching Upolu before to-morrow, owing to an adverse current, but make it just after sundown. We ran along Upolu for a couple of hours, the scenery enchanting; abrupt mountains, not so high as in Tahiti or Hawaii, nor so strangely awful as the Marquesan highlands, but with a great beauty of outline and colour, the thick jungle looking from the deck of the ship like soft green moss. Through the glass I could see a high, narrow waterfall drop into the sea. Breaths of the land breeze began to come out to us, intoxicating with the odours of the earth, of growing trees, sweet flowers and fruits, and dominating all, the clean, wholesome smell of breadfruit baking in hot stones. Soon masts of ships began to show, and the smoke of Apia. The signal-flag was carried up to the foretopmast and laboriously tied on by a black boy, when the pilot came quickly on board. It was not quite dark, but we thought it better to dine on the *Janet*, though we were burning to get on shore. While we were eating, people began to arrive in boats to offer their welcome to Samoa. Louis and I started off, leaving Lloyd to follow in the ship's boat. It was a dream-like thing to find oneself walking along Apia beach, shaking hands and passing *talofas* on every side. We spent the evening on shore and, after ordering horses for the early morning, went to bed tired out.

1 May

Woke at six to hear the horses coming for us. When last we rode out to Vailima the road was but a bridle-path almost closed in by the bush. We can now ride two abreast, or even three, if we like. Tin Jack was much delighted to see pineapples growing wild, and bewailed his mistake in having settled on a low island. Lloyd rode ahead to a native village on the road with a packet of sweeties for some little girls who used to dance for us when we lived in the bush near by. We found Lloyd waiting for us; only one of the little girls was about. After we left the village the road plunged into the forest. The tall, liana-draped trees, carrying ferns in the forks of their branches, cast a grateful shade, and we rode slowly, to enjoy all to the utmost.

There was a crowd of black boys at Vailima cutting down and burning trees and brush. I believe they are runaways from the German plantations. There are a good many noble trees, of great height and girth, left standing. A little, wooden house has been run up, from the balcony of which we could see the masts of the *Janet* as she lay at anchor and past her far out over the sea.

It is odd how little is known of Samoa, even by its inhabitants. In Sydney I asked particulars concerning a turbine wheel in case I should want one in Vailima. The man I consulted assured me it would be quite useless to attempt such a thing, as a friend of his just from Samoa, who had lived there a long time, told him there was not a tree of any size in Upolu, and none whatever of hardwood. On the contrary, in the bush are numbers of magnificent timber-trees, very hard and beautiful in colour. One in particular, a light yellow, is very like satinwood and another seems to be a sort of mahogany. We took photographs, and after a couple of hours reluctantly tore ourselves away.

A native man, an old friend, stopped us on the way back to Apia, holding the bridles of our horses that we should not escape him. A woman we were acquainted with passed; she turned and stopped, cooing like a dove, every limb and feature expressing surprise and delight.

After an inordinate luncheon I opened some boxes we had left here and took out various articles suitable for presents. At the main store we found our bush friend and his little daughter waiting for us with a large basket of oranges. Louis gave the child a shilling and told her to choose from the shelves a piece of cotton print. She was dazzled by the magnificence of the offer, and after long deliberation chose the ugliest piece of the lot. I gave an old woman a print gown, upon which she purred like a cat and kissed my hands. Our old friend Sitione (wounded in the late war)* came up and spoke to us, looking very ill, his arm bandaged and in a sling. The doctor tells Louis he thinks very badly of the arm and fears he must amputate it. There was also something wrong with Sitione's eye which was bandaged.

Sitione was suffering from the effects of an old wound got in the last wars, some of the bones in his shoulder being shattered; they were finally removed, and Sitione recovered entirely with only a scar or two to show where the doctor had operated. Sitione, I was told, received this wound while doing a very brave and dashing act. During one of the many Samoan wars his party had fallen back a short distance, leaving an open space between them and the enemy; in this opening Sitione perceived that a friend of his had fallen and was unable to arise. The enemy were already rushing forward to take the man's head, as is their custom, when Sitione bounded back in the face of their guns, caught up his friend, and brought him into safety with a hail of bullets whizzing after him, and a shattered shoulder.

A little boy brought a basket of chilli peppers I wanted to carry on board with me. There were no vegetables to be had, as the Chinaman's garden, the only one in Samoa, had been washed away by a freshet. At half past three we returned to the *Janet*, where Doctor Steubel, the German consul-general,★ Baron von Pritzfritz, captain of the German man-of-war lying in Apia harbour, and another German whose name I forget paid us a visit. We talked a few moments and drank a glass of champagne; then the whistle sounded, our friends bade us good-bye, and at about four we steamed out. Our little house in the bush was visible to the naked eye from the deck of the steamer.

3 May

At about three o'clock we sighted an island known by various names — Swayne's Island, Quiros, or Olesenga — a small, round, low island surrounding a triangular brackish lagoon like an ornamental lake in a park. It is inhabited by a half-caste man known as King Jennings, his family, and about eighty people from different islands. The original Jennings was an American who married a Samoan wife. He left Samoa in a huff after having built a man-of-war for the government, for which payment was refused. As the motive power of the ship came from wooden paddle-wheels, turned with a crank by hand, it is hardly surprising that the complaint of her extreme slowness and the great labour involved in working her should have been brought forward as reasons for non-payment. She had a complete armament of great guns and all the equipments of a proper man-of-war. Jennings, in a fury of indignation and disappointment, shook the dust of Samoa off his feet, and with his wife and family set up a little kingdom of his own in Quiros. Here he blew out a passage through the reef, built two schooners of island wood, floated them off with barrels, and sold them to the German firm at Samoa.★

A flag was hoisted on Quiros, the stars and stripes, with what appeared to be a dove in the field. We asked with some curiosity what the dove indicated. They told us that a night-bird came and cried about the settlement for months; this was supposed to bode sickness; so to propitiate the ill-omened bird it was added to the flag.

There is a good road on the island, excellent houses, a church, and a schoolhouse containing an imported half-caste schoolmaster. From a tall building used for storing copra men were already laying a temporary wooden track down to the landing for the copra trucks to run upon. This busy scene was brought to an end by Mr Henderson's information that he would not take in cargo until our return voyage. This is a rich, low island with plenty of soil, and is said to bring in a very comfortable revenue, which might be still larger did King Jennings care to make it so.

Mr Henderson and Louis went on shore; while they were away I tried to make a Mexican sauce, called *salsa*, with the chillis from Samoa and the onions from the Nuieue graves. The chillis burned my hands dreadfully, and the sauce turned out to be too hot to be used except as a flavouring for soups, for which it was excellent.

Mr Henderson and Louis came back with some return labour boys for Danger Island. One who had signed to serve five years had been waiting another three for a vessel to take him home. He was once disappointed, and nearly died of it. I am thankful he had this opportunity. (The 'labour boys' do, sometimes, die of homesickness. A black boy called Arriki whom we hired from the German firm, did so die after we left Samoa. The man to whom he was assigned by the German firm told me that both Arriki and a friend of his began to droop and become sullen, and then went quite mad; soon after they died at about the same time from no apparent disease, but he said he knew the symptoms — 'just plain homesickness for a cannibal island'. Arriki, in a moment of confidence, once described to me his life in his own land. It seemed to consist of flight from one unsafe spot to another, with death hunting on every hand. Both his father and mother had been killed and eaten, with the most of his friends; and yet Arriki died of homesickness.)

I can see a horse eating grass on the island, and Louis has seen a carriage.

4 May

Ran through a light squall in the night and sighted Danger Island at four in the morning. At the first landing is a place in the reef where people upset in boats are sucked under, never to be seen again. Our Quiros passengers are in a wild state of excitement; ladies on the after hatch slipping on their clean shifts, and the comb going from hand to hand. The eight-year exile clutched Louis's hand, and in a voice trembling with emotion ejaculated 'coco nuk'. As we drew nearer the three islands of the group began to detach themselves. Danger Island, or Pukapuka, is the only one inhabited. It is governed by a king who allows none of his subjects to gather cocoanuts without his royal permission, and as he seldom lets any one have more than is sufficient for his food, very little copra is made. Here the nuts, contrary to the usual custom, are dried in the shell to prevent cockroaches from devouring the meat, and conse-quently the copra is very fine and white; but the quantity made is so small that it does not pay to keep a trader on the island.

We could see the natives gathering on the beach in great force. They seemed thunderstruck at the sight of a vessel with furled sails moving so rapidly against a strong head wind, the *Janet* being the first steamer that had touched at Pukapuka. As soon as our passengers were recognised, a joyful shout ran up and down the beach, and canoes were launched and paddled out to meet us. When they were just abreast of us Captain Henry blew the steam-whistle. The natives were appalled; every paddle stopped short, and the crowds on the beach seemed stricken to stone. Our Pukapuka passengers tried to encourage the people in the canoes to come nearer, calling to them from the deck of the ship, but it was some time before they took heart and resumed their paddling. The King, a shabbily clad man of rather mean appearance, was among them.

The meeting between the long-parted friends was very pretty and touching. I like their mode of showing affection better than ours. They took hands and pressed their faces together lightly with a delicate sniff, as I have often seen a white mother caress her baby. One elderly woman, I was sorry to see, had bad news; she looked very sorrowful, and when a young boy came up to greet her she threw her arms round him and wept aloud. All the rest, however, were sparkling with excitement and joy. The sheep, which the strangers saw for the first time, were studied with much interest. A group of middle-aged, respectable men stood off at some distance and whistled to the sheep as though they were dogs; getting no response, they ventured a little nearer, when one of the sheep happened to move. The crowd fell back in dire confusion, and one man who had been in the van, but now occupied a rear position, asked in a trembling voice if the bite of those animals was very dangerous.

Before our passengers left us, each shook hands with all on board and bade us farewell; they said 'good-bye, sir', to Louis and 'good-bye, mister', to me. As they paddled away I took out my handkerchief and waved it. One woman, the proud possessor of a handkerchief of her own, waved hers in reply and kept it up until I, at least, was tired. I like to think of the pleasant evening at Pukapuka, the gossip, the news, the passing of presents, and the exhibition of treasures and foreign curiosities.

6 May

Sighted Manihiki at half past twelve, an outlying, low coral island with enclosed lagoon, very thinly wooded with cocoa-palms and pandanus trees.

Quiros, the first Spanish navigator of the Pacific, gave to an island the name 'Gente Hermosa' (Beautiful People), which has always been ascribed to Olesenga or Quiros Island; but since the memory of man Quiros has been uninhabited until the advent of the American Jennings. It is very possible that the navigator meant Manihiki, or its neighbouring island Rakahoa, as the isle of beautiful people. It is significant that Manihiki is always conspicuously marked on even the smallest maps of the world, no doubt from the fact that its delightful people have attracted so much attention from seamen that the place has acquired an artificial importance out of all proportion to its few square miles of reef.

The regular diet of the Manihikians is composed almost entirely of cocoanuts. The pandanus seeds are boiled and chewed, but never made into foodstuff as is done in the Gilberts. There are pigs and fowls in abundance, but these are only killed on great occasions, such as marriages or deaths. Sucking pigs are not killed, but only large ones, the larger the better. There are no white women on Manihiki, and but three white men — an absconding produce-merchant, a runaway marine, and a young Englishman who was wrecked on a neighbouring island. These men live on the bounty of the natives, and though they dislike eating copra, or 'cocoanut steak', as it is called, they seem to thrive very well upon it.

We landed on the beach as there was no entrance to the lagoon. The aspect of the reef was not very reassuring as we rowed toward it, but our men took us through a narrow, tortuous passage, and in a few minutes we were shaking hands and exchanging salutations with the natives, a pleasant, smiling crowd with many beautiful children. We were delighted to find that we had arrived at a most interesting period, that of the yearly jubilee. No one could tell us how this institution, which is known in other islands besides Manihiki, first arose. For one week out of every year all laws are held in abeyance, and the island gives itself up to hilarious enjoyment without fear of consequences, singing, beating the cocoanut-wood drum, and dancing according to the old heathen customs. At any other time the punishment for heathen dances is most severe.

The three 'beach-combers' were all well dressed, in coats and trousers, and very good-looking. One man said his present way of life 'had an air of loafing on the natives' which he disliked, but they all seemed proud of their high position as whites, with the exception of the ex-marine, who had fallen under the scorn of his companions for becoming 'kanaka-ised'. Still, that they were under some subjection, we could see, but owned themselves well used. They do not exactly *like* copra, but, as one said: 'We have no right to complain; they give us what they have.' They had had no tobacco for months, which they felt a great privation. When a ship comes in, the natives, men, women, and children, often smoke the strong trade tobacco until they fall down insensible, sometimes becoming convulsed as in epilepsy.

The trader, a half-caste, had already boarded the *Janet* in a boat of his own, but his wife, a stout, good-natured, sensible-looking woman, was waiting on the beach to receive us. She at once took possession of me as her right, and I was triumphantly swept off to her house, the crowd at our heels; here we were regaled on cocoanuts, while all the population who could crowd into the room gazed on us unwinking. The windows, also, were filled, which cut off the air and made the

ani kiki - Natives ith adopted white man.

place rather suffocating. The children were made to sit down in the front row so that the older people could see over their heads. One old woman made me feel quite uncomfortable. Her eyes remained fixed, her jaw dropped, and nothing for a single moment diverted her attention from what she evidently regarded as a shocking and wonderful spectacle. Natives have said that the first sight of white people is dreadful, as they look like corpses walking. I have myself been startled by the sight of a crowd of whites after having seen only brown-skinned people for a long time. Louis has a theory that we whites were originally albinos. Certainly we are not a nice colour. I remember as a child the words 'flesh colour' were sickening to me, and I could not bear to see them in my paint-box.

The room was neat and clean, as were all the houses in the village. Most of them contained a bedstead cut out of imported hardwood with a spread of gay patchwork, and a mat-covered sofa, very high and wide. In an inner room were great stacks of pearl shell, not, I should say, of the very best quality, and much smaller than the law allows in the Paumotus. The shell is gathered in the lagoon by native divers. Very few pearls are found, probably because the shell is taken so young. Leaving the trader's house, we started to cross the island, which is very narrow; Louis thought about one hundred and fifty yards and I no more than one hundred yards. On the way we passed a crowd of dancers, ranged in two rows, the women on one side, the men on the other, in front of the 'speak-house'. The dance was more like the Marquesans' than we had ever seen. The European costumes in which most of the people had dressed for our reception rather spoiled the effect, though many wore wreaths and headdresses made of dyed leaves. The native dyes give beautiful, soft colours, yellow, red, and pink, which they also use in hats and mats, some of the latter being exquisitely fine and as pliant as cloth.

We found the lagoon of crystal clearness and dotted with little islands. Numbers of small vessels were lying at anchor; no doubt they

King of Manikiki with the island judge on right hand.
In front a beachcomber.

Manihiki dances.

had been collecting the shell. Though it was very lovely to look at, we did not stay long on the borders of the lagoon, being driven away by an ancient and fishlike smell. On our way back we went into the church and the speak-house. In the speak-house, a very good building of coral, were stocks which were used to punish malefactors. These stocks consisted of a couple of ring-like handcuffs fastened, one above the other, a foot from the ground, at the side of a post. The church, a thatched coral building without flooring, was really beautiful. The seats, with backs, are in rows, each with a fine, narrow mat spread over it. On either side run galleries, the balustrades elaborately carved and stained with yellow, red, and pink dyes. In the middle of one balustrade the word 'Zion' was carved. The pulpit was a mass of carving and inlaid mother-of-pearl; the altar, which ran round it, was covered with fringed mats extremely fine and flexible and worked in different colours.

Among many others we made the acquaintance of a man who had been in Samoa, blown there in a storm. There were with him one other man and three little girls. It began to blow, he said, the sea rose very high, and the air and sky grew black. Suddenly his boat capsized and 'my girls', he said, 'swim — swim — swim in the sea'. With their help he got the boat righted and gathered up what he could of his cargo, green cocoanuts and copra, and ran for Samoa. 'Was any one frightened?' I asked. 'Only the other man,' he said. We met two of his little girls; one seemed clever and had picked up a little Samoan and a little English while she was in Apia. We asked her name. 'Anna,' she proudly answered. The other called herself Anna Maria.

Lloyd had photographed the King in his royal robes, a pair of white duck trousers and a black velveteen coat; over all was worn a sort of black cloth poncho bordered with gold fringe. Suspended from the neck of royalty was a tinsel star and on his head a crown of red and white pandanus leaves. Later in the evening he appeared in a pair of black trousers and a frock coat. In common with his subjects, the King is not of commanding stature. None of the islanders we have yet seen on this cruise can compare with the Kingsmill people in haughty grace of carriage, nor are they in any way so fine a race physically though most charming in manner. After dinner, finding the trader's wife and the missionary's wife having tea on deck, I gave them each a wreath, which delighted them extremely. We hired a native boat to take us on shore again for the evening; the man to whom the boat belonged begged us to go to his house, but I wished first to take a present, a print dress, to Anna.

Found Anna's house and gave my present. We were offered cocoanuts, to our great embarrassment, but Louis fortunately thought of saying '*paea*' (a rather vulgar Tahitian word signifying 'I am full to repletion'). They understood at once and seemed greatly amused. Anna gave me a hat of her own manufacture and then we went with the boatman to his house. A party of young girls followed us, wrangling together as to which had chosen me first. It seemed to be settled amicably, for one girl ran up to me while the rest held back, and catching me by the hand said: 'You belong me.' The boatman's wife, a sensible-looking woman with a pathetic smile, was ill, he said; we were afterward told that she had consumption. Again cocoanuts, and once more we got off with '*paea*'. When we left, the lady presented me with a large mat and a fine hat. I had nothing with me to give in return, so took the wreath from my own hat (I always wear one in case of an emergency) and also gave her an orange (a rare luxury) I had in my pocket. I afterward sent her a piece of print of the best quality. From the boatman's we went to the speak-house, where the dancers were assembled. As we came out of the bush toward the main road we heard a clapping of hollow sticks and whelp-like cries; at intervals a sentence was shouted. It was curfew. At eight o'clock several high officials parade the street, clapping sticks together and crying out: 'Remain within your houses.' No one obeys, but it is etiquette to keep off the main road when the officers march. We saw that the people kept to the coral on either side, so we did the same. When we first came on shore this evening, Louis, seeing a little girl about four carrying a naked boy, patted him on the shoulder; he howled, whereupon the little girl laughed and ran away. As we waited for the procession to pass, the little girl came up behind Louis in the darkness and, slipping her hand in his, nestled close to him. Her name was Fani, also Etetera; she was neat as a little statue, as tight as india-rubber; so was her sister; so was 'Johnny Bull', who had walked hand in hand with Louis all afternoon. The type is well marked: forehead high and narrow, cheek-bones high and broad, nose aquiline and depressed (the depression probably artificial), the mouth large, with finely chis-elled lips, the bow of the upper lip sharply defined, the eyes, of course, admirable; and altogether there is a strong appearance of good nature and good sense.

Part of the night Louis had a second satellite in the form of a beau-tiful boy, so that he walked between him and Fani, hand in hand with each; but Fani was his affinity. The whole island seemed interested; the King, not too well pleased, suffered Fani to sit beside Louis in the speak-house on the sofa of honour during the dance. Women came up and commented on the resemblance between Fani and Fanny and Etetera and Teritera (Louis's Tahitian name). On a table in front of us were the lights — a half shell of cocoanut-oil with a twist of fibre swimming on top and a glass bottle with the same oil and a wick. In the side of the bottle a round hole had been ingeniously cut through the glass for the conven-ience of cigarette smokers. While we were sitting there, waiting for the dance, Tin Jack came in wearing the false nose and wig. At first there was a general feeling of alarm, but most of the people soon penetrated the disguise and were greatly amused. One old dignitary, however, never dis-covered the jest, and was very much frightened, asking me several times in a trembling voice if it was the white man's devil. Louis's little girl did not even shrink, but looked up into his face with smiling confidence.

The room was so dark that we could hardly see the dancers, so Louis and I concluded to make a few calls and go back to the ship. We had been asked to spend the night by some people as we passed their house in the afternoon, so we thought to go there first. However, the man who had been blown to Samoa caught us at the door and would have us go to his house first. By this time all the people knew my name and were calling me Fanny. When we thought we had done our duty by the mariner we said we must now visit the people who had asked us to sleep in their house; the man offered to guide us there, but instead took us to the house where Fani belonged. It was a very large house and the people seemed to be all asleep; but in a moment they were broad awake and in a state of lively excitement, with the exception of one very old man who remained lying in his bed and yawned drearily. Louis tried conversing in a mélange of Samoan and Tahitian, with appreciable success. We drank cocoanuts until we were '*paea*', and rose to go. A large fish was laid at our feet in a plaited basket, then taken up and carried to our boat. This was a handsome present, as fish is a great rarity. Fani's father followed me with an immense number of large sponges tied on a long pole. We were again haled away from our destination, this time by the boatman, who took us back to his house, waking, I fear, his sick wife, who, however, was all smiles. Pleaded '*paea*' and turned our faces toward the boat, having given up our first intention in despair.

On the road we passed the schoolhouse compound where a double row of people were singing and dancing. The men were squatted on their haunches on one side of the path, the women on the other; down the centre an oldish, very respectable-looking man, with the appearance of a deacon, directed the dance, a staff in his hand. We were received with shouts of welcome and a bench set out for us. I was envious of the big town drum, made of hollowed cocoanut wood and covered with shark skin, very like one I had already got from the Marquesas, and deputed the trader to buy it for me. With the arrival of Mr Henderson, who came sauntering down the road, the deacon heartened up to a sort of frenzy, suddenly bounding along the path and throwing his body and legs about with the most grotesque and mirth-provoking contortions. We sat here yet awhile, and at last tore ourselves away from the most charming low island we have yet seen, Fani's father still following with the sponges. I sent back, by the boat-man, a piece of print for Fani, sufficient to make a gown for her mother as well as herself. It was the correct thing to do from the island point of etiquette, but all the same a pity, for the less Fani covered her pretty brown body the better she looked.

7 May

Fani, her papa and her sister, first thing in the morning with a basket of green cocoanuts and three packets of dyed pandanus leaves. Fani at once possessed herself of one of Louis's hands, the sister the other, while the lovely 'Johnny Bull', who was on board almost as soon as they were, hovered about smiling, and when he saw a chance slipped an arm round Louis's neck. Johnny Bull was a tall lad of fifteen, and I was told a half-caste, though he did not look it. Louis, having been taken up by Fani, was considered quite one of the family. It is easy to see how the copra eaters came by their 'billets', and how decently whites must have behaved here, that this little creature should have come up to Louis in the dark as naturally as a child to its mother. The sisters stayed by him until the whistle sounded. They were thoroughly well-behaved, obedi-ent children, neither shy nor forward. No doubt Louis could have eaten copra from that day forth at the father's expense.

One of the beach-combers was wrecked on Starbuck Island, his ship the *Garston*; he lost all he possessed, and says he is passionately eager to get away and very sick of living on cocoanuts; and yet, when offered a chance to work his way home on the *Janet*, he asked anxiously if it were a 'soft job', refusing any other. Louis gave him the better part of a tin of tobacco, but he got very little good from it. The hands of the natives who had adopted him were stretched out on every side, and one cigarette was his sole portion.

Have gone to another station on the same island, a very bad landing, so Lloyd and I concluded to remain on the ship, but Louis, more venturesome, went on shore with Mr Hird. They were nearly pitched into the water as the boat struck on her side on the reef. The black boys all went, with the seas breaking over them, to shove her off. The town is described as most delightful; very neat, with one straight, sanded thoroughfare bordered by curbstones; the houses with verandas, some of the verandas with carved balustrades. The heat is very great. Louis sat on the sofa in the missionary's house, the boat's crew lying on the floor and being fed with dried clams strung on cocoanut-fibre sennit. At the same time they were interviewed by the missionary himself, a fine, bluff, rugged, grizzled Raratongan, universally respected. Two old men asked for the news, giving theirs in return, their latest being that Tahiti had been taken by the French;★ they added a rider that the French were 'humbug', which was refreshingly British. 'One white man he say Queen he dead?' queried one man anxiously. They were assured that it was the Queen of Germany, and not Victoria. 'Methought', said Louis, '*in petto*, it was perhaps Queen Anne.' They are all well up in the royal family, and most loyal subjects, the island flying the Union Jack. The only 'white man' in the settlement was a Chinaman, dying for curry-powder. It seemed impossible to get away without carrying half the settlement with us, and even after we thought they were all off, two young girls and a boy were discovered trying to stow away. We returned to the first landing yet again, but by that time I was sound asleep.

8 May

Sighted Penrhyn at five o'clock, but did not attempt to go in as it is an exceedingly dangerous passage, and the night was black, with heavy squalls. Lloyd and I had to leave our sleeping place on the after hatch and take refuge in the trade room where we slept on the floor. In the morning I went to look up my wet pillows and mats. Suddenly I heard

Penryn Island.

a shout: 'Mrs Stevenson, don't move!' I stopped short, hardly moving an eyelash, but curious to know the reason of this command. I soon found out; the captain threw up one corner of a large tarpaulin showing me the open hatch on the brink of which I was standing. On the last voyage a seaman was terribly injured by falling down the forehatch. He lay two hours insensible before he was reported missing and a search made.

9 May

We enter the lagoon very early in the morning; a most perilous passage, the way through the reef seeming but little wider than the ship itself; the captain calls it two ship widths. Our route, until we dropped anchor, was studded with 'horses' heads' as thick as raisins in a pudding. There would be a rock just awash on either side of us, a rock in front almost touching our bows, and a rock we had successfully passed just behind us. We were all greatly excited and filled with admiration for the beautiful way Captain Henry managed his ship. She would twist to the right, to the left, dash forward — now fast, now slow — like a performing horse doing its tricks. The native pilot was on the masthead nearly mad with anxiety. It was the first he had had to do with a steamer, and he was convinced that the *Janet* was on the point of destruction every moment. At last, quite worn out with such breathless excitement, we came safely to anchor in front of the village, a cluster of native houses gathered together on a narrow spit of land, or rather coral. A big wave, a short time ago, washed over the village from sea to sea. Our men are working hard getting out the boxes for the shell we are to take in, and the mates are making new boxes, hurrying as fast as their natures allow. There is quite a fleet of pearling boats hanging about. One has just come in filled with natives; the colours are enchanting: the opaline sea, the reds and blues of the men's clothing, running from the brightest to the darkest shades, the yellow boats wreathed with greenery, the lovely browns of the native skin, with the brilliant sun and the luminous shadows. Boys are already swimming out to the ship, resting on planks (bits of wreckage), their clothes, tied in a bundle and hanging over their heads, dependent from sticks. I can hear the voices of the girls and the clapping of their hands as they sing and dance on the beach. I see a man hurrying along a path, a little child with him and their black pig following like a terrier. Sometimes piggy stops a moment to smell or root at the foot of a palm, but always with a glance over his shoulder; if the distance seems growing too wide between himself and his family, he rushes after them, and for a moment or two trots soberly at his master's side.

After luncheon we went over to the village in one of the boats going for shell, landing at the white trader's house. From the first, I had been puzzled by a strange figure on the trader's veranda. When we were nearer I discovered it to be the figurehead of a wrecked ship, a very haughty lady in a magnificent costume. She held her head proudly in the air and had a fine, hooked nose. All about the trader's house were great piles of timber, and in one of the rooms a piano woefully out of tune, and other signs of the wreck of a big ship. It was a timber vessel, they told us, this last one, that went to pieces just outside the reef. Numbers of houses are being built of the boards by the more thrifty minded of the islanders. One of the sailors cast ashore still remains here, a gentle, soft-eyed youth from Edinburgh, now fairly on the way to become a beach-comber. Fortunate lad! His future is assured; no more hard work, no more nipping frosts and chilly winds; he will live and die in dreamland, beloved and honoured and tenderly cared for all the summer days of his life. He already speaks the native tongue, not only fluently, but in the genteelest native manner, raising and lowering his eyebrows in the most approved fashion as he whispers to the elderly dames matter that is no doubt better left untranslated.

When the figurehead came ashore people were terribly alarmed by the appearance of the 'white lady'. The children are still frightened into submission by threats of being handed over to her. The trader's wife is a Manihiki woman, very neat and well-mannered; we drank cocoanuts with her, and were introduced to the native missionary's daughter, an enormously large, fat girl of thirteen, but looking twenty. I believe her parents are from another island. Lloyd photographed the proud lady with a lot of children and girls grouped round her, the soft-eyed Scot familiarly leaning against her shoulder. The girls went through an elaborate affectation of terror and had to be caught and dragged to the place, whence, I believe, nothing could have dislodged them. After this photography was finished we wandered through the village, a large chattering crowd at our heels. This is the least prepossessing population I have seen since Mariki, and I am assured they are no better than they look. As we walked along I happened to pick up a pretty little shell from the beach; the missionary's fat daughter instantly gathered and pressed upon me four other shells, but as I held them in my hand living claws projected from inside and pinched me so that I cried out in alarm and threw them to the ground. Every one laughed, naturally, but an impudent young man picked up and offered me a worn aperculum, saying with a grin: 'Buy; one pearl.' 'I could not', I assured him with mock courtesy, 'deprive you of so valuable an ornament; tie it round your neck.' This feeble jest seemed to be understood and was greeted with shouts of laughter. The lad was cast down for a moment, and fell behind; pretty soon he came forward again, with a dog's bone. 'Buy,' he said; 'very good; twenty pounds.' 'I could not', I returned, 'take from you a weapon so suitable to your courage.' Of course I used pantomime as well as speech. The other young men, with shrieks of laughter, pretended to be terrified by his warlike appearance, and he shrank away to annoy me no further. Several men and women offered us very inferior pearls at the most preposterous prices, at which Tin Jack and I jeered them, when the pearls were hidden shamefacedly. They knew as well as we that their wares were worthless.

Penryn :—

Trader's verandah with figure-head from wreck

Lloyd and Louis planted their camera stand in the centre of the village, and walked about to look for good points of view. While they were away a serious-looking man delivered a lecture upon the apparatus, to the evident edification and wonder of the crowd. During his explanation he mimicked both Louis's and Lloyd's walk, showing how Lloyd carried the camera, while Louis walked about looking round him. I sat down on a log to wait, when immediately all the women and girls seated themselves on the ground, making me the centre of a half circle and gazing at me with hard, round eyes.

After the photography Louis and I went to call on the missionary. He and his wife were at home, evidently expecting us. His wife is enormously stout, with small features and an unpleasant expression; the man rather sensible and superior-looking. A number of women and the pilot who had brought us into the lagoon ranged themselves on the floor in front of us. One of the ladies, a plain body, seeming more intelligent than the rest, possessed a countenance capable of expressing more indignation than one would think possible. She wished to have our relationship explained to her. Louis and I were husband and wife; this statement was received with a cry of anger, but at the announcement that Lloyd was our son, she fairly howled; even Lloyd's name seemed objectionable. About mine there was a good deal of discussion, as they appeared to have heard it before. We drank cocoanuts under the disapproving eye of the intelligent lady, and, after receiving as a present a pearl-shell with a coral growth on its side from the missionary's wife, and another, somewhat battered, from his daughter, I gave, in return, the wreath from my hat and we departed.

Louis and Lloyd went back to the ship, but I remained, with Tin Jack, to see the church. All but three little girls were too lazy to show us the way; so, accompanied by the trio, we started on a broad path of loose, drifting coral sand. The church a good, substantial structure of white coral, with benches and Bible rests, but there was no attempt at decoration. The room was large enough to hold all the inhabitants of the village twice over. As in most of the other islands, being 'missionary' — religious — goes by waves of fashion. In Penrhyn, at any moment, the congregation may turn on the pastor and tell him he must leave instantly, as they are tired of being missionary. They have the 'week of jubilee', which means the whole island goes on a gigantic 'spree', when Penrhyn is not a pleasant, or hardly a safe, abiding-place. We stopped at the schoolhouse on the way back, a large, ill-smelling room, containing for furniture one table with pearl-shell disks let into the legs, standing on a dais. The only really neat house was the trader's, and he had a Manhikian wife.

The laws of Penrhyn, some of them very comical, are stringently enforced. There is no nonsense about 'remain within your houses' here, for, after nine o'clock, remain you must. Last night our cook was shut into a house where he was paying a visit, and was not allowed out until after the breakfast hour. There was also a rumour that Tin Jack, being seen after curfew, had to run, the police after him, to the house of the trader, where he remained until morning. Our sailors, to-day, somehow offended the natives and came running back to the ship pursued by a crowd. The children are much more prepossessing than their parents, some of them, especially the little girls, being quite pretty and well-behaved. It is much easier to restrain them and keep them within bounds than if they were white children in similar case. Every scrap of orange-peel thrown overboard was gathered up by them to be converted into ornaments. A bit of peel cut into the shape of a star, with a hole in the centre for the purpose, would be drawn over the buttons of their shirts and gowns, while long strings were worn hanging over the breast, or twined round the head and neck. The trader's little half-caste boy was clad in the tiniest imaginable pair of blue jeans, with a pink cotton shirt, and had little gold earrings in his ears.

Little girls singing — Penryn S.s.

10 May

None of our party cared to go on shore. I sent a chromo representing a 'domestic scene' to the trader's wife in return for her present of a coral-grown shell. The shell I afterward gave to the cook and another to the second steward, who, by this time, was almost insane with excitement and pleasure. We had a very busy day receiving shell and packing it in the wooden cases that are still being made on the forward deck. The black sailors work extraordinarily well and with perfect willingness and good nature. They make play of everything, and in spite of their small stature and slender, elegant figures, handle great weights with the utmost ease and dexterity. The little native boys work as hard as any in helping pack the shell. One little naked fellow of about ten, I was told, was deaf and dumb, but I should never have guessed it.

As soon as there was a movement on the ship the young girls came swimming out to us like a shoal of fish. The sea was dotted with the black heads over which they held their parcel of clothes in one hand to keep them dry, making their toilets on the lower rungs of the ship's ladder. One girl would stand at the foot of the ladder where she received the clothes of the newcomer; as the latter emerged dripping from the sea her garment was dexterously dropped over her head, so that she rose with the utmost decorum fully clad.

Louis soon had his particular following, some three or four little girls eight or ten years of age. They made him sit down and then sang to him. One of these children must have been the daughter of the indignant lady we met at the missionary's house, for her powers of expression were the same. She was, however, pleased to signify approval of Loia (Lloyd). If Louis attempted to leave these small sirens he was peremptorily ordered to resume his seat, and the singing redoubled in vigour. They had shrill voices and sang not badly. Louis bought a tin of 'lollies' from the trade room and regaled his little maids on that and plug tobacco. Oranges and biscuits were given to the people quite freely, and the leavings from our table were continu-ally passing about. The cook said the contents of the swill-pail were eaten clean, pumpkin rinds being a favourite morsel. Except for the 'lollies', the little girls generously divided with their friends, but the boys were more selfish. One little fellow who had secured a whole pumpkin rind ran about the deck with a wolfish terror, trying to find a hiding-place where he could devour his prize safe from the impor-tunities of his mates.

Tin Jack, without my knowledge (I should have stopped him had I known) donned the wig and beard and false nose; his appearance created a real panic. One girl was with difficulty restrained from jump-ing overboard from the high deck, and many were screaming and rushing about, their eyes starting with terror; Louis's little girls ran to him and me and clung to us. A fine, tall young woman kept up a bold front until Tin Jack took hold of her, when she slipped through his hands, a limp heap on the deck. I tried in vain to get near him to make him cease with his cruel jest, but he was running among the fright-ened crowd, and I could not make him hear me through the confu-sion and noise. The girl who tried to jump overboard collapsed among some bags on top of the shell, where, covering her face, she wept aloud. I climbed over to her and soothed her, and tried to explain that it was not the devil but only Tin Jack with a mask. The children were the first to recover from their terror, soon recognising Tin Jack, either from his voice, or his walk, or something that marked his individual-ity, for in the afternoon they returned to the ship, fetching other children, and boldly demanded that these, too, should be shown the foreign devil. All evil spirits, and there are many in Penrhyn, are called devils.

Speaking about the superstitions of Penrhyn, Mr Hird recalls the following grisly incident that occurred when he was stopping on the island. A man who was paralysed on one side had a convulsion which caused spasmodic contractions on the other side. One of the sick

man's family began at once to make a coffin. 'But the man's not dead,'
said Mr Hird. 'Oh yes,' was the reply; 'he's dead enough; it's the third
time he has done this, so we are going to bury him.' Mr Hird went to
the native missionary, but his remonstrances had no effect; he kept on
protesting until the last moment. 'Why look,' he said, 'the man's limbs
are quivering.' 'Oh that's only live flesh,' was the reply, and some one
fell to pommelling the poor wretch to quiet the 'live flesh'. The belief
was that the man's spirit had departed long before and a devil who
wished to use the body for his own convenience had been keeping the
flesh alive. Mr Hird thinks that the man was insensible when buried
and must soon have died.

At another time some natives had been 'waking' a corpse; tired
out, they all fell asleep except a single man who acted as 'watcher'. By
and by he, too, dropped off. The party were awakened by a great noise.
The watcher explained that he had been napping and suddenly
opened his eyes to behold the dead man sitting up. 'A corpse sitting
up just like this!' he exclaimed indignantly; 'but I was equal to him; I
ran at him and knocked him down, and now he's decently quiet again.'
And so he was, dead as a door-nail from the blow he had received.

Another thing Mr Hird saw in Penrhyn. A very excellent man, but
a strict disciplinarian, died and his family were sore troubled by the
appearance of his ghost. They had suffered enough from his severity
during his lifetime, and were terrified lest his spirit had returned to
keep them up to the standard he had marked out for them. The day
after the apparition was seen, the grave was opened, the body taken
out, and the hole deepened till they came to water; the corpse was
then turned over in the coffin and reburied face down.

At about five o'clock we weighed anchor and went through the
exciting ordeal of the passage out of the lagoon, taking with us as passengers to Manihiki a woman and her two children. After we were
quite away, outside the lagoon, a boat came after us with a quantity of
timber from the wreck; this extra and unexpected work of taking the

timber on board and stowing it away, instead of being received with grumbling by our black boys, was taken as gleefully as though it were a pleasant game of their own choosing.

The passengers slept on the after hatch with us. The baby cried in the night, and the mother quieted it by clapping her hands, yawning, meanwhile, with a great noise like the snarling of a wild beast; consequently I did not sleep well. For the first time the wind is aft and the ship very airless and close.

11 May

The captain's eyes, which have been dreadfully inflamed, are much better, thanks to an eye lotion from Swan, the chemist at Fiji, that we had in our medicine-chest.

In the evening, about nine, we made Manihiki. Mr Henderson burned a blue light which was answered by bonfires on shore. We did not anchor, but lay off and on, as we were only to stay long enough to land our passengers. Louis wished to go on shore with the boat, but as it did not get off until ten he gave it up and went to bed. I made up a little parcel for him to send to Fani, and Mr Hird carried it to her, a few sweeties carefully folded up in a Japanese paper napkin and tied with a bright-green ribbon. The child was in bed and asleep, but waked to receive her parcel which she resolutely declined to open until the next day, though earnestly persuaded by the whole family to let them have a peep inside. She appealed to Mr Hird, who upheld her decision, so she returned to her mat and fell asleep holding her present in her hands.

I am trying to paint a small portrait of Tin Jack, who is a beautiful creature, but during the reluctant moments he poses he sits with his back toward me, his eye fixed on the clock, counting the minutes until his release. We took from the island a man, woman, and boy for Suwarrow, our next stopping-place. Mr Hird had a singular dream, or rather vision, of the white trader in Suwarrow lying dead and ready for burial. He was so impressed by this that he took note of the time and feels very anxious.

13 May

I awoke at six, after a night's struggle with my mats, which the wind nearly wrested from me several times, to find we are just off Suwarrow. At breakfast Captain Henry presented me with a gorgeous hibiscus flower and Mr Henderson laid beside my plate a couple of bananas and a vi-apple, products of the island. At present there are only six people living on Suwarrow; our three passengers, counting the boy, will make nine.

I went on deck to look at the island and was told that the flag was at half-mast. Sure enough, the trader was dead; the date of his death tallied with that of Mr Hird's vision. The poor fellow was most anxious to be relieved the last time the ship was here, wherefore one of the native passengers was brought to take his place. A neat white paling fence enclosed the grave. I asked from what disease he died. 'Sickness in here,' was the answer, indicating the liver; 'a long time he no stand up; all the time lie down. Pain — cry out — cry out — then die.'

Suwarrow and its attendant isles have been planted in cocoanuts by Mr Henderson. A few pandanus are here and there and more varieties of small weeds than is usual in low islands. There is, also, a great deal of fine, feathery grass, worthless, unfortunately, for feeding animals. Mr Henderson tried goats upon it, and sheep, also, I believe; they ate the grass greedily but did not thrive, and soon dwindled and died. It was found, on examination, that the grass did not digest but remained in balls in the intestines. The cocoanuts, though most of them were planted eight years ago, do not bear very heavily; Mr Henderson thinks they were not planted deep enough. He says they should be planted four feet under the soil, the sprouts being about five feet high. Bananas planted in imported earth are growing well, and some have taken kindly to the native soil; also chilli peppers from the high islands. Vi-trees are in full bearing, the hibiscus is gaudy with blossoms, and cotton-plants, not indigenous, but now become wild, flourish luxuriantly.

Suwarrow at some former period must have been a thriving and important settlement. One has the feeling that stirring events have happened here and that its history should be wild and romantic. At present it is very like the desert stronghold of a pirate. The pier is a very fine one and must have cost much money and labour; a number of houses are clustered near it, giving at first sight the impression of a village; there are beacons to guide the mariner and a 'lookout' on the opposite side of the island. Turtles are caught occasionally, and large crabs and excellent fish. There are also birds, very good eating, and in the season innumerable eggs of a fine flavour may be gathered. One bird, no larger than a dove, lays an egg as big as a hen's, out of all pro-portion to her size.

I first walked over to the weather side; here I found it delight-fully cool, but the tide was high, forcing me to the shingle, so I returned, marking on the way a fine, clear pool where I mean to have a bath to-morrow. The room where I am writing looks as though it were meant for a church or a schoolhouse; but of course that is only conjecture. It is a large room, long and narrow, with double doors at each side, a single door at one end, and four unglazed windows. The windows are protected by foot-wide slats arranged to move up and down like Venetian blinds; both doors and slats are painted green. The roof, open to the peak, is neatly thatched with either pandanus or cocoanut leaves, I am not sure which. A table, originally very sturdy, but now fallen into the rickets, holds the dead man's books: 'Chetwynd Calverly' by W. Harrison Ainsworth, 'The Mystery of Orcival' by Gaboriau, and an advertisement book about next of kin. Behind the table is a cotton-gin, the 'Magnolia', with a picture of the flower indifferently well done on its front. I sat awhile on one of the two wooden benches that help furnish the room and studied the walls, over which are scrawled names: Etelea, Mitemago, Saviti, Patawe, Polohiu, Atolioinine, Salhisi, Kari, Fuehau, Laku, Mitima, Paopave, Munokoa, and many others.

In another large house of a single room, roofed with corrugated iron, I found all sorts of treasure-trove from vessels that had been wrecked on Suwarrow. Piled up in one end of the house are ship's blocks, oakum, strange, antiquated firearms, iron parts of a ship, and the two stairs of her companionway. There is a single oar, and a tool-chest with rope handles at either end, the word SWEDEN on it, and the top covered with canvas; an iron gate, two steering-wheels, a winch, a copper blubber dipper green with verdigris, the handle of wood and iron; two life-preservers, one marked *Levi Stevens*; small, glass-bottomed boxes for searching the bottom of the sea, wheels, hatch-covers, and I know not what. At the other end of the room a ladder leads up to a loft, where sieves for guano, a harpoon, a double-handed saw, and iron shell baskets are heaped together. Two immense iron tanks, painted red, stand at either side of the seaward doors.

Next to this house came the 'office', with a little cubby partitioned off one side. I looked through the pigeonholes of the cubby and found a packet of thin sheets of tortoise-shell and a large parcel of a native woman's hair. Mildewed maps hang on the walls, the ceiling is adorned with ten rusty cutlasses, old ledgers lie about, and a bag of cotton lies on the floor as though it had just been dropped there. On one of the sides of the room is a broad, white band with painted black letters 'PEERLESS wrecked on Suwarrow Island'. In one corner stands a box of bits of old iron which are put in with cocoanuts when they are planted. It is called 'cocoanut manure'. This reminds me that the Paumotuans plant with their cocoanuts a rusty nail and a ship's biscuit. In the outer room sixteen decaying muskets are ranged in a rack. Shelves are filled with all sorts of tools, nails, axes, bush knives, tins of sardines and salmon, and a quantity of mouldy shoes in children's sizes only; among the shoes were a toy chest of drawers and a box of moulting feathers.

Passing another building containing miscellaneous wreckage, blue and white china among the rest, I came to the manager's house, a large, wooden-floored structure with a thatched roof. Here I found a native man at work on accounts, his old dog at his feet, which were wrapped up in the Union Jack to keep them warm. This room was evidently designed by a sailor and gave one quite the feeling of being on board ship. Instead of windows there were port-holes, three on either side, with a couple flanking the front door. Covers, painted black to imitate iron, could be screwed over the ports like deadlights on shipboard. The doors, one in either end, opened in two parts, being divided across the middle. The furniture consisted of two bedsteads of native wood with cocoa sennit laced across them to serve for mattresses. A couple of bunches of bananas hung from the roof. Against the wall hung the death certificate of the dead man, which, in such cases, must be the only proof that the death was due to natural causes, and not a crime. I copied the certificate.

> *Samuli lee aho 2 ...*
> *he motu nai mate he malu va he tau*
> *fro ia gauali 2 1889 Ka Papu*
> *Ko Maro tolu ne ha nie ne tamu*
> *Ka Patiti ma miti San ma*
> *J ketiti ma Paemani Koe tau wine*
> *Kwenia kia mounina kelie iki lagi ke*
> *he tan ban nei kua hobooko kiai a tautala*
> *June ati 2—1890*

Next comes 'government house', as Louis calls it, neatly thatched, the floors of wood, and separated into two rooms by panelled wood from a wreck; the rooms are connected by a wide, open doorway, the arched top and sides edged with brass. In one room is a table with a Bible and other books lying on it, a home-made sofa covered with a mat; two corner shelves, spread with newspapers cut in points where they hang over, are filled with miscellaneous books; chests, a compass-box, and a water-monkey with its neck gone stand about. On the walls are some rather pretty engravings, a few framed and one glazed. On each side of the house are small, square windows protected by solid wooden shutters that drop down when not upheld by a stick. The front and back doors are strong and divided across the middle. In the back room are two home-made bedsteads, sennit crossed, one with a mosquito curtain. Chests are on the floor, mats lie about, and a roll of fine mats is lashed to the ceiling. In front of the house, the gable end, are two large, rusty, iron boilers such as are used on ships. Inside the compound, which is neatly fenced with whitewashed palings, are two small, mounted cannon with a couple of vi-trees growing beside them. Returning to what I call the church, I passed a tool house, a large room filled with rusting tools. Two small casks of fresh water lie waiting there in case a boat should come ashore in distress for water. There is also an immense cistern sunk in the ground, filled with rain-water caught on the iron roofs, but that, I believe, is kept locked.

Leaving the dog that boarded us at Auckland, and some cats, we departed from the most romantic island in the world, regretting that to us its history must always remain a mystery unsolved.

16 May

Arrived at Danger Island. Boats put out to inform Mr Henderson that, despite all their promises when we were here before, there is no copra ready, it being the season when the natives collect subscriptions for the church and hold the 'Me' meeting. 'No tobacco,' says Mr Henderson with malicious glee as he orders the people off the ship. To my joy he says to the captain: 'Can you make Nassau by night!' The captain can;

and we arrive the same night and lie off and on until morning. We give Nassau a blue light, and the inhabitants respond with a bonfire, keeping it blazing all night, apparently afraid if they let it go out we may steam away.

17 May

Nassau is a small high-low island enclosing a lagoon which has now dwindled to a pond. It is triangular in shape and roughly measures five miles round. We could see that the ground rose up from the beach at a considerable slope, and between the ti-trees I could make out that grass was growing. With a glass I could distinguish a breadfruit tree. Nassau has no anchorage and the landing was thought to be too dangerous for me to attempt, so, to my great disappointment, the men went without me; from the description they gave when they returned, and from the outside view, it must be the loveliest of all the high-low islands. There are many pigs and fowls, and all the high-island fruits flourish exceedingly; turtle abound, both the green turtle beloved of aldermen and the turtle that produces the shell of commerce. The owner of the island had not visited the place for two years, so the few people living there felt as though they had been marooned. They sent two pigs on board, and offered Mr Hird a large piece of tortoise-shell which he refused because of its value. There were some forty boxes of copra ready for sale, but, as the sea was high and the landing bad, Mr Hird did not care to take it. Mr Henderson, however, gave them what 'trade' they wanted, some fifteen dollars' worth, as a present.

When Louis came back he gave me the following account of his visit, starting from the very beginning:

'First thing in the morning we saw the whole population gathered on the beach. As we came nearer in and lowered a boat it was a strange thing to see the two women dancing like jumping-jacks for joy. All three men came down to the edge of the reef. H. signed to them from the bridge to jump in, and swim, which two of them, Joe and Jim, did, the boat meeting them half way. We could see them scramble in solemnly and shake hands with Johnny, who was at the steer oar, and sit down. They had a good many old friends on board, Joe especially, and it was a treat to see the absurd creature dance up to them for all the world like a clown in a pantomime. A little later, seeing Lloyd come out from under a blanket where he had been changing plates in the camera, he made us all nearly die laughing with his pantomime of terror. He called everybody "old man"; and was always either laughing himself or the cause of laughter in others. He said they had no fish; "got no canoe," he said; "why not make one," asked one of us; "Too much wo'k!" cried Joe with infinite gusto. He is very strong, and in reality most industrious, only he is simply marooned and means to do nothing needless. After breakfast we go ashore. The third man and a dog met us on the reef; and singular thing, the dog is afraid of us. At the house we are introduced to Mrs Joe, Mrs Jim and the five children, the whole party like crazy folk, dancing and clapping their hands and laughing for mere excitement. On into the island, a garden-like place, with limes, bananas, and figs growing, and the ground in many places carpeted with turf. Not in all, however, and as I had bare feet, and the morning was hot, I presently turned back and arrived alone at the settlement. Mrs Joe was out waiting for me with a green cocoanut; while I was drinking she tried to abstract my ring. Failing in this she led me into a shed where Mrs Jim was, piled up pillows at my back, supported me in her arms and proceeded to feed me like an infant with cocoanut pudding. Mrs Jim, meanwhile, patted and smoothed me, and both at the pitch of their excited voices plied me with questions as to my age, country, family, wife and business. When they heard my wife was on board, they cried out with regret that she had not come; and Mrs Joe intimated that she was dying to go on board to see her but lacked clothes. (Both were quite well dressed, Mrs Joe a comely fellow, in blue, Mrs Jim in red.) They began at once to build up a heap of presents for the *fafine* (lady). In the meanwhile, or concurrently, they were all through my pockets and robbed me of all I

111

possessed; all my money, tobacco, matches, and my pocket handkerchief; some capsules I saved, telling them they contained poison, and (more fortunate than the rest) my cap. They were perfectly good natured when refused anything, but returned again to the assault like flies. Mrs Jim offered to give me her baby in exchange for Lloyd, which I accepted. When the party arrived they were all subjected to similar pillage; though, being so many, scarcely to the same endearments. (I was simply petted, smoothed, caressed, and fed like a pet animal.) The scene was one of the wildest excitement and I am sure they all had headaches. All came down to the reef to see us off; Joe and Jim were to take us out; the ladies stood a little back up to their knees, and when the boat was launched, I saw Mrs Joe make a sudden plunge under her skirts, and next moment her gaudy *lava-lava* was flying in the air for a signal of farewell. When a native woman dons a civilised garment she still retains her native garment, the *lava-lava* twisted round her body. Once we were clear of the breakers under the able pilotage of Joe, "this is very beastiness" said he severely, to one of our black boys who volunteered advice. Jim and he stood upon the thwarts, "good-bye, old man", heels up, head down, and next moment they were pushing for the shore.'

19 May

Quiros (the Jennings) in the morning. After Nassau it seems commonplace and tamely prosperous. We walked across to the lagoon which is very large and only slightly brackish. Lloyd and Tin Jack took a swim, and I went back to the women. After drinking many cocoanuts we returned to the ship.

20 May

Mrs Jennings and her sister-in-law, with a singing boat's crew Samoan fashion, visited us. Unfortunately, one of the ladies became seasick, which cut their visit short.

Girl in Tokelau Islands.

21 May

Fakaafo, of the Tokalau group. Louis and I went on shore very early in the morning. There was a big swell and all our boatmen had different views at the same moment, the consequence being that we broached to and were nearly swamped. I got drenched from head to foot and felt very cold. We walked about the village and were taken to the house of the King. The Queen spread a mat on the ground for us and we sat down beside her; she was holding a precocious little baby in her arms, her grandchild, I presume, for she looked quite an old woman. The King came to the opening of the hut and, thrusting out his head and shoulders, shook hands with us and tried to converse. Cocoanuts were offered us, but I felt too chilly for that refreshment. It seemed a languid place; the very children soon tired of following us.

As I felt symptoms of rheumatism from the wetting I had got, I hunted up the trader, a pallid Portuguese, and asked if his wife could lend me a gown. He said if we crossed the island we would find a board house, belonging to him, where his wife would give me a native dress. As we drew near the place several handsome, smiling women joined us; we all sat down on the veranda and waited for the trader, who was not far behind us, and I was soon clad in comfortable dry clothes. We refused cocoanuts but accepted brandy and water. I gave the trader's wife the wreath from my head and a gold ring, after which we came back to the ship, very nearly upsetting our boat in the surf. I had with me a number of plain gold wedding rings; I always wore a few that I might take them from my own hand to offer as presents.

In the afternoon the trader's wife sent me a present of a hat. The trader used the most puzzling English possible; in passing Lloyd's room he caught sight of a guitar. 'Who that music?' he asked. When told, he asked to have the guitar put in his hands and demanded that Lloyd be sent for. In the meantime he examined the instrument and

found two broken strings. When Lloyd came the trader said he wanted two fine guitar strings. Not having too many, Lloyd was loath to
part with the strings, but the man was so bent on having them that
the box of strings was sent for. On Lloyd asking the man about his
own guitar, to our surprise he said he had none at all, and yet he
went on choosing out strings with the utmost excitement. 'Really,'
said Lloyd, 'I can't let you have *all* those; I will give you this lot but
no more; and I don't see what you want with them if you have no
guitar'; apparently, he wanted them to 'play with'. Then it occurred
to us that he might have some other sort of instrument on which
guitar strings could be used; but no, he said he had no sort of instrument whatever. At last, after great perplexity and wild endeavours to
find out what he would be at, Lloyd suddenly, as if by inspiration,
asked: 'Do you want to buy *this* guitar?' That was the mystery. As we
had only one guitar we could not give it to him, so the poor fellow
sadly returned both strings and instrument.

22 May

We celebrated the anniversary of our marriage in front of the trade
room. (We forgot it on the nineteenth, which was the real anniversary, but thought there would be no harm in a belated celebration.)
Champagne was set to cool in wet towels, and at about four we gathered together at the appointed place, each person to do what he
could for the amusement of the others. Tin Jack gave a reading from
Shakespeare, standing in a pulpit that was part of our cargo. Mr Hird
sang 'Afton Water' charmingly with much grace and feeling. Lloyd
sang, and Louis, taking what he saw before him as a text (it was an
advertisement of St Jacob's oil), mounted the pulpit and delivered
a sermon.

Sight land, Atafu, where I hope to get Tokalau buckets, which are
very useful in place of portmanteaus.

23 May

Mr Henderson went ashore very early this morning, at Atafu. He boasts that he ate three chicken legs as well as half a breast and quantities of taro. As I have a little rheumatism from wearing my wet clothes so long at Fakaafo, and it rains, I decided to stay on board and take a dose of salicylate. Later the sun comes out; my rheumatism flies before the salicylate, but too late; Louis has gone in the boat and there is no other for me. I spend a dreary time watching the people with an opera-glass. The wind occasionally brings the sound of singing to my ears. Then the opera-glass gives me a headache, and I try reading, first 'Olla Podrida', which I cannot manage, and afterward the South Pacific Directory,★ with which I succeed better. The boat comes back at dinner time, everybody talking at once about the curious experiences they have had.

24 May

To my regret I did not feel well enough to go on shore. A trader, the brother of the man who wished to buy the guitar, told me his wife was coming to see me and introduced his son, a fine, little, brown fellow of about eleven. Mr Hird informed me that he is quite a travelled youth. He, himself, told me he had been to Sydney, and when I asked, 'To San Francisco?' he replied: 'No, but I have been to Frisco.' This child was on board a schooner when she was nearly destroyed by fire, and also when she was in imminent danger of being shipwrecked. The fire was an incendiary act. One of the sailors had several times been very impudent to the captain of the schooner and was regarded as a dangerous character. He, one day, in a fit of rage, attacked the cook with a knife and nearly murdered him. The captain, who seemed a pitiful fellow, was frightened at the thought of putting the man in irons and bungled to such an extent with the handcuffs that the culprit, himself, obligingly put them on. The supercargo asked that the culprit be confined in the cabin next his, but the captain was alarmed at the idea of having him so near. It was not long before he managed to get loose, set the ship on fire, and jump overboard. A few hours after the fire they were nearly driven on a rock before a heavy squall. When they were so close that they could almost have jumped on the rock, the vessel stopped dead and remained perfectly quiet. The rock had taken the wind out of her sails, and the backwash held them off.

By and by the trader's wife and her friend, a handsome woman with a haughty, high-bred expression, came on board. With a simplicity that was almost cynical, the trader explained that at one time there had been a great many German sailors about the islands, so, as his wife had yellow hair, he just took it for granted that she was a German half-caste. She certainly did look very like a sentimental German governess, with her yellow hair and blinking eyes, but I perceived at once that whatever else she might be, she was certainly an albino. She brought me a basket and a small Tokalau bucket. In return I gave her a gold ring which she replaced with three tortoise-shell rings and a thicker one ingeniously tied in a true-lovers' knot. I gave the friend a wreath and received a hat as an exchange present. These people are desperate flatterers; we call this 'The Isle of Flatterers'. A native met Mr Henderson in Louis's hearing 'You *handsome* man!' he cried, his voice thrilling with emotion as he eagerly studied Mr Henderson's face. 'You *good* woman!' said Mrs Trader to me continually, her eyes melting into mine with admiration and affection as she tenderly embraced me. I asked for a lock of her beautiful hair, which, after asking permission of her husband, she gave me; I pinned it in my diary and she wrote under it, '*Fani mai feleni*' (Fanny, my friend) and her own name, 'Amalaisa'; then she fanned me, and caressed me, and flattered me, and finally, getting hold of my photograph, pressed it to her bosom and face, saying: 'All same you.' I wonder if they really do 'rub noses' anywhere! All I have seen is a pressing together of the two faces with a slight inspiration through the nostrils. While I was sitting with

Amalaisa and her friend, holding a hand of each, I became aware that a very ragged but superior-looking young native man had joined our party. 'That boy, King,' whispered Amalaisa, so I shook hands with his majesty and called Louis to be introduced. The last words of royalty were 'You *good* woman', delivered in most seductive tones.

Most of these natives are suffering from a skin disease which covers them with whitish scales and is contagious. I trust we have not all caught it. The scaliest boy in the island has been walking about all day with his arm round Louis's waist, patting and smoothing down his hands with a purring: 'You *good papalagi*' (foreigner).

When it came time to part Amalaisa gave me another hat and put more sentimental expression into her *tofa* (farewell) than one would think possible. We shook hands, Amalaisa suddenly kissed me and was gone in a flash.

Louis has written here the following account of his adventures in Atafu: 'Immediately on landing I was surrounded by boys more or less scaly; the little girls fled before us in a squadron, looking coquettishly back; if they came too near the boys cast handfuls of stones upon the ground by way of a hint. "You *Peletania*?" (British) they asked, one after another and again and again, always receiving my affirmative with "*Peletania — Aloha!*" taken in an indrawn breath. One boy walked all the way, caressing me. "You good *papalagi*," he cried at intervals. I suppose I had fifty of our escort. Presently we found some twelve stalwart dames sitting on a wall. They made me sit by them, sent for cocoanuts, caressed me with the most extraordinary fervour of admiration, and breathed, from time to time, in an emotional chorus: "*Peletania — Aloha!*" Although not accustomed to the offer of gallantry based upon political considerations, I suspected something was intended; and presently one of the boys was called by the ladies and stood forth as an interpreter. "All these girls he laugh at you" (these ladies smile upon you is what he meant). "You flatter me," said I. The disappointment caused by this miscarriage was inconceivable. A little later one of the boys asked me: "You want wife?" "I got wife on board," I said. "Wife on board," cried he with unmistakable scorn, "no good!" The new-comers laid traps for me as to my nativity. I could hear them asking and hearing what I claimed to be; and then they would come up and ask in a fine, offhand manner: "You Melican?" (American). Certainly we have no possession more loyal than Atafu. Another specimen of Atafu English (they all speak some) is this: I had given a boy a stick of tobacco; another asked for one. "No," I said, "all done." "Eet ees feen-ished," said the boy who had the stick; but the boy who had it not regarded me with a playful smile. "You go hell! no done."

'I saw the cure for scaly itch, invented by old Jennings of Olesenga — a barrel sunk in the earth where they are smoked with sulphur. The girl who was undergoing treatment was the most European little soul — skin of a fair brown, eyes a light hazel, hair golden chestnut. Strange that folk of a low island should so incline to fairness. Amalaisa first claimed me as "*mai feleni*"; hearing of my wife, she transferred her allegiance and began to write her love-letters; the factitious nature of this sentiment (*me judice*) didn't prevent its being an immense success.'

27 May

We expect to make Funafuti, the first of the Ellices, by daybreak; at nine o'clock there was no sign of the island. 'Bad steering,' growled the captain. 'We've run past it, and now we have to turn round and run back.' At about two we anchor in the lagoon, and almost imme-diately the traders are aboard, two wretched-looking objects. One was a half-caste from some other island, with elephantiasis, very bad, in both legs. There were recent scarifications as though he had been attempting the Samoan plan of tapping. The other trader was not thin but the most bloodless creature I ever saw; his face, hands, legs, and feet were without sunburn, smooth, and of a curious transparent texture like wax. It seemed an over-exertion to raise his large, heavy eyes when he spoke to us. The two men had pulled the boat in which they came. The pallid one panted and held both hands over his heart as though suffering acutely. I asked him if he liked the island. 'Not at all,' he answered and went on to describe the people; he said he could not keep chickens, ducks, or pigs; no one could, for their neighbours, jealous that another should have what they had not, would stone the creatures to death. The same with the planting of fruit-trees; the soil was good, and there were a few breadfruits and bananas, but any attempt to grow more is frustrated. The young trees are torn up and even the old ones are occasionally broken and nearly destroyed. Before the great earthquake in Java★ there were plenty of good fish fit for eating. The half-caste can remember when a poisonous fish was a thing unknown; now all outside the reef are poisonous, and many inside. The worst of it is that a fish, to-day innocuous, may to-morrow become deadly. Turtle do not come to the islands at all; so there is no food besides copra except what chance vessels may bring. I fear this poor man is simply dying of starvation. A steward on board the missionary ship, who knew a little about medicine, had told him that he only needed iron and good food. 'They gave me a bottle of iron,' he said, 'and I got better on that, or I'd be dead by now, but how could I get the nourishing food?' I suggested his leaving the island, but the loyal soul replied that, though he knew he could save his life by doing so, he would not desert his native wife and children.

The half-caste told us several stories that sickened us to hear and yet were most interesting. In 1886 he was away from Funafuti. During his absence two American vessels, under the Peruvian flag, came to the island and distributed presents right and left to all who came to receive them. Naturally, the people were delighted, and when it was proposed that as many as liked should go to Peru to be educated by these kind people, they flocked on board in crowds. The King, anxious that as many as possible should participate in this good fortune, blew his horn, which is the royal summons. On the return of the half-caste two thirds of the population had gone, and the King was in the very act of blowing his horn again to gather in his remaining subjects, now reduced to the very young and the very old. It is needless to add that the vessels were slavers, and the entrapped islanders were never seen again.

Throughout the islands (Funafuti and her chicks, one might call them) there are not now above one hundred and fifty inhabitants all together. They have a bad name — are said to be a dirty, rough, dishonest lot; dishonest, that is, as far as cheating goes, but they do not steal. No wonder they are dishonest, for they learned in a good school. Here is another tale of the half-caste. Mata, of Samoa, come to buy copra; there was none but what had been engaged by another vessel, the price being one and a quarter cents. 'I'll give you two,' said Mata promptly, which offer was as promptly accepted. But Mata's scales weighed nothing higher than one hundred and four pounds; so, though he paid two cents, he left with tons for which he paid nothing.

Resterau, the pallid trader, had sailed with both 'Bully Hayes' and 'Bully Pease', of whose names I am quite sick and hope I'll never hear them again (two somewhat picturesque desperadoes of the South Seas, now dead fortunately for the rest of the world). Louis and I went with Mr Henderson over to the island, where we met the wives and children of the traders, handsome, healthy, and with excellent manners; two young girls were quite beautiful. Resterau's wife had but one eye and was a plain, kindly old body.

After a little, Louis and I strolled across the island, becoming more and more amazed by what we saw. Everything that one naturally expects to find on a low island is here reversed. To begin with, the fact of the poisonous fish being outside the reef is contrary to what one has reason to expect. The soil is very rich for a low island, with ferns and many shrubs and flowering plants growing. We saw a little taro and quite a large patch, considering, of bananas. There was much marsh and green stagnant pools, and the air was heavy with a hothouse smell. The island seemed unusually wide, but what was our astonishment when we pushed through the bushes and trees to find ourselves not on the sea beach, as we had expected, but on the margin of a large lagoon emptied of its waters almost entirely by the low tide. The lagoon was everywhere enclosed, but the traders told us there was a blow-hole outlet into which the natives had thrown piles of coral hoping to block it up. A little girl had once fallen into the lagoon when the tide was turning; three days after her body was found far out at sea. It was then that the blow-hole, where she had been sucked through, was discovered. Off on one side there seemed to be an opening by which we hoped to reach the beach. We crossed a bit of mangrove swamp, climbed over loose piled-up shingle that rang with a metallic sound very unlike coral, and at last reached the beach. I wandered away from Louis, gathering shells, but was recalled by a wild shout. I found Louis bending over a piece of the outer reef that he had broken off. From the face of both fractures innumerable worms were hanging like a sort of dreadful, thick fringe. The worms looked exactly like slender earthworms, more or less bleached, though some were quite earthworm colour. They lengthened out and contracted again until I felt quite sick and had to fly from the sight. Afterward Louis broke other pieces of rock; one kind always contained worms; another kind, lighter in colour and firmer in texture, contained much fewer worms, also empty holes in the process of closing up; still others were close and hard and white, like marble. I got a good many shells, and after a fruitless search for some other way across the island than round the inland lagoon, I gave it up and we retraced our footsteps; that is, for a certain time, when we became lost, or as Louis indignantly put it: 'Not lost at all; we only could not find our way.'

The two traders dined with us, and I was glad to see that the bloodless man ate a large double helping of meat. Lloyd, fortunately, thought of giving him some stout and asked Mr Henderson if the man were the sort to give stout to; Mr Henderson thought it a good thing to do, and Louis explained to the trader that it was given him as medicine, not as a beverage to be handed round to others, asking him to promise that he would drink it all himself. He readily enough gave the promise but said in that case Mr Henderson would have to smuggle it over to him, as he must drink it in secret. I also gave him a large and small bottle of iron, all that we had, telling him when that was done to put nails in his drinking water. I went to bed early, very tired, but was driven below by repeated squalls, and slept on the saloon floor.

Not long ago the *George Noble* called at this island, her destination being the island of Piru (pronounced Peru). The natives who were on board heard the word and fled incontinently, nor could they be persuaded to go back; the dread word 'Peru' was enough.

28 May

Left Funafuti early this morning. After every one was off, Lloyd photographed the ship's company to the delight of the black boys, who posed themselves with great dramatic effect.

Arrived at Natau after dark. Mr Hird called to us that there was another vessel close at hand. We rushed on deck and saw a schooner putting up a light. In a few moments the mate was on board the *Janet*. There is no landing at this island, and an unusually heavy swell will make a big surf in the morning. The only one of the Ellices I have as yet seen gave me such an unpleasant impression that I shall not be disappointed if I cannot go ashore.

29 May

Early this morning we anchor near the schooner. She is painted white and looks just like the *Equator*. (We made a former cruise, our second, in the *Equator*, a little trading schooner.) Louis says that every time he looks at her he expects to see ourselves. There seems to be great excitement aboard the little vessel; canoes filled with people are going to and fro, continually, between her and the shore. Only one canoe has as yet come near us; it was filled with women who paddled about the ship, following my movements; one of the women handsome, and the others by no means plain. The canoe was very long, tapering off into a beautiful fish's tail, something like this: and was ornamented at both ends with mother-of-pearl let into the wood in bands and patterns. The people here wear *ridis*, not so good as the Gilberts, however. The *ridis* are too full, too much like ballet-dancers' skirts, though the colour is pleasantly gay, a mixture of dull red, blackish maroon, and faded yellow. The surf, as I expected, was too high for us to get on shore dry, so we did not attempt it.

In the afternoon the schooner (of 80-ton burden) began to fill up with natives; we were told that she was going to take a party of one hundred and eighty people on an excursion round the group, for which a lump sum of twenty-five tons of copra was paid. The decks of the little vessel were closely packed with laughing, chattering people; the hum of their voices came to us like the sound of bees. It was just so, not very long ago, that slave-ships used to carry them away. 'What a haul that would be for labour!' remarked Tin Jack when he first caught sight of them.

There is a small enclosed lagoon in this island. Tin Jack, while on shore, broke off some of the reef coral and found it full of the same living worms as Louis discovered before on the other island, only here there were two varieties; one like a pallid earthworm and the other something like a small centipede. Tin Jack brought me a wreath of gardenias, and a spray of scarlet leaves. Mr Hird brought me a bunch of jack-fruit leaves to polish my Tokalau buckets with. Some young banana plants were sent on board, I suppose for friends on another island. (This must have been a high-low island, though in many atolls the earth is brought in schooner loads in which trees and flowers flourish.) Tin Jack was strongly tempted to stop here as is his custom at most islands. The trader at Natau was a rather dreadful-looking person, apparently afflicted with leprosy. He shook hands with me, to my dismay, for his fingers were dropping off. 'I think I've got some native disease,' said the poor fellow as he held out his hand.

30 May

Still a heavy swell and the surf too strong for boats to venture in. A great crowd of natives on shore and many canoes drawn up on the beach. Pretty soon the canoes swarmed about the ship and we were overrun with eager venders of merchandise, mats, chickens, and eggs. One man followed me about beseeching me to buy a silver half dollar. 'You want buy money?' said he. 'How much tobac you give?' I bought one mat for ten sticks of tobacco, one for a comb, and one for a pattern of calico. I saw Mr Henderson, in the midst of the harassing business of weighing copra, stop and paint a broad mark, with violet ink, down the breast of a fine young lad who swaggered about afterward with a conscious air of superiority.

For a long time we saw no women, but at last a canoe containing two, pretty and young, was seen paddling wildly up and down beside the ship; the women were shouting for a sight of the '*Beretani fafine*' (white woman). I was called, and showed myself, whereupon they threw up their hands and shouted with excitement. Soon after this I met on the companion stairs the captain, half dragging, half persuading one of the young women I had seen in the canoe to come down to the saloon. Naturally she did not understand that he was only trying to bring her to me. At the sight of me she gave a cry and, breaking loose from the captain, flung herself upon me and clung to me like a frightened child. I could feel her heart beating against my breast and she was trembling from head to foot. As she held me she bent down, for she was taller than I, and smiled in my face. Plainer than words her smile said: 'You are a woman, too; I can trust you; you will protect me,

will you not?' I put my arm round her and talked to her in English
and tried to soothe her fears. She understood my English as well as I
her smiles. I brought her into the saloon and Louis gave her sweetmeats; she turned to me with a gesture that asked if they were safe to
eat. She had already a bit of ship's biscuit tightly clinched in her hand,
and of that she alternately took a bite with the sweetmeats; but at the
sound of a footstep she was trembling again and would throw her arms
round me with the same pathetic, questioning smile. I placed a wreath
of yellow and red tulips on her pretty head — she was a lovely young
creature — and the captain brought her a necklace of large blue beads
and a pair of earrings. All the while, though I did not know it, the girl's
father was hanging about the companion way with a very dangerous
expression on his countenance.

After a little, another woman, seeing that no harm came to the
first, was persuaded to come down to the saloon where she stood,
quivering and starting like a timid, wild animal, ready to fly at a sound.
The difference between this place and Manihiki is very marked. So far
from there being any fear shown in Manihiki, the very children
pushed through the darkness to clasp the white man's hand, and after
that there was no getting rid of the gentle, affectionate, little creatures.
I remember, at Manihiki, seeing Louis sitting with a tall boy of fourteen, beautiful as an angel, holding him round the neck, a young girl
leaning over his shoulder, while a little child nestled up to his breast.
But these islands were a favourite recruiting place for slavers and,
worse still, a haunt of the loathsome 'Bully Hayes'. I gave a wreath to
the other girl also, and after Lloyd (they seemed to have no instinctive
fear of either Lloyd or Louis) had sprinkled them with scent from a
bottle of 'Jockey Club' they paddled to the shore to be met by a crowd
of friends who rushed into the surf up to their necks to hear the news.
The wreaths, necklaces, and earrings were taken off and examined,
criticised, and tried on by all who could get hold of them; the excitement was tremendous. All the while the young girl was in the saloon

Mrs Stevenson and native body,
hand in hand.

the three large port-holes were entirely closed up by the faces of men, who watched every movement with the keenest anxiety.

In the meantime the ship was noisy with the squawking of fowls and the squealing of pigs. The latter are of a curious mouse colour and most amiable creatures. Later on our pretty girl, accompanied by an elder sister, very handsome, and the startled one who had visited me before, came back to the ship. Lloyd took the younger girl's photograph at the end of the bridge. I had to stand beside her with my arm round her for some time before she would keep in one spot long enough for the camera to be pointed at her. Though much less frightened, she was still suspicious. She brought a chicken and some cocoanuts for a present to me, also another fowl which she wished to exchange for a comb, and a mat to exchange for cotton print, both of which I gave her. The startled one brought some shells which she wished to have me understand cancelled the gift of the wreath. I wish I knew how to explain that I do not want return gifts; but that might be an unpardonable breach of etiquette.

I was sitting on a box near the trade room when a fine, intelligent-looking man, a missionary from another island, came up and began talking to me. Unfortunately, his English was so hopeless that I could understand but little that he said, except that a native he presented to me was the King, and that if we would call at the island on our way back there would be an immense load of copra ready. The King had a look of breeding, and only one of his ear-lobes hung down to his shoulder in the native fashion, the other having somehow miscarried. The outer rim of the ear is sliced round and grafted against the jaw, thus making a much larger hole than can be managed at the Gilberts with mere boring and stretching.

Moving through the crowds on deck were three unmistakable lepers, one with elephantiasis also. The toes of the man with elephantiasis were dripping blood, not very pleasant for us barefooted people. I have asked the steward to hang all the mats, some of which are very handsomely decorated, over the side when next we anchor and let them be thoroughly washed by the sea. Just before we left the King asked for me; he had brought me a present of a large mat, a bunch of husked cocoanuts, and a very fine *ridi* of different colours. The *ridi* is the only garment worn by the women in most of the atolls. It is a thick fringe, shorter or longer, according to the prevailing fashion in *ridis*, made of pandanus leaves cut in strips, oiled, and smoked. In the Gilberts a man may not lay his hands on a *ridi* under penalty of death, even when the garment is not in active service. I bought one, also, not so fine, from a woman for seven sticks of tobacco. I had nothing to give the King in return for his present — I am bound to say he seemed to expect nothing — so I pulled a gold ring from my finger and gave him that. He was overcome by the magnificence of the gift, as were the crowd who gathered round him to examine it.

During dinner we weighed anchor and shoved off. The captain had expected to meet the schooner at this island; there were no signs of her until late at night, when she was sighted, apparently on a wrong tack. The captain fears they may be out longer than they expected and the provisions run out; however, there are always the twenty-five tons of copra at hand in case of an emergency, and the passengers can eat their currency, which is more than we would be able to do. The *Janet* has taken to her old trick of rolling, which makes things very uncomfortable. When I went to bed the cackling of hens, the crowing of cocks, and the grunting of pigs gave quite the effect of a farmyard. Our three cats seem to be getting the 'rattage' well under; at least there are no more rats on deck and the old, businesslike Tom now takes his ease and sleeps all night.

31 May

The Island of Nanui. A very violent surf and very broad. Louis goes on shore and returns with a mat. Tin Jack is in great feather as the Nanui people speak the Gilbert Island tongue which he knows.

Louis is instantly accepted as a *kaupoi* (rich man), though he cannot imagine why, as he was clothed only in an old, ragged undershirt and a *lava-lava*.

1 June

Still at Nanui. Mr Henderson asked his black boys, as he was afraid of a change of weather, to work to-day. He said it was a case of necessity, so they consented and fell to like good fellows. After work was done they all gathered together, as is their custom on Sunday, and held a service. It was strange to hear them singing a Scotch hymn tune with words in their own tongue — or tongues, I should say.

2 June

Still taking on copra. Johnny, one of our men, the cleverest one, brought his wife, a native of Nanui, to see me — a strapping fat wench of sixteen, though she looks twenty-five. I gave her some cotton print and a silk handkerchief. A little after Johnny came, with a most serious countenance, to ask Louis to go on deck, where he found a large, mouse-coloured pig and a great pile of cocoanuts awaiting him. Among the people on deck I saw a man the facsimile of the leper at the last island; involuntarily, I looked at his feet, and, sure enough, the poor fellow had elephantiasis also.

The captain offers to make me a plan of a surf-riding canoe. There was a light rain last night which the captain thinks must have fallen on my eyes, as they are inflamed and swollen to-day. When rain in these latitudes touches the captain's eyes, which happens often on the bridge, he is affected in the same way.

4 June

At the Island of Nanomea. Two traders come on board, the company's trader known through the groups as 'Lord —' and an 'independent' trader, a pathetic figure of an old man with both legs bound up; he said he suffered from boils. Soon after, the missionary and his wife came on board, both Samoans, the woman a fine, kindly looking creature with a very sad expression. I said as much to Louis and she wished my remark translated. With the aid of a dictionary Louis told her what I had said. 'I am sad,' was the reply. She brought me a present of a mat, and I gave her a print gown. I bought, also, a few mats from the people. One man followed me about, insisting that he and I should be brothers. He had a mercenary countenance, wherefore I refused steadily the proffered relationship. In spite of me, however, he managed to thrust a bunch of cocoanuts into my cabin door to ratify the tie.

The surf is very high. When the boats went off, the one containing the traders and the missionaries turned over, end for end, and the poor, old 'independent' was nearly drowned. The missionary woman dived for him again and again, and we could see people carrying him along the beach after she rescued him. Several canoes smashed during the day and some bags of copra were lost. In the evening we had a long discussion as to whether Lord — is a gentleman, I taking the affirmative with no more to go upon than the way he raised his hat.

7 June

Have been lying at Nanomea, the last of the Ellices we shall visit, for three days, unable to get the cargo on board till to-day owing to the fearful surf. A good many canoes are broken to pieces, and our own boats have had many escapes. While I was looking through the glasses a great wave swamped one of our boats and pressed her down out of sight. In a moment black heads popped up everywhere and the boat was hauled on shore. Another boat was just on the point of crossing when the steersman was snapped off his perch and flung into the sea; he was almost instantly back and crossed in triumph. Every success was cheered from the ship by the watching men.

It is always a great pleasure to the natives to help raise the ship's boats to the davits for the night. They know that white sailors make a sort of cry or 'chanty' when hauling on a rope, so they, too, try to do the correct thing. The result is a noise very like a mob of schoolgirls let loose, a confusion of soprano screams. No one would suspect the sounds to come from the throats of men. Our own black sailors are the same; we hear them screaming and laughing in the forecastle exactly like girls. We are so used to island life that it has but just struck us as odd and picturesque that our almost naked sailors (they wear only a short *lava-lava* round their loins) should be working in wreaths like queens of the May.

It is only to-day that any women have been able to get on board. Not knowing there were any on deck, I started toward the trade room. There was an instant loud cry of '*Fafine! Beretani fafine!*' and I was in the midst of them. The two who seemed of higher rank than the others took possession of me, and it was explained to me by our Johnny that they had come prepared to make a trade. Each had an elaborate *ridi* for which she wanted two patterns of cotton print. The bargain seemed so unfair that I added a necklace apiece of yellow and white beads. They were enchanted with the necklaces, calling everybody to look at them. Then they began pulling off their rings to put on my hands; I did not like taking their rings, but I need have had no scruples, for one of them with prompt energy removed a gold ring from my finger to her own. These exchanges made, they fell to examining my clothes, which filled them with admiration. The next thing, they were trying to take my clothes off; finding this stoutly resisted, they turned up my sleeves to the shoulders. Their taste differed from mine, for, while I was thinking what a cold, ugly colour a white arm looked beside their warm, brown ones, they were crying out in admiration. One woman kissed my feet (the island kiss) and sniffed softly up and down my arms. She was plainly saying to the others, 'She's just like a pickaninny; I would like to have her for a pet,' holding out her arms as she spoke and going through the motions of tossing and caressing a baby. My hands and feet were measured by theirs and found to be much smaller (they were large women made on a more generous scale than I). 'Pickaninny hands and feet,' they said. The discovery of vaccination marks caused great excitement, especially as one of them could proudly show similar '*Beritani*' marks. Whether they were real vaccination scars or only accidental, I could not be sure. She, however, declared that they were true *Beritani*. Suddenly they all began calling out names; there were now five or six women sitting in a circle round me on the floor of the corridor at the head of the companion stairs. In a moment all their husbands' heads appeared at the doors and windows. My sleeves, in spite of my struggles, were dragged to my shoulders and, to my dismay, my petticoats were whipped up to my knees. At that I began to cry, when the men instantly disappeared, and except for an occasional sniffing the women behaved with more decorum. One woman was most anxious that I should stop on the island with her. I really think she had some hope that she might keep me as a sort of pet monkey. At last they were warned that the ship would be off soon, so they fled to their canoes.

For some time eight or ten canoes, loaded with people, hung to the ship's sides, rocking to and fro with her as she rolled. It was a beautiful sight, and Louis and I leaned over admiring them. Suddenly a lovely young girl (we were told she is to be married next week) climbed up to me like a cat, pulled off a ring, and pushed it on my finger. I ran back and got a blue-bead necklace for her and she climbed down in a state of great delight. The beads will doubtless serve as wedding jewels, for she did not put them on but tied them up carefully in a bit of cotton stuff. We watched the canoes go over the surf; one, filled with women, upset, but nobody appeared to mind so small a mishap.

Mr Hird tells us a story it is well to remember. There was some sort of disturbance at Penrhyn, where his vessel was trading, and all on the ship were afraid for their lives to go ashore except himself. The moment his boat touched ground he dashed up to a little maid of seven, the chief's daughter, and, taking her by the hand, calmly walked to where he wished to go.

Last night, as we were sitting round the lamp, some one looked up and perceived that all three port-holes had as many faces looking through them as could find an eyehole. Mr Henderson went into his room and arranged a few conjuring tricks. When he returned he made money disappear in a box, bits of cork change places, etc. While speaking to one of us he carelessly tore off a piece of newspaper and handed it to a man at the porthole, but as the man's fingers closed on it the paper disappeared. '*Tiaporo!*' (the devil!) he cried, his eyes almost starting from his head. This was followed by the throwing up of money which apparently fell back through the crown of a hat and jingled inside. The last and most thrilling feat was after Mr Henderson had been pulling money from all our heads, noses, and ears. He seemed to be retiring quietly to his room when he gave a start, looked up in the air over his head, and with a leap caught a silver dollar that seemed to be falling from the ceiling.

I forgot to say that in the afternoon Louis was dictating to Lloyd, who used his typewriter. All the air and most of the light was cut off from them by heads at the port-holes. I watched the faces and saw one intelligent old man explaining to the others that Lloyd was playing an accompaniment to Louis's singing; the old man several times tried to follow the tune but found it impossible. He did not appear to think it a good song, and once, with difficulty, restrained his laughter.

9 June

We should have picked up Arorai yesterday at four o'clock, but somehow missed it and did not arrive until this morning. An atoll about six miles long, the first of the Kingsmills (or Gilberts). Natives swarmed round the ship in canoes built somewhat after the pattern of the American Indian birch-bark canoe. The pieces are tied together with cocoanut sennit and the boats leak like sieves. Louis, Lloyd, and I went on shore in the afternoon, Louis, to my distress, for it was very hot, with a hammer to break off bits of the reef for examination and Lloyd with the camera. Louis found the rock he wished to break but was a little afraid to use the force necessary. Seeing a powerful young man standing near, he offered a stick of tobacco for the job. The fellow smiled with delight, took the hammer, and struck one blow. 'Too much work,' said he, dropping the hammer.

Lloyd and I were taken in tow by an old man and led to the house of the missionary, who was himself on board the ship; but his wife and family, a handsome young Samoan woman with a pair of sickly twins, were at the door to give us welcome. We drank cocoanuts with her and took a photograph of the group.

There is very little soil on the island, which is subject to severe droughts; yet there are a number of breadfruit and jack-fruit trees growing luxuriantly, not many, however, old enough to bear. The village looked clean and prosperous. Children and women were pulling weeds and carrying them away in baskets. Lloyd and I strolled along a wide avenue that ran through the town for about a quarter of a mile, stopping once to photograph an old woman who had evidently dressed up for the ship. She was standing in the doorway of a neat house built of stockades tied together — the first I've seen in these islands. The house belonged to a trader who was abroad at the time. Returning, we saw two women, tall and superior in carriage and looks to the common people, marching abreast toward us; they were dressed in gala-day *ridis* of smoked and oiled pandanus strips and swung the heavy fringe from side to side, as they walked, in the most approved and latest style. As they came nearer to us their four eyes were fixed on the horizon behind us, and they swaggered past as though unaware of our existence, though we were attended by a following of the greater part of the village. I stopped and looked after them, but neither turned a head.

At this island I remember that the women wore what looked like doll's hats as ornaments on their heads. They were about the size of the top of a tumbler.

At the veranda of the mission house we found Louis entertained by the old man and indignant at receiving no attention from the missionary people; we suggested that his chopping at the reef in the hot sun had convinced them that he was a lunatic.

We had heard of a sick trader, so we all three went to his house with an immense tail of followers, who seated themselves outside in a circle eight or ten deep while we talked to the sick man. A forlorn being he looked, lying on a mat, his head thrust out into the open through the thatched sides of the hut to catch what air there was. He had been ill a month and a half, he said; the whole population had been ill, also, his wife and children with the rest. With them it came first as a rash, then a fever, followed by convalescence. He had no rash, but after feeling very badly for a week or two, fell down in a fit, foaming at the mouth and black in the face. Since then he had been suffering from an intolerable pain in the head and could not stand for weakness. I asked if he had proper food, which Louis followed by asking if his appetite was good. When he could get anything to eat, he replied, he liked it well enough, but he could not get anything. A bit of fish or a chicken he could relish, but the people seldom fished and a chicken was impossible. His food consisted almost entirely of pounded pandanus seeds, in which there was about as much nourishment as in chopped straw. His hands and feet were pallid and bloodless and he looked very near the end. He was born, he said, in Colton Terrace, Edinburgh. 'I'm frae Edinburgh mysel',' said Louis. 'We are far frae hame,' returned the poor fellow with a sigh. We went at once to the beach to get a boat, intending to consult 'Hartshorn', our medical authority,★ as to his case, which I believed to be suppressed measles. Louis spoke to Mr Henderson about sending the man a case of soups to begin with, anything heavier being dangerous in his weak state and semistarved condition. Mr Henderson, who is generosity itself, seemed rather hurt that we had not taken it for granted that anything the man needed would be supplied him at once. Mr Henderson's only fear was that the man would, in the usual native custom, give all the food away. He first divides with his family, and then they divide with the outside relations, so that provisions sufficient for a month may only last a day. It is an amiable weakness, certainly, but one could wish that the recipients of his bounty showed a little more gratitude. Fishing would be no more than play for them; but I fear neither fish, flesh, nor fowl can save him now.

The missionary who came aboard showed Louis his eye, in which he was blind, the effect of measles, and begged for a cure. Of course there was none, but Louis advised him to live as generously as possible and, instead of a continual diet of pandanus seeds, to try and get some fish. As soon as it was dark the sea was crowded with fishing-boats, lighted up with flaring torches, made by wrapping sennit round a dry cocoanut leaf; so we hope our poor trader may receive some benefit, also. We could see that they were scooping up in their nets many flying-fish. The light from the torch attracts the fish, which come to the surface of the water round the boats and are then dipped up in little nets on the ends of long poles.

While I was resting after my excursion to the island I heard a great commotion; a native had been discovered trying to stow away in the hold among the coal. Two large men could not overpower him, and for a long time he refused to come out. One of the white firemen finally leaned over the open hatch and held out a stick of tobacco. 'Won't you come out for that?' he asked with an insinuating smile. 'He is making signs that he will,' he continued, looking at me quite proud of his cleverness. Sure enough, up came the native, a beautiful youth with a sullen face and blazing eyes. He strode haughtily past the fireman, looking neither at him nor his proffered tobacco, sprang upon the side of the ship, where he balanced himself a moment, and then jumped into the sea and swam ashore. I sympathised with the boy and was sorry he was caught, the more especially that another man had chosen a better hiding-place and was not discovered until we were well at sea.

When we left the island we should have signalled a boat, but a canoe lying at hand, we took that instead. We waded out toward the canoe, but, as the water began rising above my knees, I stopped in alarm when a native caught me up in his arms, unawares, before I had time to arrange my skirts, and I was carried out, willy-nilly, my legs waving frantically in the air. I tried to shield them from the view of the ship with my umbrella, which I was unable to open, but I fear my means were inadequate. The canoe was a fourth filled with water; its owner sternly commanded Louis and me to bail and Lloyd to paddle.

From the last island we took on some passengers — two cats in an onion crate — and at this island exchanged them for a woman and a sickly baby. I was much amazed at seeing the mother spread a thick, dry mat on the wet deck for her own comfort, her baby being plant-ed on the cold boards. I made her take it up and lay it beside her on the mat, which seemed to amuse her a great deal. As the baby still shiv-ered, I got an old *lava lava* of Tin Jack's and wrapped it up in that, charging the mother not to dare remove the *lava-lava*.

This is the island where, in 1871, three slave-ships, the *Moroa* (bark), *Eugenie* (schooner), and a barkentine, name unknown, came for 'recruits'. The King, in his fright, offered them all his people except the very young, the very old, and a few young girls reserved for his harem. It is needless to say that his offer was accepted. I have since met and conversed with a man who was on board one of these ships.

12 June

Arrived early this morning at Onoatoa. The missionary's child is named Painkiller.★

13 June

Noukanau in the morning. Met the German 'labour' brig *Cito*, after recruits, doubtless for Samoa; then ran over to Piru and back again to Noukanau at night. At Piru we met the American schooner *Lizzie* with two passengers.

At Piru came on board a man named Cameron, another named Briggs, and a person with an Italian name I forget. Briggs said he made much more money by 'doctoring' than by trading. A strange disease, he told us, had broken out in the island; the Samoan wife of a trader had died the night before and many others were down with it. It is contagious, and the natives take no care to avoid infection. I said it was measles, which Briggs denied, declaring it was typhus. I asked him where he got his knowledge of 'doctoring'. 'Straight from my father,' said he; 'my father was the celebrated Doctor Briggs, and if you buy a bottle of his patent medicine you can read an account of his life on the wrapper.'

Cameron is a Scotsman with a twinkling, hard blue eye, the daft Scotch eye. He followed every word we said with sly caution (partly, no doubt, in consequence of drink) as though he feared being trapped into some dangerous admission. He was one of the men of the *Wandering Minstrel*★ that was so mysteriously wrecked on Midway Island, and was afterward charged by the captain with not reporting the fact of there being other starving castaways left on Midway when he was rescued. To us he denied this vehemently, and said he at once delivered a letter written by the captain. Louis tried to get a hint of how and why the vessel was wrecked, but failed. 'Mosey', the Chinaman who was in the boat with Cameron, was afterward wrecked again on the *Tiernan*, the schooner we so nearly took passage in ourselves, when we were accidentally marooned at Apemama during a former cruise. Louis got this much from Cameron — but I am sure very little, if any, of it is true — that he had written an account of the wreck which, with the log he kept on the boat, had been left on one of the islands we are about to visit, for safe-keeping. Before Cameron

Mrs Stevenson being carried ashore —
— Apia eng.

Tom Day — a Trader on Nukanau Isl

left he had given Louis a signed order for the apocryphal manuscript. Of the two men we brought one back with us, Captain Smith, who, having lost his schooner on this island, remained as a trader. He seemed a modest, intelligent young man, rather above the South Sea average. Tom Day, however, is — must be — the 'flower of the Pacific'. Tom is fifty years of age, with a strong, alert figure and the mobile face of an actor; his eyes are blue-grey in deep orbits, blazing with energy and drink and high spirits. 'Tom Day' is not his real name, he says, and Tom Drunk would do quite as well; he had found it necessary to go to the expense of a shilling to have it changed, as he had three times deserted from men-of-war. 'I've been in prison for it,' he said cheerfully, 'and I got the cat for it, and if you like you can see the stars and stripes on my back yet.' He took pleasure in representing himself as the most desperate of ruffians. Tin Jack asked him to go back to Sydney with him. 'I couldn't leave my old woman behind,' said he; 'and besides, you see, I got into trouble there. The fact is, I've got another wife there, and I think I'd do better to keep away.' He then began to tell of a quarrel he'd had with his 'old woman' when he took her to Auckland. How she chased him along the street with a knife in one hand and a bag of sovereigns — his entire fortune — in the other; he begged for the bag of sovereigns, trying to lay hold of it and at the same time avoid the knife wielded by the 'old woman' (a young native girl, no doubt), who alternately lunged at him with the knife and cracked him over the head with the bag of sovereigns. The bursting of the bag, which scattered the sovereigns in every direction, fortunately ended the quarrel. He mentioned Maraki, on which Louis called to mind a story he had been told many times over.

'You are the Tom Day who had a native's head cut off,' said he; 'now tell me the story,' which Tom presently did. A native had shot at him without provocation. Some one said: 'Don't shoot; it's a white man.' 'A white man can cut a bullet as well as another,' was the native's reply as he fired. Tom put his hand to his ear, found that the shot had grazed it and his head, and the blood was running from the wound. Infuriated, he rushed into the house for his rifle, but when he got back the man, frightened at what he had done, had disappeared. Tom tried to persuade the people standing about to go after the man, pinion him, and fetch him back to be tried. To this they objected; they could not get him, they said, as he was a chief and had people to protect him. One of the men came close to Tom. 'Better we kill him,' he said in a low voice, which Tom imitated. 'If you do,' was Tom's answer, 'fetch me the head.' Then turning to us with an apologetic air he explained that 'If I had not asked to see the head they'd just have gone and killed some poor, inoffensive fellow and I'd never have known the difference.' That night he was called up by the men who had the head, sure enough. 'I made 'em stick it up on the wall', said Tom, 'and then I got a light and looked at it. I jerked it down and slung it as far as I could; and, by golly, the old woman was in the way, half scared to death, and it took her on the side of the head and knocked her down, and I had to pour three or four pails of water over her, for she had fainted dead away.'

'And after that', he continued with an air of virtuous indignation, 'they wanted to make trouble about it in Sydney — they said I had killed a man. What did they mean by it, I'd like to know? I never killed no man; I only told them to fetch his head so I could be sure it was him.'

It was very cold last night and my bed and tent and things nearly blew away; I could not leave them and go below where it was warmer, but had to stay and hold on to my belongings lest I should lose them entirely; so to-day I lashed everything securely. No one stayed on the hatch but Lloyd and me. The onions alongside Lloyd's and my beds are decaying, and smell horrid, as do a great lot of sharks' fins drying over our heads.

15 June

Waked to find that we were lying off Tapituea, Tin Jack's station. He had packed the day before and was all ready to land, his pig tied up and lying on deck. Tapituea looks a large and dreary island, the whole lee side submerged, making it very dangerous. We could not venture inside the lagoon, and even if we did we should have to anchor far away from the landing-place. It was a long time before any one came on board, but finally a Hawaiian who spoke a little English came out in his canoe. As Tin Jack appeared to be rather depressed with the news from his place, and it was almost impossible to land his stuff, we left Tapituea and ran on to Nanouti, where he thought he might prefer to stop. He has a sort of partner at Nanouti, known as 'Billy Jones's cousin'. The partner was soon on board, a man with a big head and one hand blown off by dynamite. A new arrangement was made with Tin Jack, who said he preferred staying in the ship as long as possible. We are now to carry him on with us, and land him at Nanouti as we return. A pleasant-looking young native came on board with the trader. He wore a rosary round his neck, which reminded me that there were Catholic missionaries on the island; I therefore made a little parcel of four Catholic pictures for them, and Louis put in his card; Tin Jack added a bag of garlic.

We left Nanouti before dinner, had a beautiful golden sunset, and are now steaming on to somewhere else, Apemama, I trust. To-night the evening star is extraordinarily brilliant, with the blue fire of a diamond. Last night Mr Hird came to the hatch and called out in a most excited voice: 'Osbourne, we are just passing the equator!' Lloyd jumped out of a sound sleep and ran aft, crying: 'Where is she? I don't see her!' It was a sorry joke; we were crossing the line, and it was not Captain Reid's schooner, on which we had passed so many delightful months.

A NOTE
ON A
PREVIOUS VISIT
TO APEMAMA

It seems easier to explain our relation with Tembinoka, King of Apemama, at whose island I hoped we would call, by giving an extract from a former diary written on the trading schooner Equator:

We have been now about a month on the island of the redoubtable Tembinoka, an absolute monarch, who holds the lives of his subjects (our own also) in the hollow of his hand. He says: 'I kill plenty men, him 'praid (afraid) now. I no kill any more.' That he does not mean to kill any more his subjects do not believe, nor I, quite, myself. He once shot five men, one after another, as they sat in a 'moniap' (native house) where they had been brought to be examined by him concerning some breach of his laws. There were seven men in all, but two escaped and are still at large in another island. He says his father had a head house where he hung up the decapitated heads of his enemies or in other words, people who differed in their opinion from him or whom he did not like (a friend of ours afterward saw this moniap *with its grisly decoration of skulls). No missionaries and no white people are allowed on Tembinoka's islands (he rules over three) with the exception of Johnny, an inoffensive, dying 'poor white', who lives some four miles from the village. We did not know in the least whether we should be allowed to remain, and waited with some anxiety for the appearance of his Majesty. In the meantime the whole ship was in a commotion, scouring the decks and getting everything into apple-pie order; I did not know that the* Equator *could be brought to such a pitch of cleanliness. Finally the King's steps arrived, were made fast to the sides, and the royal boat was seen to put out. We thought it more dignified to remain in the cabin and show none of the curiosity we felt concerning this very remarkable man. We had been told that he was grossly stout, and that was all the description we had been able to get from the stupid people we had talked with; consequently, we were not prepared to meet the most magnificently royal personage that it has yet been our lot to behold, a gentleman by nature and a king every inch of him. He gave us a long and careful study; afterward he said it was first the eyes and then the mouth he judged by. We passed muster, Louis's eyes being specially commended, and were told to come ashore and remain as long as we liked as his guests. The next day we chose a spot*

where we thought it would be pleasant to live, and Tembinoka ordered his men to carry houses and set them up there for us. The captain and Lloyd stayed at the King's palace all night; the next morning they were alarmed to see Tembinoka shooting into the village with a rifle. He explained that his men were lazy and should be at work, so he was reminding them that accidents were possible. The whole trembling village set to work like bees, and by the time I came over, one sleeping house was up, a little thatched bird-cage with flaps on all sides to raise or lower as one likes, and an open-sided cook house for Ah Foo (a Chinese servant we brought from the Marquesas). The King sat on a mat and directed proceedings. He motioned me to sit beside him and asked for a cigarette, of which he is very fond. Whenever a native has to pass the King, or come near him for any purpose, he must crouch and crawl; even his Majesty's own sister did so when she came to join our party.

We have had a little ripple of excitement on the usually smooth current of our existence. To go back to the beginning: Soon after we were settled in 'Equator town', as we call our hamlet, the King proposed sending the royal cook to learn from Ah Foo. The man was an insolent, handsome fellow, with no intention of either learning or working, and either lay on the floor of the kitchen or squatted smoking, while Ah Foo, who was in mortal terror of Tembinoka, prepared the dishes which the royal cook, without doubt, passed off as his own productions. This went on for some time, and as the King's meal hours are the same as our own, interfered a good deal with Ah Foo's work and consequently our comfort. The climax was reached when the cook, too lazy to walk down to the well for a can of water for himself, came softly behind me as I was watering my plants and impudently snatched a dipperful from my pail. We then took the first opportunity to let the King know how things were going, advising him to send a man who was willing to learn. Since then his Majesty's steward, a capable, serious man, has accompanied the cook. Shortly after our complaint we

*heard several rifle-shots from the palace, and soon after met the cook,
who passed us hurriedly, without the usual salutations, his countenance
bearing the marks of furious anger and fear. It seems that he had been
the King's target, running and crouching behind piles of stones, the
bullets flying after him. Tembinoka came over a few days later and
apologised for having possibly alarmed or annoyed us. He said he had
no intention of killing the man, which he might have done easily, being
a dead shot, but only wished to frighten him. He said he had killed
enough people to show the rest what he could do, but thought it a good
plan to remind them occasionally that he had a rifle and the power to
use it as he pleased. 'More better him 'praid' (afraid), were his words.
As may be imagined, the cook bears us no good will, knowing that our
complaints had turned that fearful rifle against him. However, he
dropped his insolent airs and became almost obsequious.*

Since we have been here, the schooner Tiernan *came in for copra.
While she was lying in the lagoon, the King spent most of his time
aboard and some seven hundred dollars of his money (he spent nearly
one thousand on the* Equator*); then he got very drunk, going on
steadily a little worse or a little better, according to his headaches. Day
before yesterday, he gave a feast and dance to which he did not invite
us. At noon he came to say he would lunch with us. His eyes were wandering and his voice excited and almost boisterous. It was plain that
royalty was not far from being vulgarly drunk. We could see that he
had been worried by our visits to the palace having ceased and wished
to have an understanding that there was no ill feeling on either side.
He demanded beer, saying that he had been drinking gin and port
wine, and dozed off in his chair, starting up in a few moments much
mortified. I noticed that even in this stage of semi-intoxication, he used
his knife and fork in our fashion, and not as he had learned from the
'South Sea merchants'. It is an unending pleasure to hear the King
say: 'I want to go home.' There is an element of appeal in it, reminding one of a child who can bear the tedium no longer. It is always*

directed to Louis or, he being absent, to me as his representative. He wanted to go home very soon after that luncheon. In the evening we could hear the dancers in the big 'speak house', clapping, stamping, and singing. The sounds were so savage, so like an immense pack of dogs fighting in a mass, that we did not realise what it was, but thought that some form of riot was going on. An absolute tyrant like Tembinoka walks amid dangers of which he is fully conscious. Tembinoka dead drunk was not an idea to contemplate with serenity, and the sound of a single shot did not tend to reassure us, so we laid our pistols where they would be handy. Louis's idea is that no one would attack the King unless he were absolutely certain of killing him instantly, in which case we had better wait here until the enemy came for us. I think on the contrary, that the commission of so enormous a crime would make a pause. The terrors of the deed would fill the childish minds of the natives to the exclusion of anything else and there would be a short time of confusion in which nothing would take place but shoutings and aimless running about; then would be our time to rush in and take possession of a stout wooden house inside the palace walls, and the King's arms, and really the King's throne. There would always be the chance, a very slight one, to be sure, that we might still be in time to save the King's life. I do not quite understand what Louis's tactics would be, but aside from any other consideration, there must be but one commander and he should be absolute even though the others do not agree with him.

After the shot (which was only aimed at a dog, though that we could not know) we listened and found that there was no interruption to the singing and dancing, which reassured us. In the night, Louis, being restless and not sleepy, took his flageolet and wandered off into the woods, playing as he walked, until I lost hearing of him. About midnight, or a little later, I was out a short distance from the house watching with some anxiety for his return. Pretty soon I saw him coming along the main path toward our house. I also saw a dark figure dogging his steps. I called to him, telling him what I had seen. He was convinced that it was an hallucination of mine and I was quite ready to believe him, but as we talked I caught sight of the man running toward the palace. I pointed him out to Louis, who dashed off in pursuit. When the man saw he was outdistanced, for Louis is a fine sprinter, he turned the face of the cook, smiling suavely. I heard 'sea language' in Louis's biggest voice, and saw him leaping strangely in the moonlight, like a grasshopper. He came back in fits of laughter, saying he had kicked the cook, who fled in terror.

Ever since the cook found we had turned against him I have had an uneasy feeling that some one was about our sleeping house in the night, and several times I was certain a hand was cautiously feeling about inside our door flap. It seemed a foolish notion, so I had said nothing about it until this night, then Louis said he, too, had distinctly heard the same thing. We cannot complain to the King for he would kill the man instantly, and we do not go so far as to desire his death. We have not seen or heard from him since. Ah Foo thinks he has gone away in fear of his life. I have it in my heart to be sorry for the fellow, for his terror must be extreme, and we who have brought this upon him belong to the feared and hated white race.

We are getting to be rather anxious concerning the Equator. *She was to be gone two weeks, but it is now over a month since she left us. The* Tiernan *met her at Butaritari, she leaving the day before Captain Saxe of the* Tiernan. *Captain Reid intended to go to Maraki to take a man known as 'the poisoner' over to another island, Taravao, I think. Now Taravao is so near to Maraki that Peter Grant had been over there in a small boat. There may have been trouble in Maraki — certainly it was imminent — which has kept the captain, but still it is a long time. He promised, if the schooner were lost and he was saved, that he would make his way here somehow. In these dangerous and uncertain waters one is easily made uneasy. Fortunately for us, the* Tiernan *was able to let us have some stores. Our salt beef was finished,*

*and we were absolutely sickened of wild chickens shot by Ah Foo with
the King's gun.*

*I had a little strip of coral dug out, got rotted leaves from under a
tree, put them into the hole, and into this I emptied the half-decayed
filth that was left in the onion basket. I should think I have nearly two
dozen onions now growing finely. I have invented a salad for Louis of
which he is extremely fond. In all these islands there is one cocoanut
that has a sweet husk, used for cleaning the teeth. In Butaritari the
baron often caused me great embarrassment by chewing a brush for me.
This sweet nut when green has a little crisp portion at the stem end
which I cut up and made into salad with oil and vinegar, or rather oil
and lime-juice, as we have no vinegar. We have put out a bottle of sour
toddy hoping to get vinegar from that.*

*My diary ends here, abruptly; I had too much on my hands to find
any further time for writing diaries, for Ah Foo fell ill, and I must be
cook, purveyor, housemaid, and what not, as well as nurse. Ah Foo
announced his illness (something alarmingly like diphtheria) in these
words, 'Me sick: no can work; no can cook — no good any more —
more better you kill me, now,' offering Louis, as he spoke, a large,
keenly sharpened carving knife and his bared throat ready for the sac-
rifice. He was severely ill for some days, needing almost constant attention. His undisguised surprise that I would stoop to nurse a Chinaman
was pathetic, and his gratitude afterward was sometimes shown in
unexpected and embarrassing ways, as, for instance, when he insisted
on shooting several men who waked me from an afternoon nap by
singing Christmas songs beneath my window; or when he proposed to
burglariously enter a trader's house to steal something for me that could
not be procured otherwise.*

It seemed a rash thing to let the Tiernan *sail away without us as
we had finished, not only our own supplies, but the King's also. True,
Mr Lauterbach, the mate of the* Tiernan, *let us have several kegs of salt
beef, and Reuben (which was the nearest we could come to pronouncing*

his name), the King's majordomo, had fetched three big hawkbill turtles from another island. The turtles were for the King's own larder, but he sent us a generous portion of each; we, of course, divided accordingly when we opened our kegs of beef. But these provisions would soon be finished, and if, as we each feared but dared not say, the Equator were lost, 'cocoanut steaks' might become our sole diet. Indeed, I had packed the most of our belongings in some large camphor-wood chests ready to go on board, and we had even chosen our bunks when a picture of Captain Reid's face if he arrived to find us gone rose before my mind's eye. 'Louis,' I suddenly whispered, 'I don't want to go.' Without a question Louis immediately cancelled our passage and the Tiernan sailed away without us. Not many days afterward she capsized and sank in a very odd way. A heavy gale that had piled the sea up into enormous waves was followed by a dead calm. The Tiernan, lying quite helpless, was rolled over, further and further, until she 'turned turtle' and sank. Years after the mate, Mr Lauterbach, whom I had supposed to be drowned, came to see me in San Francisco. He, he told me, with some natives, managed to turn over a boat that floated out upside down from the schooner. With only the carcass of the ship's pet pig which they had picked up and what rain fell from the sky for sustenance, the boat went drifting off. I am not sure that they had an oar, but Mr Lauterbach caught a native sleeping-mat that was floating on the water; the castaways took turns in holding up this mat, which thus served as a sail. They could not hope for a rescue in these unfrequented waters, so Mr Lauterbach tried to work toward an inhabited island with only the position of sun and stars for guidance. When he did make land, after an incredible length of time to have lived without food or water, there were, as I remember, only himself, one man and a demented woman left living in the boat. None of our party, except, perhaps, Ah Foo, would have been able to endure such hardships — if, indeed, we had not gone straight down with the schooner — the most likely thing to happen. So it was as well that I asked to go back to our meagre fare to await the Equator.

16 June

Early this morning we were lying outside the lagoon of Apemama, just alongside the little island at the entrance. There was no sign of life, so, after waiting awhile, a boat with Mr Henderson, Tin Jack, and Louis went to find out the reason. They came back with the news that the King was away visiting his island of Kuria, so off we started to hunt for him. Arrived at Kuria, a boat came out to tell us that the King was ill from the sequelae of measles; also it brought an insulting letter to Mr Henderson, signed by the King but written in a white man's hand; Mr Henderson, very angry, showed the letter to Louis, who proposed that he should be present at the interview with the King. To this Mr Henderson consented. Of course we all went on shore; Louis and Lloyd and I took our presents with us; from Louis a chibouk, from Lloyd a filled cartridge-belt with a sheathed dagger, mine being the King's own flag after my design. I thought it very generous of Mr Henderson that he advised me to keep my flag back in case the King came on board, so we might get a better effect by breaking his colours man-of-war fashion — this after the insulting letter and before what promised to be a very unpleasant interview.

Our black fellows pulled us across in splendid style, passing the King's returning messenger, who made a fine though unsuccessful spurt to catch up with us. As we rowed along the beach surprised cries of 'Pani! Pani!' (Fanny! Fanny!) ran through the *moniaps* (native houses) where the King's wives were sitting. The King, looking older and thinner, received us in the native fashion with no apparent aston-ishment. The presents were given, and then Lloyd and I left the party to get their explanations over, the King smoking his chibouk the while with great enjoyment, while the cartridge-belt hung over his shoulder.

We soon found the *moniap* of the harem and sat down beside the King's mother. The women received us with fervent expressions of welcome and pleasure. We passed through several houses on our way,

153

and in every one our attention was called to a 'devil box'⋆ similar to one we bought from the medicine-man at Apemama, then the only one in the three islands. In the centre of the big *moniap* was a circular piece of 'devil work' with a ring of sacred white shells about it. Tin Jack followed after us, and we got him to act as interpreter. It seems they have been suffering here severely with measles, though there were only four deaths, two men and two women. Children escaped with slight attacks, but grown people were very ill, the King himself being at one time very near death. The first question put to us by the women was concerning Louis's health; then what had we done with our devil box? Butaritari had lapsed into heathenism when we arrived there, but, by showing a magic lantern which included some Bible pictures among the slides, we quite unconsciously reconverted the whole island, King and all. I fear that our accidental reconversion of Butaritari to Christianity has been offset by our having inadvertently strengthened these Apemamans in their heathen superstitions. A sick foreigner comes, is cured by means of a devil box manipulated by a 'dog-star' (doctor), and naturally he desires to possess an article so valuable, going so high in his offers for it as the worth of a ton of copra. The foreigner is a very clever and learned man. 'He savee too much,' they say. And when measles falls upon the land the first thought is the devil box, and a praying place for devil worship is erected in the very centre of their *moniap*. I wish I could find out if they really worship the spirit of evil or whether, having been enlightened by the missionaries, they have not given their god that name. If the latter, how much better to have accepted their god and shown them where they had mistaken his attributes? And that reminds me that when I heard the people with the scaly disease on the other islands erroneously called lepers I wondered if that could have been the leprosy of the Bible that was miraculously cured. The darkest people turn quite white when covered with the scales.

But to return to Tembinoka, the King. Louis, fortunately, was able to clear up the misunderstanding caused, no doubt, by a white man, though the King loyally refused to give the name. Louis proposed that the King should apologise for the insulting letter, at which his Majesty looked very black, indeed; but when Louis told him that under the same circumstances an English gentleman would certainly offer an apology, his countenance cleared, the apology was handsomely made and accepted, and so, all being well, the King proposed to go on board. We wished some of our party to be on the ship to break out the flag at the right moment, so hunted up our black boys who were filling bags with grass for the ship's sheep; Mr Hird went off with them, and the rest of us begged permission to accompany the King, who invited us to ride out with him to his boat in the royal litter. I was told to get in first, then Lloyd, then Louis and Mr Henderson together, and then his Majesty. The black boys passed us on the way with Mr Hird, and afraid that the flag might be forgotten by some mischance, Mr Henderson shouted: 'Hird, elevate the royal bunting.' That was because the King would have understood had he said: 'Break the flag.' The black boys put their elegant backs into it and were in time to send up the flag in fine style. Every one cried out in admiration; it could not have had a better setting than the 'long, low, rakish black' steamer. The King, who steered his own boat, and was greatly pleased to learn that the Hawaiian King was a good sailor as well as himself, had been smiling on Louis, and Louis on him, in the most melting way. He now directed his attention to the flag, and there was no doubt but the sight gave him the keenest gratification. We came down to the cabin, where 'champagne was opened', and then Mr Henderson left Louis and me alone with the King.

The moment that Mr Henderson was gone the apathy that in these islands 'doth hedge in a king' broke down. The dear old man clasped Louis in one arm and me in the other and kissed us and wept over us for joy. He told us how, day after day, he looked through his glass out over the sea pretending to himself that he could see us coming back. Sometimes, he said, he deluded himself so far that he beheld our very faces. This day he had been looking out as usual and was not surprised when our boat came near; he had seen it all like that before in his day-dreams. Suddenly he recognised a particular dress I wore that he had given me. 'Then I felt like this,' he said, making a gasping sound of surprise and emotion — 'O-o-oh!' — and pressing his hand on his breast with a dramatic gesture. Often, he said, he made an errand over to his taro pits that he might look upon the place where our houses had stood. 'I too much sorry,' he said; 'I want see you.'

The time came to say good-bye until the *Janet* came back on her return voyage; the flag was hauled down and presented to the King, and he went off in his boat with a very depressed countenance.

Reuben is now called 'the governor'. As we were sitting at dinner some one said: 'The anchor's coming up. There's a man at the port wants to speak to you, Mr Stevenson.' We all looked up, and there, grinning like an ape, was 'Uncle Parker!' (Uncle Parker was a servant the King had lent us when we visited him before.) He thrust as much of himself through the port-hole as was possible, and we all climbed up and shook hands with him. He told us that there had been further trouble with the impudent cook, and in consequence the King had shot him. Louis gave Uncle Parker a magnificent gift of six sticks of tobacco. The King said he had sent us ten mats by Captain Reid. On this island is a house of refuge, an octagon to which criminals may run. I am told that the people have a system of palmistry.

17 June

Maraki. We stopped at the wrong settlement, and, as men were seen on the beach, Mr Henderson sent a boat for them in case they wished to go on with us to the other settlement. One was a stranger, the other an old friend known as the 'passenger'. We were forced to kidnap 'the passenger', Paul Hoeflich, a very pleasant, agreeable German, when we were on the *Equator*. Mr Hoeflich had taken passage on the schooner from Butaritari to another island, only a few miles distant, where he meant to start business as an independent trader. All his worldly goods, including the stuff for stocking his store, were on board the *Equator*. It was the beginning of the bad season, and we had continual contrary winds with heavy seas. In vain we cruised round and round his island — we could not make a landing. We were losing much time, so my husband informed Mr Hoeflich that he must join us in a trip to Samoa, our next destination. It so fell out that Mr Hoeflich, who had helped greatly to lighten the tedium of a long voyage in bad weather (we arrived at Apia in a somewhat wrecked condition, with one foretopmast gone), took an immense liking to Samoa and remained there instead of returning to the Gilberts. He has prospered exceedingly and blesses the day he was kidnapped. At this time, when we met him he had come back to the line islands for a final arrangement of his affairs preliminary to settling permanently in Samoa. We heard his meagre news and he heard ours, and drank stout with Louis and Lloyd. It was pleasant to meet him again. He expects to be in Samoa in a twelvemonth. Left the silk dress, 'blackee coat', and other presents with him to forward to Maka and the Nan Toks, and I gave a gold ring to the Hawaiian missionary for his wife. This missionary expects to return to Honolulu on the *Morning Star* in company with Maka, so our presents will fall in at the right moment. Louis also sent one of his photographs to a young Hawaiian I met under peculiar circumstances when we were here before. We stayed a very short time, and then, with several sails set, took our way toward Jaluit. A sheep and a pig struck attitudes and dared each other to fight — a comical sight. Both were delighted when the strained situation was broken by a chance passerby. The black boys are playing cards in the forecastle. Mr Hird and Foo-foo (black boy) sang in the evening.

A NOTE
ON A
PREVIOUS VISIT
TO MARAKI

*As we neared the end of our walk we came into quite a large village.
The aspect of the people was more savage and ugly than we had hereto-
fore seen, the faces brutal and unintelligent. Half-grown children, and,
indeed, some more than half-grown, were entirely naked. The young
boys were like little old men, their faces hard and their eyes haggard
and anxious. I saw one with St Vitus's dance, several with hydro-
cephalus, and a number who had affections of the eyes. Many of the little girls had their heads entirely shaved, with the exception of a small
tassel at the nape of the neck which gave a very curious effect. The
older ones wore their hair bushed out to a great size. Almost all wore
necklaces of braided hair with an oval bit of red or white shell hanging
to it like a locket. One haughty, impudent, fat young fellow, evidently
a beau, swaggered about with a white handkerchief, twisted most
ingeniously into a crown, on his head. Almost all of the women wore
a girdle of flat, round beads (made of cocoanut shells) above the* ridi.*

As we walked along the village street the whole population joined
us. We stopped at the sight of a church neatly made of wattled cocoanut
leaves bearing at the peak of its front gable a belfry of braided leaves.
There was actually a bell in this belfry which looked as though a breath
would disperse it. The floor of the church is covered with mats, which are
renewed each new year. A very odd thing was an arrangement of strings
which, inside of the building, crossed each other with a sort of pattern
just above a tall man's height. All along these strings, at regular intervals, strips of bright-hued calico were tied — I thought in an attempt at
ornamentation, but was told it was for a game of the children. I should
like to see the game played. Indeed, I do not believe it to be a game.
(We found afterward that these decorations were for the purpose of*

propitiating 'chinch', a terrible evil spirit — the devil, in fact.) We asked
for the missionary; a fine-looking young Hawaiian came up to us, salut-
ing us with the pleasant 'Aloha!' His house was our appointed place of
meeting with the captain. The missionary, we were told, was in council
with the 'old men'.

This island is a republic governed by the 'old men'. To arrive at
the distinction of being an 'old man', one must be either very rich or
have performed some prodigy of valour in war time. Accompanied by
the Hawaiian, we wandered along to the Council House. The mission-
ary looked extremely like a mixture of native and Chinese — a large,
imposing man with a long, thin, white moustache and thick, grey hair.
As we sat outside in the circle surrounding the Council House, con-
versing with the Hawaiian, it occurred to me that I might buy one of
the cocoanut beaded girdles worn by most of the women. The Hawaiian
turned to one of them and asked what she would take for her girdle; a
dollar was the answer; at that I handed a half dollar and two quarters
to the young man who, saying that it was too much, gave me back half
the money. 'They sell them for two fish-hooks,' he said, 'and this is
simply extortion; however, as she has seen the money she will do her
best to get it, so you might as well give her the half dollar.' The
exchange was made, and after a moment's confabulation with a crowd
of her neighbours the woman demanded the other half dollar. At this
the Hawaiian asked for the piece of money she had, took it, and gave
back the girdle. In an instant the whole place was in an uproar. Men
bounded up with furious gestures; the old men in the Council House
shouted with threatening yells, while the Hawaiian, leaping to his feet,
his eyes flashing like a cat's in the dark, defied them all. Fearful that
harm might come to him after we were gone, I begged him to let me
give the people whatever they might ask for, but he would not hear of
it, and matters were the worse for my offer, as the people evidently
understood it had been made. Finally, leaving the crowd in a state of
ferment, we walked away with the Hawaiian to his very pleasant

house, he entertaining us on the way with a list of the laws made that day by the 'old men'. They were as follows: 'Dancing, one dollar fine; concealed weapons, five dollars; murder, fifteen; stealing, twenty-five, and telling a lie, fifty dollars.' Pretty soon the crowd began surging round us; there was more furious talk, the Hawaiian looking very fine as he walked toward the mass of people, shaking his fists and, I am bound to say, interlarding his language with English oaths. When he had forced the crowd back by, I really think, the fire of his eye, he laughed in their faces contemptuously and turned to me translating the meaning of the scene. The 'old men' had made another law, against him, placing him under tapu so that he could neither trade nor be traded with. I felt very miserable at being the innocent cause of so much trouble. He said he did not care a rush and meant to leave the island anyway. He had married a native of Maraki, bringing her home to visit her people, with whom she had proposed they should stop, but now, he said, she was as eager to go as he was. When we left he presented us with a girdle that he had somehow got hold of and his wife gave me a young fowl. I, very fortunately, had a handsome wreath of flowers on my hat which I took off and gave the wife. It was amusing to watch the dandy of the village, the haughty and insolent fat young man who had been too languid to see us before, trying to keep all speculation out of his eyes when I passed over the wreath. He could not do it. The red imitation currants held his gaze like fish-hooks.

We sailed away quite gaily from Maraki, fell into a calm, and had to turn and come back again, so had yet another day, and all together four, before we really got away. All the time, more or less, we were over-run by the traders, who came to beg drink and buy and sell.

We have now seen the South Sea 'bad man' of the story-books, Peter Grant. He always comes with 'Little Peter', a kindly, simple lad who has been on the island since he was thirteen and speaks excellent English with the native tossing and eyebrow lifting. (Little Peter died from poisoning some years after; it was supposed to be a murder.) Peter Grant is the most hideous ruffian I have ever beheld. The skin of his face has the quality of a burn scar and is crossed with wrinkles in places where no other human being has wrinkles. His forehead is narrow and retreating, his eyes very light, with a strange scaly look, not a pair in size, colour, or movement, and set too close together in a large, gaunt face. His nose, hooked at the end until it almost touches his upper lip, is unusually bony and is bent over to the left as though from a blow. His coarse-lipped, stupid mouth is creased with slashes like cuts. One of his unpleasant peculiarities is what Louis calls 'crow's-feet between the eyes'.

The next to the last day at Maraki Lloyd and I went ashore with the captain, who had, as he said, 'business to attend to' with a missionary. (The Hawaiian missionary who was to travel in the Morning Star *with our dear Maka of Butaritari.) I knew the business had something to do with a* tapu *put upon Peter Grant some six months ago, but that a concerted attack was to be made upon the old missionary I did not suspect or I should never have gone. We were met by my friend the young Hawaiian, who accompanied us to the missionaries' house. There the best seat was offered me, all being received with dignified hospitality as they dropped in, one horror after another. Little Peter was appointed interpreter. The missionary was charged, first, with having instigated the natives to* tapu *Peter Grant. It was supposed he denied this, but in reality he did not. Head and shoulders above the rest he sat, a fine, massive figure, with impenetrable Chinese eyes, master of the situation. I only noticed once any sign of perturbation in him; that was when the head of the 'old men' was brought in to be questioned. The missionary made a quick attempt to put the old man on his guard, but was instantly checked by a trader, who leaped to his feet and shook his fist in the missionary's face, ordering him to be silent. The missionary smiled contemptuously, but a thick sweat gathered upon his face and neck, his hands trembled slightly, and his great chest rose and fell, slowly and heavily. Feeling that to gaze upon him was an indelicacy, though I was doing so in sympathy and admiration,*

I made a slight movement to turn away; as though he knew my thought, the missionary suddenly looked me in the eyes with a charming smile, fanned me a moment with a fan that lay beside him, then handed me the fan with a bow.

Fortunately, the attempt to warn the 'old man' had been enough, for he seemed idiotic in his apparent endeavours to understand what was wanted of him. The charge against the missionary then changed to theft. He was said to have stolen a murdered man's property. In answer to that he said: 'Then place the affair in the hands of either the first man-of-war that comes to the group or the Morning Star,' *which is daily expected. The traders all cried out with fury at the mention of the* Morning Star, *and, all speaking at once, charged him with instigating the natives to all sorts of evil when he should be setting them a good example. For the first time he retorted, saying that the missionaries came only to try to make the people better, and that the only difficulty was the wickedness of the white men. I am sorry to say that I got the impression that there was something in danger of being discovered which would have been to the disadvantage of the missionary, but not exactly what the traders were looking for. They were too stupid to see that, and were forced to come to a pause, having gained nothing. Both Lloyd and I had a distressed feeling that we might be confounded with their party in the mind of the missionary, but he reassured us with his eyes, and, pushing aside those in his way, shook hands with Lloyd and then with me. I held his hand and pressed it and said all that eyes and smile could manage.*

As we went out of the house the missionary's wife made me a present of a fowl. The Hawaiian joined us as we passed his place and his wife ran out with another fowl. I had made up a little parcel for her, a red comb, a bead necklace, a bottle of fine scent, and a striped blue-and-white summer jersey, with a large silk handkerchief for her husband. The next day they, with their little daughter, came to pay us a visit on board, fetching with them three young fowls and a very fine, beautiful mat of a pattern I had not seen before. Louis was greatly pleased with my friends and promised to send the man his photograph. When he said good-bye, to our surprise he asked for Louis's card, which was a piece of civilisation we were not prepared for. We have touched at no island where there has not been at least one person we were sorry to leave and should be glad to meet again, though this was the only place where these friends were foreign to the land.

18 June

Very hot weather. Our sails are still up, and one of the boats hanging over the side has its sail also set. It looks very odd.

19 June

Jaluit, the German seat of government for the Marshalls. We could see the commissioner's house, painted a terra-cotta red, looking very pretty under the green trees. Went on shore, a blazing hot day. We were all dressed up for the occasion, Louis with his best trousers, yellow silk socks of a very odd shape, knitted by his mother for a parting present, dirty white canvas shoes, and a white linen coat from the trade room that could not be buttoned because of its curious fit. It was hoped, however, that a gold watch and chain might cover all deficiencies. I wore a blue linen native dress, entirely concealed by a long black lace cloak, and on my head a black turban with a spotted veil. Our feet were certainly the weak point, my stockings being red and my shoes cut in ribbons by the coral. Not having gloves, I put on all my rings which flashed bravely in the sun. On board ship our appearance caused a decided sensation and was considered most respectable, and reflecting great credit on the *Janet*. The commissioner received us at his door, offered us wine, and while we were drinking it in came Captain Brandeis,★ a political refugee from Samoa,

Majuro Station — Marshall Islands. Specimen
Marshall Is. canoe.

a slender, sallow man with a small head and the most extraordinary eyes of glittering blackness which seemed to shrink from meeting one's gaze and yet to challenge it with a nervous defiance. He was pale, and I thought he was prepared for an unpleasant meeting with Louis; that wore off very quickly, and the two were soon deep in conversation, I talking twaddle with the commissioner that Louis might have the captain alone. Louis is fascinated by the captain and I do not wonder; but his eye is too wild, he is too nervous, and his nose is not to be depended on — a weak and emotional nose. A man, I should say, capable of the most heroic deeds, sometimes preternaturally wise, and sometimes proportionately foolish; a born adventurer, but never a successful one.

The commissioner showed me the 'garden', an acre or so of high-island plants grown in foreign soil brought in vessels. The commissioner's room was decorated with trophies of native arms, armour, etc. He promised to have a native sailing chart made for Louis. These charts are very curious things, indeed, made of sticks, some curved, some straight, caught here and there by a small yellow cowry. The cowries represent islands, the sticks both currents and winds and days' sailing. The distances between the islands have nothing to do with miles, but with hours only. These charts are very little used now, only one old chief knowing how to make them, but the time was when each young chief must pass his examination in the charts, knowing them by heart, as they were never taken to sea but kept at home for reference and continual study. We lunched with the commissioner and, the steam-whistle calling us soon after, we went on board to start immediately for Majuro.

20 June

At Majuro early in the morning, a pearl of atolls. The lagoon, large and round, but not so large that we cannot distinctly follow the coastline. At the entrance it is broken into the most enchanting small islets, all very green and soft, the lagoon clear and in colour like a chrysoprase. Mr Henderson offered us a little house on the windward side, so we took our mats and blankets and a lantern with us in the boat. The house was the old 'lookout' consisting of a single room with lattice-work running along two sides of the wall under the roof; this lattice served for windows. The door had a padlock so we could lock it as we came and went.

I had taken my paints with me and made a little portrait of a native girl called 'Topsy' by her white husband. She was a very small, very thin creature, greatly given to dress. She seemed to live with several other women in a sort of boat-builders' shed, where I would always find her, her thick hair shining with oil and carefully braided, a different head-dress for a different hour — her keys hanging below her rows of necklaces, busily employed at something or other; sometimes it was a necklace she was stringing on shreds of pandanus leaves, sometimes a new print gown she was cutting out with a most capable, businesslike air; or she might be feeding her monkey ('*monkaia*', she called it) or her gentle-eyed dog; or, most interesting task of all, sorting her possessions into order. She had two pretty large camphor-wood chests quite filled up with cotton prints, coloured handkerchiefs, and various accessories of the toilet. She dressed for the portrait in a gown of cheese-cloth drawn in at the waist by a white cotton belt edged with blue and white; the yoke of the bodice and the sleeves were trimmed to match, and the hem of the skirt was marked with a black braid. Her hair, smoothly drawn back over her little rabbit head, was ornamented by two bands worked in a design with beads, and her necklaces were innumerable. On one arm she proudly showed me the word Majuro tattooed and on the other, Topsy. It seems that she was a castaway from another island, every other soul in the canoe being lost. She was absolutely ignorant, and when something was said about her heart, gravely assured us that she had no heart, being solid meat all through. Topsy sat for her portrait

White Trader and family –
taken at Majuro, Marshall Is.

most conscientiously as though it were a photograph, not moving a hair's breadth, nor hardly winking. After each sitting she returned to exactly the same position. I tried in vain to make her take it more easily; when I talked to her (she knew half a dozen words of English) she responded with stiff lips, trying to speak without moving them. I took her a wreath which delighted her, and just before we left I came across a red silk bodice with a smocked yoke and embroidered cuffs; just the thing, I felt, for Topsy. The captain, Louis, and Lloyd were with me when I gave it to her. She instantly slipped off her upper garments, showing a very pretty little figure, and we all together robed her in the bodice. Topsy is quite a great lady with her female attendants, living in her boat-house, sleeping on her mat beside her two chests with her dog, and that rich possession the '*monkaia*'. Some one the captain knew took a large monkey to Savage Island, but the people would not allow it to remain; it was, they said, derogatory to their dignity.

There are broad, well-kept walks on Majuro, and to cross the island to our cabin was like passing through a palm-house. When somebody remembered it, fresh palm toddy was brought to us in the early morning, and once tea. (Fresh palm toddy tastes like sweet champagne and is very wholesome; sour or fermented toddy is quite another thing.) Louis slept on shore with me one or two nights, and then, as it rained a good deal, it was judged better for him to remain on board. The next night I slept alone. At about two in the morning I waked with the consciousness that some one was in the room besides myself. I peered about without moving and saw two native men who moved into the moonlight so I could see them distinctly. I said, 'Who's there? What do you want? Get away with you!' in the gruffest voice I could assume, and after a few moments' hesitation, they made off. One evening, while Louis still slept in the lookout, quite late, the room became filled with a peculiar and pleasant fragrance. For some time we could not make it out, but it finally occurred to us that it was the scent of pandanus nut. Some native, overcome by curiosity, must have crept to the house so softly that we did not hear him, but the pandanus he had been chewing betrayed him. As they all seemed to think that I should not stop alone so far away, Lloyd came over and slept on Louis's mat. Some of the pandanus nuts here I like very much; they are juicy and of fragrant, tart flavour like a good apple.

One day while I was talking to Topsy at her door, the monkey being fastened by a long, light chain to a tree close by, a girl fell down in a fit. Her head struck a woman's lap, but the woman hastily thrust her off so that she lay, half smothering, face down, in the sand. She sniffed, and moaned, and clicked her teeth together, but neither frothed at the mouth, nor protruded her tongue, as I supposed people did in fits. Not a soul moved to help her, but '*monkaia*' leaped on her head like a demon and began biting and plucking at her hair and face. I tore him off with difficulty, the men and women standing by quite helpless with laughter. I had to threaten a woman with physical violence before she would drag the girl away from the monkey while I held the brute. The next morning, while I was painting at Topsy's portrait, the girl who had the fit sat on the floor beside me watching the process. My bottle of oil and a basket of coral just given me were standing between the legs of the easel. Suddenly the girl lurched forward, upsetting the bottle of oil, and had a fit with her face in the basket of coral. The instinct of saving property brought Topsy to my aid this time, however, and together we dragged the girl to a safer position.

One afternoon I asked the name of a particularly bright-looking girl who came to visit the ship. 'Neel,' was the reply. 'How did she get that name?' I asked. 'Oh, it came in this way: She was a sharp little child, and some white man said she was sharp as a needle, so they called her needle.' Neel is the nearest they come to pronouncing it. I was told that Neel was a capital mimic and actress. I made an offering of a wreath and she agreed to give me an example of her skill if all the white men went away. First, she said (Johnny, a half-caste, interpreting), she would represent a well-known native woman, with an impediment in her speech, on a visit to a neighbour; immediately her round, fat face twisted itself into a thousand wrinkles, and her thick, protruding lips became pinched and thin, on one side lifted like a harelip. She spoke like a person with a cleft palate, very garrulously, making polite inquiries about different members of the family she was supposed to visit, but never waiting for an answer. After this impersonation she assumed a prim air and, with a dry, nipping precision of speech, and neat little persuasive gestures, gave us a bit of an English missionary's sermon. The voice was a man's voice, and the English accent in speaking the native words perfect. Had I not been aware that the girl was speaking, I should have felt certain I could pick out the man by his face; I knew it, and his figure, and his umbrella.

I am told they go in for 'devil work' here; they call it 'bu-bu', which reminds one of the negro word. When their old witch women (they are always old) wish to lure a vessel to destruction they run up and down the beach shouting their incantations, waving, as they run, a long stick with a red rag on the end. A man whose vessel was wrecked on these islands told me that as the ship neared the rock where they struck they could distinctly see an old woman rushing along the beach waving her red rag.

A Mr R— told Lloyd that in New Ireland he had had a similar experience to that of Tom Day. A man had attacked him, and he had said to the bystanders: 'I'll give an axe for that man's head.' The next morning he discovered the head stuck on his gate-post. He said he had often bought victims set apart to be eaten for ten sticks of tobacco. If he paid up honourably, the natives were honourable in return, and never after molested his man.

One evening I stopped at Mr M—'s to wait while some one went on board for my key, which I had forgotten. Tin Jack, who was there, promptly presented me with a fine piece of stag-horn coral belonging to our host, following up the coral with presents of elaborately worked mats, some of which he gave in his own name and some in Mr M—'s, until he had made me the embarrassed recipient of four. The captain, who dropped in, was also requested to make choice of a pair of the best. Poor Mr M—, feeling that it would be more graceful to give his own presents, then offered me a curious fish preserved in a bottle which Mr Hird, much to my distress, scornfully refused on my behalf as a present 'unfit for a lady'.

The Marshalls seem a very damp, rainy group of islands, but, in consequence, breadfruit grows on most of them, and bananas on many. We had expected to fill up with copra at Majuro, but measles has been ravaging the islands. The King himself, whom we had wished greatly to see, old Jebberk, lay dying and *tapued* to whites. Two other Kings came to visit us on the vessel, both very fine, intelligent-looking men. One was dressed in a mat breech-clout and a comical red shirt or jacket, and had his hair done up on the top of his head Japanese fashion. The other wore a red-and-blue-figured petticoat, very full at the waist, where it was gathered in with native cord. Around his neck he had a pink shell necklace, and his hair was done in the same high knot as affected by the first King. We had finished luncheon when the last King came, so he had his alone spread at one corner of the table. I gave him a wreath, of the best, for his queen; he admired it greatly, and examined it over and over. Finally he turned to me saying, 'What you want?' pointing to the wreath. He meant to ask what would I like for a return present. I said 'Nothing', which was a mistake, afterward cleverly rectified by Louis. The King asked through an interpreter how long it would be before the *Janet* sailed, as all his things were at his own village, and he wanted to get some mats for me. Louis replied that we were sailing almost immediately but that when we returned we would be most happy to receive his present. This proved satisfactory, and the King was put at his ease.

Kai buke — one of King of Majuro —
— and white trader

24 June

Left Majuro.

26 June

Again at Jaluit. Went to see the commissioner, where we found our island charts awaiting us. Louis and the commissioner and Captain Brandeis tried to make out the names of the islands by comparing the charts with our European map, but failed; a man who had been thirty years in the islands was consulted, and afterward a native, but still they were baffled. It was finally settled that the thirty-year resident should see the maker of the charts (now absent) and get a complete key to be sent to Samoa. Lloyd bought some German beer, which is excellent, and I bought two jars of sweeties, a couple of Pleasant Island baskets, several pieces of tortoise-shell, and some abominable sausages. The commissioner gave me two shells and Captain Brandeis gave me a lovely one, also a black mother-of-pearl shell, such as the Gilbert Islanders use for trade.

Left the same day, towing out a schooner.

27 June

Arrived at Namorik. Louis went on shore and met a wicked old man who afterward appeared in the 'Beach of Falesá'.

28 June

First thing in the morning at Ebon; anchored in the passage nearly opposite the wreck of the *Hazeltine*, American schooner. Left early in the afternoon.

1 July

Arrived Apiang, lay outside. Louis ill. Captain Tierney came off in a canoe. No copra. The missionaries in power and a general *tapu*. On to Tarawa.

3 July

Aranuka, one of Tembinoka's islands. Louis still ill. He was lying in his bunk when the King and his people came on board. A pleasant-faced man, who, with the rest, was shaking hands with me, asked for Louis. I said he was ill, whereupon he demanded to be taken at once to the sick man. I guessed that he was a medicine-man. Louis said he stood beside his bed, with the gently soothing, insinuating, professional manner of the European practitioner, asking his symptoms and very anxious to know if there was a 'dog-star' in Samoa.

A little later a soft hand tapped me on the shoulder; I turned — it was the King, Tembinoka himself, smiling and holding out both hands to me. He looked much better and was greatly concerned at Louis being ill. Mr Henderson is going to take the King's boat back to Apemama for him with his harem and court.

4 July

Got under way at eight o'clock with about two hundred deck passengers — all the King's wives and body-guard and retainers generally — and steamed down to Apemama flying the royal ensign at the main truck. The whole ship, every plank of her, covered at night with sleeping natives. Among the rest were babies and three dogs, the latter with strange, glassy, white eyes. The King's favourite wife had a snub-nosed puppy, which, when it became restless and whined, she put to her breast and suckled. All the head women had their devil boxes, taking the greatest care of them. They consulted me about ours through every interpreter they could find. They always referred to the box indirectly; the interpreter would be told first to ask if I had not carried away from Apemama something very precious. Upon my answering that I had, questions were then put as to its whereabouts, etc. Louis and I were talking to the King on a different matter in which the escape of hissing steam was mentioned. His Majesty jumped to the

...arem and little son of King Tembier...
...this passage from Arinka to A...
...ingmill Islands.

conclusion that we were speaking of the devil box, and assured us that we need feel no alarm when the shell inside (representing the devil, Tiaporo) made a noise. We had only to give it a very small bit of tobacco and that would settle him. He thought it a good sign, and that the shell was in proper mediumistic order when Tiaporo was noisy, though he confessed it would be better if we had a 'dog-star' handy. A quarter of an hour later all the King's women were in a state of ferment concerning our devil box, the news of Tiaporo's behaviour causing the most excited comments.

The getting on board of the people was a wild affair of noise and confusion. Boat after boat was unladen, and piles of the most extraordinary household goods blocked up every space that should have been kept clear; at least twenty-five large zinc pails came from one boat. There were sewing-machines, large rosewood musical boxes, axes and spades, cutlasses, unwieldy bag pillows, every conceivable sort of bag and basket, cocoanut shells of toddy syrup, and shells of water; old nuts, new nuts, every sort of nut; also large packages of the native pudding (giant taro pounded up with pandanus syrup and cocoanut milk, baked underground in taro leaves), and piles of neatly done up sticks of what we call sweet sawdust, made of the beaten pandanus nut. There were camphor-wood chests of every size, and mat packages without end. One woman was trying in vain to find a place for her ear piercer, a stick of hard, black seaweed, some two feet long, tapering from the circumference of a couple of inches in the middle to a smooth, sharp point at either end; round each side of the centre, where it was intended the hand should grasp it, was a ring of yellow feathers worked with human hair; these looked just the same as the royal Hawaiian feathers — also those on the peace spears I got at Savage Island — but I have never seen the bird that produces them.

Our black boys are almost insane with excitement and 'Tom Sawyered' to such a degree, showing off before the court ladies, that it was a wonder and mercy none were killed. When they were raising the boats to the davits, Louis said they were upside down more often than not, doing herculean feats of strength. The harem ladies were gathered together aft and a *tapu* placed round them. Ladies of a lower station found what places pleased them best and had a much gayer time than the great ones, for the black boys sang, and danced, and shouted with merriment the whole night through. The very old ladies of high rank — the King's mother, hopelessly drunk on gin, which she carried everywhere with her, the King's aunt, and one or two others — spent the night on the captain's bridge. The people all showed the utmost affection for us, our old friend and servant 'Snipe' in particular. ('Snipe' was one of three slave girls lent us by Tembinoka when we lived at Apemama, in Equator Town. The other two we called Stodge and Fatty.) She would seize every opportunity to get beside me, when she would smooth my hair, fondle my hands, and alternately put her arm round my waist and poke me in the ribs with her elbows, giggling sentimentally the while.

Quite late at night Uncle Parker sneaked down to the saloon and squatted on the floor with a kindly grin. He was not in the least surprised nor offended when Louis hustled him out. I had not had the heart to do it myself, as I should.

Among the rest of the people was a man who had known us in Butaritari; he gave us full news of our Cowtubs (retainers) there. Tembinoka's governor, whom we had known as Reuben, who now says his name is Raheboam, begged that I would speak to the King and ask that he might go away with us. I assured him that it would be useless; the King could not afford to part with a man of his talents and acquirements, which is quite true. In the forecastle were the unfortunate exiles of Piru, among them our 'Boat's crew' looking very pretty and pert but grown no larger. Some years ago, I do not know how many, a large party of the natives of Piru, thinking to see the world, bought return tickets from the Wightman line to one of the other islands. They were warned that they must take their chances of a schooner going back to their own place. No schooner did; but they were carried on from island to island, each trip getting a little nearer home. The boy called 'Boat's crew' had been a servant of ours at Apemama, one of their halting places. They are to be taken on to Nanouti, a station so much the nearer home. An old man who was anxious to die on his native soil is still living and looks a hundred years old, his head entirely bald except for a tuft at the nape of his neck.

5 July

At Apemama, landing the court. Tin Jack had to sell a pet canoe he was taking to his station to the King, who insisted on having it. It cost five dollars and the King gave twenty for it; so, as a commercial speculation, it was no loss. When the King came on board this morning he laid a fine mat on my lap.

Later a great wailing arose from the forward deck. A woman who had taken possession of another woman's husband was being sent away with her people of the Piru party, and conceived it her duty to have an attack of nerves. She did not do it so well as they manage in France, but it was of the same order, and reasonably creditable. Her hysterical kicking and choking cries, when held back by her companions from drowning herself, was the most effective part of the performance. She soon gave it up, probably because of the lack of interest shown by the bystanders.

In the evening we had a farewell dinner with Tin Jack, champagne, toasts, speeches, etc. At night a party went on shore with fireworks; Mr Henderson answered with a display from the ship. As I was watching them I overheard a conversation between a white fireman and our cook about the dangers of the land. 'Why, one of my mates', said the fireman, 'got lost in the bush once, and it was a whole day before he got a drink of water. I wouldn't take the chance of that for all the money you could give me.' I reminded him that wrecked sailors had been known to suffer from thirst; he had never thought of that, he

ill Islands: — King Tembenoka and suite
"J. Nicoll" at the King's Island of Ap-
gig visiting for King and wives.

said, but anyhow it didn't seem the same. The fireworks were very successful, and I think pleased our black boys more than any one else. The ship rang with their shouts and musical, girlish laughter. All afternoon they had been scraping the ship's sides under water; it looked very odd to see them kicking like frogs and working at the same time; yet, after all this, they were ready for more dancing and songs. Louis and I agreed that we would willingly pay a high price for only Sally Day's superfluous energy to use at our discretion. All these men are from cannibal islands, but do not like that fact referred to. When Mr Hird teases them about it they declare they were mere infants when they were taken away and can remember nothing about the savage customs of their people.

6 July

Off Apemama, our black boys lying in a row under the awning, one reading the Bible (it was Sunday) and another playing hymns on an accordion. The King took breakfast with us, and we bade him good-bye, not so sadly as before, because now we have some hope of seeing him again.

7 July

Nanouti first thing in the morning. Went on shore after breakfast to 'Billy Jones's cousin's' place where British colours were flying. Tin Jack wished to be photographed in his new place in the midst of his new surroundings, so we had the camera with us. Lloyd and I wandered about and were astonished at the number of houses we saw piled up with dried cocoanuts not yet made into copra. We were told that a famine was feared and these nuts were stored as provisions. Speaking of provisions, we were struck by the difference in the condition of our Piru friends since we were fellow passengers with them on the schooner *Equator*. Then they were in the most abject poverty, hardly a mat among them, no food, only a few shells of water and a few old nuts. When we took them off Apemama they came as rich people, with bundles of fine mats, stacks of 'sawdust' food and dried pandanus fruit (very good, tasting like dried figs) and quantities, generally, of the best food produced in Apemama. The people all have cotton-print clothing as well as fine *ridis* and baskets full of tobacco with plenty of pipes.

While Lloyd and I were walking about in Nanouti, Tin Jack went back to the ship quite oblivious of the fact that we were left prisoners on account of the tide, for the entire day. When we arrived we had to take down part of the wall of a fishing ground to land at the house. We left the ship at ten and were tired, hungry, and very cross at being so deserted. Lloyd finally went off to try and find a canoe, hoping to reach the ship in that way and get something for me to eat. I had got very wet in crossing the surf in our own boat and was dressed in a filthy gown and chemise lent me by a native woman. I asked for a dry gown when I arrived and the woman gave me one she had cast off; I did not know what to do, as it was quite transparent, so I had to stay in the inner room. Tin Jack, hearing of this, demanded a chemise for me. The woman removed the one she was wearing, in a dark corner, folded it up, and then pretended to take it out of a trunk which she opened for the purpose. After this piece of either pride or delicacy I felt bound to put it on. As my head ached, I lay down on a mat, with an indescribably filthy pillow under my head, and tried to sleep. The people of the house, some twenty in number, came in every few moments to look at me; if the children made a noise they were smacked, thereupon bawling loudly enough to raise the roof, and occasionally a crowd of outside children would be beaten from the house with howls and yells. I never saw so much 'discipline' administered before in any of the islands. Outside my window a child was steadily smacked for crying for at least half an hour. I actually did fall asleep once, but was quickly awakened by a savage dog fight just under where I lay, the house standing high on piles. This house, belonging to

the trader, was one of the best I had seen, containing four rooms separated by stockades, with a lofty, airy roof, while along the shady side
ran a neat veranda. The whole house was tied together with sennit, the
sides and ends thatched as well as the roof.

Lloyd, having searched for about an hour and a half, had found a
canoe, and a native willing to take him off for the high price of ten
sticks of tobacco. In the meantime, Tin Jack, awakening to a sense of
the enormity of his behaviour, had despatched another canoe from the
ship with some sandwiches, a tin of sardines (useless with no tin opener),
and a bottle of stout without a corkscrew. When Lloyd discovered this,
he would not wait a moment, but tried to get back to me. In spite of
all he could do, he was landed in the surf some two miles short of
where I was. He struggled along the reef, sometimes knocked down
by the surf and most of the time up to his armpits in water. He had
on shoes of leather which became water-logged, and the nails, coming loose, tore the soles of his feet, adding to the difficulty of walking.
He also cut his ankle on the reef and grazed his leg, both serious
things to have happen here. (A scratch from dead coral is apt to cause
blood-poisoning and is greatly feared. The captain of a man–of–war
was said to have lost his leg in this way.) There was also the fear in his
mind that, thinking he had landed, I might have given my leavings to
the natives. I really cannot imagine why I did not; I several times made
a movement to do so and then something distracted my attention. It
was quite dark before the ship's boat could get in for us, and very chill.
Tin Jack, most eager in his apologies, had a bad quarter of an hour.

A cat, I hear, has been added to our ship's company. At Majuro a
man who had been shipwrecked there, and was taken on board the
Janet for Sydney, had a pet cat. One of the sailors found her swimming
round the ship trying to climb up the steep sides. An oar was put out
for her and she climbed in, almost drowned.

I begged a fish from one of the black boys, and with a nut, a pinch
of cayenne pepper, an old dried lemon, and some sea water, I made

girls' Costume

'miti' sauce and gave Louis a nice dish of raw fish for his dinner. He relished it very much, and ate all I prepared.

Raw fish may seem a strange delicacy for a sick man, but, properly prepared, there is nothing better than fresh raw mullet. I first learned this in Tautira, a lovely native village on the 'wild side' of Tahiti. My husband was alarmingly ill with pneumonia, and had sunk into a state of coma. There was no way to reach civilisation except by means of our yacht, the *Casco* — and the *Casco* was gone to Papeete to have her masts repaired. Crushed by this catastrophe I was gazing stupidly out over the village green, trying to gather my wits together, when my attention was distracted for a moment by the spectacle of a tall, graceful, native woman entering the house of the chief of Tautira, amid the acclamations of a great crowd. I vaguely remembered that for many days there had been preparations making for an expected visit from Moë, 'the great princess'. In about half an hour there was a tap at our door; there stood Moë with a plate of raw fish prepared with miti sauce. Speaking perfect English, she told me that she had heard there was a sick foreigner in the village whose wife was troubled because he would not eat, so, she said, she had made this dish herself, and if we could only get him to taste it he would eat more, and convalescence would follow immediately. At first Louis turned his head to one side wearily without opening his eyes, but by the advice of the princess I slipped a morsel between his lips; to my surprise he swallowed the bit, then another, and finally opened his eyes and asked: 'What's that?' Several times a day the princess came with her plate of fish and miti sauce, which was soon eagerly watched for and devoured by my invalid, and within the week Louis had so far recovered as to be able to walk over to the chief's house, where we took up our abode with him and Moë.

The raw fish, as prepared in Tahiti, instead of being revolting in appearance, as one might imagine, is as pleasing to the sight as to the taste. The fresh white meat of the mullet is cut into neat little strips about half an inch wide and a couple of inches long and laid side by side on a plate — of course it is carefully freed from skin and bones — and covered with miti sauce. Miti sauce is made of milk pressed from cocoanut meats (an entirely different thing from the refreshing water of the green drinking nut), mixed with about one third the quantity of lime-juice, a few tiny bits of the wild red pepper, and a little sea water. This sauce seems to cook the fish, which takes on a curdled look, and curls up a little at the edges as though it had just been boiled.

8 July

Remained all day and left at night. A long reef, and much trouble in getting Tin Jack's things clear of the ship. Heard the labour brig *Cito* had been landing rifles and cartridges. Tin Jack gone; he left late in the afternoon, the boat taking him to the reef, where we could see him being carried over it on a native's back. There were still fifty bags of copra to come on board; these were packed out to the boat on the backs of natives and our black boys. Mr Henderson gave Tin Jack two black pigs and a very fine, handsome mat; I gave him a supply of medicines carefully labelled, and a pillow with an extra case. When we left we blew the steam-whistle in farewell, burned a blue light, and let off two rockets, to which he responded with a rocket from the shore. One of our rockets was let off by the captain (who is quite ill) on the bridge. It shot at us and fire was sputtering all about the bridge, to our terror. A woman has been following me about all day trying to get me to adopt her little half-caste boy. She tried to bribe me with a mat, which in the end she gave me as a present. I gave her a bottle of scent. Everybody bargaining for shells, even the black boys and Mr Stoddard, the engineer. When the boat returned from landing Tin Jack it brought me from him an immense spear, very old and curious.

Tin Jack came to a sad end. He possessed a certain fixed income, which, however, was not large enough for Jack's ideas, so he spent most of the year as a South Sea trader, using the whole of his year's income in one wild burst of dissipation in the town of Sydney. One of his favourite amusements was to hire a hansom cab for the day, put the driver inside, and drive the vehicle himself, calling upon various passers-by to join him at the nearest public house. Some years ago when Jack was at his station he received word that his trustee, who was in charge of his property, had levanted with it all. Whereupon poor Jack put a pistol to his head and blew out what brains he possessed. He was a beautiful creature, terribly annoying at times, but with some-thing childlike and appealing — I think he was close to what the Scotch call a natural — that made one forgive pranks in him that would be unforgivable in others. He was very proud of being the orig-inal of 'Tommy Hadden' in the 'Wrecker', and carried the book wher-ever he went.

9 July

Piru. I am disgusted by the apathy of our exiles. Except one woman, they did not even raise their heads to look on their native land. There was no excitement, no appearance of interest. The Samoan missionary and friends of his, all well-dressed, superior-looking peo-ple, came on board. The missionary demanded, in a high and mighty way, that paper, and envelopes, and pen and ink be brought him. Lloyd was working the typewriter to my dictation, which amused them all extremely. Mr Clark, the missionary from Samoa, has just been here. To our disappointment we have missed him by only twenty-four hours. He has gone, they say, to Apemama, to try and persuade the King to allow them to land a missionary. I think he will not succeed. The King fears the power missionaries get over the peo-ple. The traders have also been on board, the braggart Briggs and a Mr Villiero from the Argentine Republic. Mr Villiero's father was Italian, his mother Tyrolese. He seems an intelligent, pleasant fellow, and I talked a long time with him. A few years ago, he tells me, a man died on this island who was once secretary to Rajah Brooke.★

He asked to bring his wife and his adopted daughter, a half-caste Tahitian named Prout, to see me.

I was talking to the two traders to-day when Briggs said that he used to carry the lepers from Honolulu to Molokai. 'Did he know Father Damien?'★ I asked. After much searching in his memory, at last he said he did. 'A Catholic priest he was, who seemed to be all right when I knew him, but some pretty ugly stories have come out about him since in Honolulu, I understand.' I gave them Louis's pamphlet without a word more.

The tides very low; there is a good deal of copra here, and our black boys worked last night until two in the morning, and to-night they expect to be up still later. One of the black boys is ill with a sore throat, headache, and diarrhoea. We gave him some castor-oil and laudanum, not knowing what else to do. The captain very weak, indeed, with intense headache, sickness, and an intolerable burning in his stomach. There is an odd dryness of his skin, not like fever. He has taken no nourishment but barley-water for days. Louis is better, the haemorrhage having stopped.

10 July

Still lying off Piru. Mr Hird came back yesterday with a sickening account of the man Blanchard who was supposed to be implicated in what was called 'the Jim Byron poisoning case'.★ Blanchard has contracted some terrible disease which makes it necessary for him to lift up his eyelids with his fingers when he wishes to look at one, and has swelled his nose to a monstrous size. Blanchard is, he says, an American, and when he first met the man, some years ago, had some pretentions of being a gentleman, but has now fallen to a state of degradation that is horrible. Blanchard spoke of the murder and confessed that he knew it was to be done and that he was there when it was done.

11 July

Still at Piru at ten o'clock p.m. Mr Villiero has come on board with his wife, a handsome young woman, to whom I gave a wreath, some lollies for the children (all adopted, her own being dead), and a piece of lace. A little later Mr Hird brought in several traders and gave them luncheon.

Lifting anchor.

12 July

Left Piru last night, arriving at Noukanau this morning. We carry with us a native man, as an exile, to this island. The Samoan native missionaries told their people that for certain crimes it was allowable to kill the offender. Such a case occurred, and the guilty person, who richly deserved his fate, was put to death. Then the native missionaries said that the taking of life called for capital punishment. Fortunately, at this juncture, a white missionary from Samoa appeared in the missionary ship, and it was arranged that the avenger be exiled for an indefinite period. As this man has large possessions in Noukanau, it is to be hoped that he may not experience much discomfort. He is a fine-looking, respectable man of early middle age and had his family with him.

The ship all morning has been filled with crowds of natives (among them the inevitable leper with elephantiasis), all chattering like monkeys. I have bought from them three pronged shark's-tooth spears, one for a striped undershirt, the other two for a couple of patterns apiece of cotton print. I also bought a mat with rows of openwork running through it, just like hemstitching, and for a florin I got an immense necklace of human teeth. A little while ago, in some of these islands, especially Maraki, a good set of teeth was a dangerous possession, as many people were murdered for them. I trust mine were honestly come by — at least taken in open warfare.

Last evening our pigs fought like dogs, biting each other and rushing about the deck like mad. The noise they made was more like barking than grunting or squealing. The cook has cut his leg; Mr Hird has a bad cold; the engineer, Mr Stoddard, is sneezing, and Louis feels as though he had caught the cold also; the captain still very bad; he caught more cold last night. Lloyd's wounds, from the reef on Tin Jack's island much better. I bound them with soap and sugar first and then covered them with iodoform.

We have been to two settlements to-day and are now returning to the first. At the second Tom Day came on board and had a meal; also Captain Smith. Our coal is very low; hardly any left, in fact, and we are all burning with curiosity as to where we are going next — to the Hebrides, Fiji — or perhaps to Brisbane. Spent the evening talking to Tom Day. He told many tales of Bishop Patterson★ and of hunts for necklace teeth. A father who has good teeth often leaves them as a heritage to his children. They are worth a great deal — or were. He has known many murders for teeth. My necklace seems a gruesome possession.

13 July

Left Noukanau in the morning; arrived at Piru at eleven o'clock; left at one, Monday morning, for Onoatoa. Louis had a long talk there with Frank Villiero. Land here is divided into large and small lots; the large, one and a half acres, the small, half an acre. There are never any smaller divisions. A large lot is quite enough for a family to live on. Some great families own many lots and have picked as many as fifteen hundred nuts in one month. Pieces of land are confiscated for theft, or murder, by those who suffer loss through the crime. A piece of land so taken from a murderer can be regained by the criminal pouring a bottle of oil over the body of the man he has murdered. But this is never done if the person fined bears malice or enmity toward the dead man. The island was formerly in a far more prosperous state owing to the fact that a large proportion of the inhabitants were then kept as slaves.

The duties of the 'old men' (the democratic islands are supposed to be ruled by the 'old men', who meet in a body to make laws) are really the demarcation and recording of lands; they can go back for generations in the division of island lands. The population of Piru is about twenty-five hundred; the police, at present, number about one thousand men uniformed in blue jumpers, jean trousers, and a wisp of red on the arm. There are three districts, each being patrolled at night by the police, who call the roll of every grown person, and must be answered. The fines go one half to the teacher (for his private benefit), one fourth to the old men, one fourth to the police. Villiero has seen a policeman receive no more than ten cocoanuts for a whole year's work, and he must find his own uniform of which he is not proud. Every portion of the island is owned and the demarcations owned. They are a mean lot here; their fights mere broils, and very little feeling is shown for each other. A canoe drifted away, or a man dead, is almost instantly forgotten. Little or no sour toddy is drunk since the missionaries came. Mr Clark, the missionary from Samoa, told them that on Sundays when a ship came up to the island they must allow a couple of men to take the trader off; formerly these boatmen were always fined.

Mr Villiero brought his wife and adopted daughter, Miss Prout, to see me in the afternoon. It was very embarrassing, for they came laden with gifts, and I had nothing suitable to offer in return. We had an adoption ceremony by which I became either mother, or daughter, to Mrs Villiero, no one quite knew which, not even her husband. Miss Mary Prout was quite the 'young person', shy and silent. Both were well dressed and wore European rings. Mrs Villiero makes all her husband's clothes. The presents consisted of a little full-rigged ship inside a bottle, the mouth of which it could not pass. Mr Villiero was three weeks in making it, working all the time, a regular sailor's present; also a large, fine mat with a deep fringe of red wool, in very bad taste, a couple of plaited mats, a pair of shells, and an immense packet of pandanus sweetmeat. When we met Mrs Villiero she threw round my neck a string of porpoise teeth, thick and long, the preliminary to adoption. With Louis's help, Mr Villiero made his will. (He was afterward lost in a labour vessel — virtually a slaver — that sank with many unfortunate natives on board as well. It was on the way to South America.) He has a feeling that his life is not safe here with some of the other traders, the poisoners, in fact. He told Louis of an unfortunate affair that happened on the fourth of July. Villiero, Briggs, and the Chinese trader made a signed bargain that they would all buy copra at a certain fixed price, with a fine of two hundred dollars to be paid by the one breaking the bargain. Soon all the custom had fallen into the hands of the Chinaman. On inquiry it came out that while the Chinaman ostensibly bought at the agreed price, he gave a present of tobacco besides, thereby evading the letter of the bargain. Following Briggs's foolish advice, the other traders armed themselves to the teeth and went at night to the Chinaman's house. Briggs and Blanchard guarded the door, while Villiero, holding a pistol to the Chinaman's head, demanded the two hundred dollars fine. Of course it was paid. When the missionary ship came in Villiero told this tale to the white missionary who advised immediate restitution of the money, and said he was bound to report the traders' conduct. I wonder that a man of Villiero's intelligence should have been led by a person like Briggs.

The captain is very weak, but Louis better.

14 July

Onoatoa Island.

15 July

At Tamana early in the morning. One of our passengers taken on at Tom Day's island and introduced by Tom as 'Captain Thomas, this old Cinderella', went on shore with all his belongings. Another passenger whom we are taking to Sydney made me a native drill which will cut through the most delicate shell, or through the iron of a boiler, or a dish, or a glass tumbler. I made holes through some red and white bone whist counters and strung them into necklaces, really very pretty. Since we were at Tamana before there has been a murder and an execution. A man from another island, indignant at being worsted in a wrestling match, watched at the church and struck a spear into his victim, who soon died. The execution was by hanging. They dragged the man up by the neck, then let him down to see if he was dead, then pulled him up again only to lower him for another look, continuing this barbarity until they were satisfied no life was left in the wretch.

16 July

Arorai in the morning. The first thing we hear is that poor McKenzie, the man who was starving, is dead, supposedly from a surfeit on the soups we left him. He ate ravenously; said in reply to a question of how he felt, 'I feel full', immediately became insensible, and so remained for three days, when he died. It did not occur to me to warn him against overeating; soup seemed such an innocent thing; I was afraid to let him have solid food at first.

'Cockroach', one of our black boys, has got his fingers badly crushed. He has been crying like a child ever since. The captain still very ill; he and I went through two medical books and both came to the conclusion that he must be suffering from inflammation of the stomach. He says he has been worse ever since one day when three black boys refused to work on a Sunday. Sally Day, he says, was very impudent, and he was too weak to knock Sally down, which fact preys on his spirits.

To-day one of the boats steered by Mr Hird suddenly disappeared in the surf, and Mr Henderson at once put out for her. She had capsized and stove a small hole in one end. Mr Hird came dripping from

Boys setting sail on
S.S. Janet Nicoll.

his involuntary bath. Fortunately, no one was injured but the engineer and Mr B— (a passenger from Jaluit) and they only in their feelings. They were waiting a long way down the reef when the accident happened, and could not get another boat in time for dinner. We killed a pig to-day, the first, our sheep being now done. Charley, passenger from Jaluit, working his way, gave me a belt of human hair. Some natives brought off a shark they had just killed, hoping to sell it to us for food. Mr Hird told a story of a shark he had seen chasing a fish. The shark could easily catch the fish, swimming in a straight line, but could not turn quickly, so the fish knowingly swam round and round him. They were very near the ship when the fish jumped out of the water. With the quickness of lightning the shark struck it with his tail straight into his mouth. There is a swordfish here with a snout like a spear, long and sharp, which follows the flying-fish. When the natives are fishing they have to be on the lookout, as he jumps at them and tries to stab them with his sword. One of our passengers knew a man who was killed by such a stab. I forgot to mention that Tom Day told me that during this present epidemic of measles he saw a woman buried alive. 'She was too weak to resist, so her husband just buried her'; the same sort of tale as Mr Hird's of Penrhyn.

17 July

Had a sharp squall in the night. Lloyd slept through it all, his things swimming in the water. I put my head out of the port and watched the rain-drops strike the sea, each producing a spark like a star. It looked as though the heavens were reversed. I often find my bath, when I take it after dark, blazing like liquid fireworks. The weather continues bad, and we are rolling a good deal. Louis much better; the captain very weak and ill. Lloyd's leg, hurt on the reef at Tin Jack's island, shows uncomfortable symptoms. I suppose I should burn it out, but it requires courage to perform that operation.

18 July

Arrived at Vanumea at ten o'clock. Left at nightfall under sealed orders, steering S.S.W.

24 July

First thing in the morning sighted Eromango about fifteen miles away, and a little later, Tanna. Eromango is the place where the missionary John Williams★ (always spoken of as 'the martyr Williams') was killed by the natives.

Some time ago a good deal of amusement was got from discussions concerning the mango and the proper way to eat it. Mr Stoddard said it should be eaten with a spoon, which is impossible. We soon discovered that he had confused the mango with the barbadine, though he would not confess it. One evening when the bread was under baked I pressed the crumb into the semblance of a spoon and solemnly presented it to him as a 'mango spoon'. This morning I found a large pumpkin hanging up to ripen. I borrowed it from the cook, and Mr Hird and I tied it up in an enormous parcel, while Louis wrote out a card in printing letters to go with it.

> For Walter Stoddard Esq.,
> — One Mango —
> With the fond love of the
> inhabitants of Eromango.

(This is gathered, with a spoon, from the finest mango swamp in the island. But beware of the fate of the martyr Williams, who died from trying to eat one with too short a spoon. O mango and do likewise.)

To make the presentation scene more impressive, I made a pair of false eyes to be worn like spectacles by hooking wire round the edges of a very large pair of green cat's-eye opercula, which Mr Henderson donned at the appearance of the pumpkin. The parcel was brought in at dinner by the chief steward with the assurance that it had come off in a boat from Eromango, sent by the people of the island. Anything more truly diabolical than the expression of the cat's-eyes cannot be well conceived. I chose very clear, dark ones, with a well-marked white ring on one side, which I made the upper, so that the eyes were apparently starting from their sockets with fiendish surprise and malevolence.

25 July

Mare Island, Loyalty group; lay off the Sarcelle passage all night, about forty-five miles from Noumea, our first civilised port and the last we shall make until we reach the end of our cruise at Sydney. A large, most strange, and picturesque island. At first sight it seemed only desolate cliffs and terraces. Here and there at wide intervals a tree, very tall and close-growing, stood up straight like a needle. As we drew nearer, however, enchanting little bays began to open up. We could make out groves of cocoa-palms and the needle trees clustered together, making a curious edging to the cliffs. In one of these bays was the mission station; we could see the white wooden house smothered in trees, the plantation of palms following the indentations of the shore-line, and stretching far back to the white and coloured cliffs that ran up into the precipitous hills. In a niche on a cliff side was a great statue of the Virgin, dazzling white in the sun. Before the mission house ran a broad, smooth beach. We could distinguish many people standing there, and a fine large boat.

26 July

At half past one, Noumea. A succession of the most lovely bays began to open up as we steamed nearer. The surf runs out some forty miles and is studded with small islands, some like little hills rising from the sea, and some miniature low islands fringed with cocoa-palms. We all don the clothes of civilisation to go on shore, looking very strange to each other.

Explanatory notes

TAPU
(PAGE 57)

The *tapu* (taboo), a form of prohibition combining religious and legal force, was one of the most important institutions regulating indigenous Pacific societies. A *tapu* person, object, action or word was in some sense set apart, consecrated or forbidden either to all or to an individual or group. Both the sacred and the impure are included in the concept of *tapu*.

RIDI
(PAGE 58)

A short fringe skirt made from strips of pandanus leaf, the traditional dress of Gilbert Islands women. See photo on page 175.

MR LOW, THE ARTIST IN NEW YORK
(PAGE 64)

Will H. Low (1853–1932), friend of Bob Stevenson and Robert Louis Stevenson, the model for the character of Loudon Dodd in *The Wrecker*.

THE LATE WAR
(PAGE 76)

In September 1888, a revolt against the German rule of Samoa through the puppet-king Tamasese led to war between supporters of rival chiefs and brought the 'Three Powers' with interests in Samoa — Germany, Britain and the United States — to the brink of hostilities. International war was avoided when the famous hurricane of March 1889 destroyed their warships in Apia harbour and the competing powers turned to a diplomatic solution.

DOCTOR STEUBEL, THE GERMAN CONSUL-GENERAL
(PAGE 77)

German consul at Apia in the early 1880s, recalled to the post after the hurricane in 1889. In *A Footnote to History* Stevenson called him 'my friend' and 'that invaluable public servant', but criticised the rigour of some of his policies and his insensitivity to indigenous feeling.

THE GERMAN FIRM AT SAMOA
(PAGE 78)

The *Deutsche Handels-und-Plantagen-Gesellschaft der Südsee-Inseln zu Hamburg,* generally called simply 'the German firm', was the largest trading firm in the Pacific. The German firm's commercial interests drove German policy in Samoa in the 1880s and 1890s. Its Samoan plantations used imported labour from the western Pacific.

TAHITI HAD BEEN TAKEN BY THE FRENCH
(PAGE 92)

The French had held Tahiti since 1842; the islanders' 'latest' news is nearly half a century out of date.

SOUTH PACIFIC DIRECTORY
(PAGE 116)

Alexander Findlay, *A Directory for the Navigation of the South Pacific Ocean,* 5th edition (London: Richard Holmes Laurie, 1884) which the Stevensons took on their Pacific cruises and consulted regularly for both information and entertainment. 'Persons with friends in the islands should purchase Findlay's *Pacific Directories*' wrote Stevenson; 'they're the best of reading anyway, and may almost count as fiction.'

THE GREAT EARTHQUAKE IN JAVA
(PAGE 120)

One of the world's most destructive volcanic eruptions occurred on the island of Krakatoa (or Krakatau), in the Sunda Strait between Java and Sumatra, in 1883. A series of violent explosions destroyed much of the island and produced massive tidal waves, which killed about 36,000 people and had far-reaching effects on weather and ecology.

'HARTSHORN', OUR MEDICAL AUTHORITY
(PAGE 137)

Henry Hartshorne, *Essentials of the Principles and Practice of Medicine*, 3rd edition (Philadelphia, 1871).

PAINKILLER
(PAGE 139)

In the Pacific islands in the nineteenth century 'painkiller' was the generic name for medicine.

WANDERING MINSTREL
(PAGE 140)

The castaways from the *Wandering Minstrel*, wrecked on Midway Island in February 1888, arrived in Honolulu while the Stevensons were there in 1889. The voyage, shipwreck and rescue were attended by elements of mystery and scandal which intrigued Louis and Lloyd so much that they used the *Wandering Minstrel* incident as the basis for the plot of their novel *The Wrecker*: hence Louis's eagerness to gather more information from Cameron.

A 'DEVIL BOX'
(PAGE 154)

The Apemaman devil box was an oblong-shaped box made of pandanus wood, standing on four legs, and containing a shell that was believed to be inhabited by a spirit called Chench. These boxes were used by wizards or medicine-men in ceremonies to heal the sick, and Stevenson was cured of a cold after undergoing such a ceremony at Apemama in 1889. He recounts the episode and its sequel — his purchase of the devil box — in *In the South Seas*.

CAPTAIN BRANDEIS
(PAGE 163)

Eugen Brandeis was the German soldier who was the power behind the Samoan puppet-king Tamasese in 1887–88. At the time of this meeting, Stevenson had already begun his study of recent Samoan affairs, *A Footnote to History*, using as one of his chief informants the American trader H. J. Moors, who had been a key opponent of the Tamasese–Brandeis regime — hence Fanny's idea that Brandeis expected an unpleasant meeting with her husband. However, Brandeis is sympathetically portrayed in *A Footnote to History*: Stevenson liked his 'romantic and adventurous character' and admired his vision for the development of Samoa, although he believed it was impatiently, often injudiciously implemented, and fundamentally compromised by links with German trading interests.

RAJAH BROOKE
(PAGE 186)

Sir James Brooke (1803–68), legendary colonial adventurer and ruler. He was made Rajah of Sarawak (part of the island of Borneo) in 1841 by the Sultan of Brunei, for his services in suppressing rebel Dyak tribes. The Brooke dynasty ruled Sarawak for just over a hundred years.

FATHER DAMIEN
(PAGE 187)

Joseph de Veuster (1840–89), the Belgian Roman Catholic mission-ary known as Father Damien, became famous as 'the leper priest of Molokai'. After his death (from leprosy) some Protestants decried the value of his service to the community of lepers at the remote Hawaiian settlement. The Rev. Charles Hyde, an American Congre-gational minister in Honolulu, wrote a private letter attacking Damien's morals, motives and achievements, which was published in religious papers around the world. Stevenson had visited the leper settlement at Molokai in May 1889, only a few weeks after Father Damien's death, and had been greatly impressed with what he saw and heard of the priest's labours, calling him 'a man, with all the grime and paltriness of mankind; but a saint and a hero all the more for that'. He was incensed by Hyde's attack, which he read in Sydney in February 1890, and struck back in his 'Open Letter to the Reverend Dr Hyde of Honolulu', generally known as *Father Damien*. The pamphlet, dated Sydney, 25 February 1890, was privately printed in Sydney and distributed in March. It has since been reprinted many times in various editions of Stevenson's work.

THE JIM BYRON POISONING CASE
(PAGE 187)

William Blanchard, an American trader, was thought to have been complicit in the poisoning of Jim Byron, an English trader, by the Swedish trader Peter Grant when they were drinking together at Mariki in 1888. The Stevensons heard of the case when they were on the *Equator* cruise, and Stevenson made inquiries in Sydney to assist the official tracing of the dead man's assets. Such tales of trade rivalry, drink, murder and the degradation of white men in the remoter islands formed the background to Stevenson's story 'The Beach of Falesá'.

BISHOP PATTERSON
(PAGE 189)

John Coleridge Patteson (1827–71) was a pioneer missionary and the Anglican Bishop of Melanesia. An outspoken critic of the labour trade, he became one of its victims. He was murdered by natives at Nukapu, a Polynesian atoll which he visited only days after labour recruiters had taken away five young men. His murder was seen as a retaliation for abuses by labour traders and, the story quickly spread, for a specific fraud in which slavers dressed in surplices and used the Bishop's name to lure islanders aboard. The Bishop's murder and the reasons for it shocked the British and spurred them to enact the first Pacific Islanders Protection Bill in 1872.

JOHN WILLIAMS
(PAGE 195)

John Williams (1796–1839) was a Protestant missionary with the London Missionary Society whose mission work brought significant social changes to the Cook Islands and Samoa in the nineteenth century.

Further reading

Campbell, I. C., *A History of the Pacific Islands*, Berkeley: University of California Press, 1989.

Crocombe, Ron, *The South Pacific*, Suva: University of the South Pacific, 2001.

Davidson, J. W. and Scarr, Deryck (eds), *Pacific Island Portraits*, Canberra: Australian National University Press, 1970.

Furnas, J. C., *Voyage to Windward: The Life of Robert Louis Stevenson*, London: Faber, 1952.

Knight, Alanna (ed.), *R. L. S. in the South Seas: An Intimate Photographic Record*, Edinburgh: Mainstream Publishing, 1986.

Mackay, Margaret, *The Violent Friend: The Story of Mrs Robert Louis Stevenson*, New York: Doubleday, 1968.

Palmer, George, *Kidnapping in the South Seas* (1871), Harmondsworth: Penguin, 1973.

Sanchez, Nellie Van de Grift, *The Life of Mrs Robert Louis Stevenson*, London: Chatto & Windus, 1920.

Stevenson, Fanny, 'Prefatory Notes' to *The Wrecker* and *Island Nights' Entertainments, The Works of Robert Louis Stevenson, Tusitala Edition*, 35 vols, London: Heinemann, 1923–24, vol. 12, pp. xv–xxiv, and vol. 13, pp. xi–xiv.

Stevenson, Fanny and Robert Louis, *Our Samoan Adventure*, ed. Charles Neider, London: Wiedenfeld and Nicolson, 1956.

Stevenson, Robert Louis, *A Footnote to History: Eight Years of Trouble in Samoa*, London: Cassell, 1892.

—, *In the South Seas* (1896), ed. Neil Rennie, London: Penguin, 1998.

—, *The Letters of Robert Louis Stevenson*, ed. Bradford A. Booth and Ernest Mehew, 8 vols, New Haven: Yale University Press, 1994–95.

—, 'A Pearl Island: Penrhyn' in *Vailima Papers, The Works of Robert Louis Stevenson, Tusitala Edition*, 35 vols, London: Heinemann, 1923–24, vol. 21, pp. 307–16.

—, *Selected Letters of Robert Louis Stevenson*, ed. Ernest Mehew, New Haven: Yale University Press, 1997.

—, *South Sea Tales*, ed. Roslyn Jolly, Oxford: OUP, 1996. Includes 'The Beach of Falesá' and *The Ebb-Tide*.

Stevenson, Robert Louis, and Osbourne, Lloyd, *The Wrecker* (1892), New York: Dover Publications, 1982.

Wawn, William T., *The South Sea Islanders and the Queensland Labour Trade: A Record of Voyages and Experiences in the Western Pacific, from 1875 to 1891* (1893), ed. Peter Corris, Canberra: Australian National University Press, 1973.